North Worcestershire (

COLLEGE LIBRA

Books must be returned not later than last date stamped below.

18. DEC. 1985		
15. JAN. 1986		
13. FEB. 1986		
13. MAR. 1986		
10. APR. 1986		
-9. JUN. 1986		
-2. FEB. 1987		

Butterworths Technical and Scientific Checkbooks

Chemistry 3 Checkbook

P J Chivers
BSc(Hons), PhD

Butterworth Scientific
London Boston Sydney Wellington Durban Toronto

All rights reserved. No part of this publication may be reproduced or transmitted in any form or by any means, including photocopying and recording, without the written permission of the copyright holder, application for which should be addressed to the publishers. Such written permission must also be obtained before any part of this publication is stored in a retrieval system of any nature.

This book is sold subject to the Standard Conditions of Sale of Net Books and may not be resold in the UK below the net price given by the Publishers in their current price list.

First published 1982

© Butterworth & Co (Publishers) Ltd 1982

British Library Cataloguing in Publication Data

Chivers, P.J.
  Chemistry 3 checkbook.
  1. Chemistry
  I. Title
  540'.246   QD312

  ISBN 0-408-00662-5
  ISBN 0-408-00658-7 Pbk

252733

NORTH WORCESTERSHIRE
COLLEGE LIBRARY

540 CHI

Typeset by Scribe Design, Gillingham, Kent
Printed in England by Hartnoll Print Ltd., Bodmin, Cornwall

Contents

Preface v

1 The energetics of chemical reaction 1
Main points 1
Worked problems 3
Further problems 12

2 Gaseous equilibria 17
Main points 17
Worked problems 18
Further problems 27

3 Ionic equilibria 30
Main points 30
Worked problems 32
Further problems 42

4 Heterogeneous equilibria 46
Main points 46
Worked problems 48
Further problems 53

5 The lattice crystal structures of some inorganic compounds 56
Main points 56
Worked problems 59
Further problems 65

6 The inorganic chemistry of some elements 69
Main points 69
Worked problems 77
Further problems 89

7 Reaction kinetics 93
Main points 93
Worked problems 99
Further problems 114

8 Organic reaction mechanisms 122
Main points 122
Worked problems 126
Further problems 136

9 Organic chemistry 143
Main points 143
Worked problems 152
Further problems 159

10 Polymerisation in organic chemistry 165
   Main points   165
   Worked problems   171
   Further problems   178

Answers to multi-choice problems   181

Index   182

Preface

This textbook of worked problems provides coverage of the Technician Education Council level 3 unit in chemistry (syllabus U76/020). It can also be regarded as a basic textbook in chemistry for a much wider range of courses, and will be useful for A level chemistry students.

Each topic is presented in a way that assumes the student has the knowledge attained either at TEC level 2 chemistry (syllabus U76/019) or parts of A level syllabuses. The aims of this book are to extend the understanding by students of basic chemical concepts, and to provide a basis for further studies in science and technology. This practical chemistry book contains approximately 120 detailed worked problems followed by some 450 further problems with answers.

The author would like to express his appreciation for the encouragement and advice of the series editors John Bird and Tony May, and for the friendly co-operation given by the publishers. Finally, the author would like to especially thank his wife Sandra for typing the manuscript and for her continuous help in its preparation, and to Mark and David for their patience.

P J Chivers
Highbury College of Technology,
Portsmouth

Note to Reader

As textbooks become more expensive, authors are often asked to reduce the number of worked and unworked problems, examples and case studies. This may reduce costs, but it can be at the expense of practical work which gives point to the theory.

Checkbooks if anything lean the other way. They let problem-solving establish and exemplify the theory contained in technician syllabuses. The Checkbook reader can gain *real* understanding through seeing problems solved and through solving problems himself.

Checkbooks do not supplant fuller textbooks, but rather supplement them with an alternative emphasis and an ample provision of worked and unworked problems. The brief outline of essential data—definitions, formulae, laws, regulations, codes of practice, standards, conventions, procedures, etc—will be a useful introduction to a course and a valuable aid to revision. Short-answer and multi-choice problems are a valuable feature of many Checkbooks, together with conventional problems and answers.

Checkbook authors are carefully selected. Most are experienced and successful technical writers; all are experts in their own subjects; but a more important qualification still is their ability to demonstrate and teach the solution of problems in their particular branch of technology, mathematics or science.

Authors, General Editors and Publishers are partners in this major low-priced series whose essence is captured by the Checkbook symbol of a question or problem 'checked' by a tick for correct solution.

Butterworths Technical and Scientific Checkbooks

General Editors for Science, Engineering and Mathematics titles:
J.O. Bird and A.J.C. May, Highbury College of Technology, Portsmouth.

General Editor for Building, Civil Engineering, Surveying and Architectural titles:
Colin R. Bassett, lately of Guildford County College of Technology.

A comprehensive range of Checkbooks will be available to cover the major syllabus areas of the TEC, SCOTEC and similar examining authorities. A comprehensive list is given below and classified according to levels.

Level 1 (Red covers)
Mathematics
Physical Science
Physics
Construction Drawing
Construction Technology
Microelectronic Systems
Engineering Drawing
Workshop Processes & Materials

Level 2 (Blue covers)
Mathematics
Chemistry
Physics
Building Science and Materials
Construction Technology
Electrical & Electronic Applications
Electrical & Electronic Principles
Electronics
Microelectronic Systems
Engineering Drawing
Engineering Science
Manufacturing Technology
Digital Techniques
Motor Vehicle Science

Level 3 (Yellow covers)
Mathematics
Chemistry
Building Measurement
Construction Technology
Environmental Science
Electrical Principles
Electronics
Microelectronic Systems
Electrical Science
Mechanical Science
Engineering Mathematics & Science
Engineering Science
Engineering Design
Manufacturing Technology
Motor Vehicle Science
Light Current Applications

Level 4 (Green covers)
Mathematics
Building Law
Building Services & Equipment
Construction Technology
Construction Site Studies
Concrete Technology
Economics for the Construction Industry
Geotechnics
Engineering Instrumentation & Control

Level 5
Building Services & Equipment
Construction Technology
Manufacturing Technology

1 The energetics of chemical reactions

A. MAIN POINTS CONCERNING THE ENERGETICS OF CHEMICAL REACTIONS

1. (i) The energy changes which take place during a chemical reaction are called **enthalpy changes** and are identified by the symbols ΔH.
   (ii) The enthalpy changes are best reported under **standard conditions** in order that values can be compared internationally. The symbol for enthalpy changes under standard conditions is $\Delta H^{\ominus}$ and these conditions are that the temperature shall be recorded between the values of 298 K, and when gases are involved at a pressure of 101.325 kPa.

2. **Definitions of some standard enthalpy changes**
   (i) The **standard enthalpy of atomisation** is the enthalpy change which occurs when one mole of an element in it's standard state at 298 K and 101.325 kPa is converted into **free atoms**.
   (ii) The **standard enthalpy of ionisation** is the enthalpy change which occurs when one mole of **gaseous atoms** are converted into one mole of **gaseous ions** accompanied by a **loss of one mole of electrons**, measured under standard conditions. It should be noted that each element has a different number of ionisation energies dependent upon the number of electrons in the element. Usually the formation of **stable metallic ions** are associated with a **loss of 1, 2, 3, or 4 electrons**.
   (iii) The **standard enthalpy of lattice energy** is the enthalpy change which occurs when one mole of **an ionic solid** is formed from it's **constituent gaseous ions** measured under standard conditions.
   (iv) The **standard enthalpy of electron affinity** is the enthalpy change which occurs when one mole of **gaseous atoms** are converted into **one mole of gaseous negative ions** by accepting **one mole of electrons**, measured under standard condition It should be noted that some non-metals can have more than one electron added for example, oxygen has **two electron affinity enthalpy values**.
   (v) The **standard enthalpy of solution** is the enthalpy change when one mole of a solute is **dissolved in a given amount of a solvent**, measured under standard conditions.
   (vi) The **standard enthalpy of dilution** is the enthalpy change which occurs when that amount of **a given solution containing one mole of solvent** is diluted with a given amount of solvent, measured under standard conditions.
   (vii) The **standard enthalpy of neutralisation** is the enthalpy change which occurs when one mole of **hydrogen ions** in solution are neutralised by a base in dilute solution, measured under standard conditions.

TABLE 1 Bond dissociation energies

Molecule X–Y	Enthalpy $B.D._{x-y}$ kJ mol^{-1}
H–H	436
F–F	269.9
Cl–Cl	242.7
Br–Br	192.9
I–I	151
H–F	621.3
H–Cl	431.8
H–Br	366.1
H–I	298.7

3 For covalent molecules the energy required to separate **one mole of covalent bonds between two atoms** in a diatomic molecule is called the **bond dissociation enthalpy** or bond dissociation energy. Some typical examples of values are given in *Table 1*, where $B.D_{X-Y}$ symbolises those terms.

4 In covalent molecules containing more than two atoms the bond dissociation energies are found for **all of the bonds** and an **average value** is derived. For example in methane, CH_4, there are four carbon to hydrogen bonds. The enthalpy required to break the four bonds is 1666 kJ mol^{-1}, and the average value is thus 416.5 kJ mol^{-1}. These average or mean values, E_{X-Y} can be used to estimate how much enthalpy is required to completely break all of the covalent bonds in a molecule. Similarly, the amount of **enthalpy released on the formation of a covalently bonded molecule** can also be estimated. As a result of calculating these values the **enthalpy of a reaction** can be determined (see *Problems 6 and 7*).

5 By considering all of the energy changes involved in converting elements from their ground states into molecules, **the enthalpy of formation of covalent molecules** can be found (see *Problems 8 and 9*). Some values are given in *Table 2*.

TABLE 2 Some average bond dissociation enthalpies

Bond X–Y	Energy, kJ mol^{-1} E_{x-y}
C–H general	412
C–C general	346
C=C general	611
C≡C general	835
P–P in P_4	201
C–Cl general	339
C–Br general	268
C–I general	234
C–F general	427
P–Cl general	328
SI–H in SiH_4	318
H–O general	464
H–P general	322
H–N general	389
N≡N	945
O=O	497
O–O general	146

$$M(g) + A(g) \atop x+$$

ΔH_4 Enthalpy of atomisation of non-metal

$$M(g) + A(g) \atop x+ \ \ y-$$

ΔH_5 Sum of enthalpies of electron affinities

Energy

$$M(g) + A(g) \atop x+$$

ΔH_3 Sum of the enthalpies of ionisation energies

$M(g) + A(g)$

ΔH_2 Enthalpy of atomisation of the metal

ΔH_6 Enthalpy of lattice energy

Datum line —— $M(s) + A(g)$ (Standard states)

ΔH_1 Enthalpy of formation

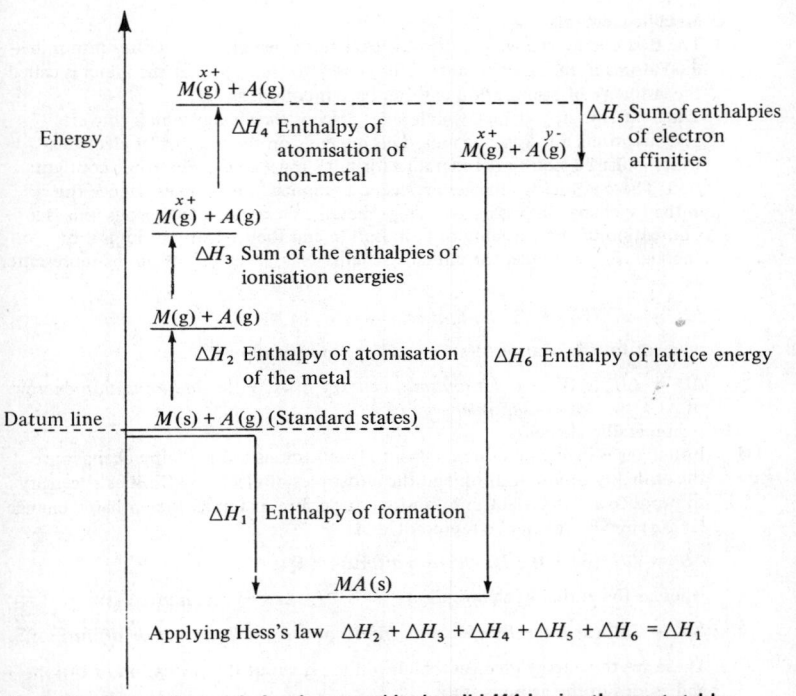

$MA(s)$

Applying Hess's law $\Delta H_2 + \Delta H_3 + \Delta H_4 + \Delta H_5 + \Delta H_6 = \Delta H_1$

Fig 1 The Born–Haber cycle for the general ionic solid *MA* having the most stable oxidation states M^{x+} and A^{y-}

6   If all the energy changes involved in the formation of an ionic solid are considered, the **lattice energy** of the solid can be found. The method was devised by **Born and Haber** as an application of **Hess's Law** of constant heat summation. They considered each change in enthalpy necessary to form the number of moles of positive and negative gaseous ions from the elements in their standard states. Then, by using the enthalpy of formation of the solid and applying Hess's law, the **Born–Haber** cycle was produced allowing the lattice energy to be found.

A general Born–Haber cycle is shown in *Fig 1* with specific examples shown in *Problems 2, 3 and 4*.

B. WORKED PROBLEMS ON THE ENERGETICS OF CHEMICAL REACTIONS

Problem 1 What are the energy changes involved when elements are changed into gaseous ions?

The elements can be considered as (a) metallic elements and (b) non-metallic elements.

(a) Metallic elements
(i) The first energy change requires the change of elemental structures into individual atoms in the gaseous state. This energy for one mole of the metal is called the **enthalpy of atomisation** and can be symbolised as $\Delta H_a^\ominus$.
(ii) The next enthalpy change which takes place is the change which converts gaseous atoms into gaseous ions. This depends on the number of electrons which must be lost by the metal to form it's most stable electronic configuration. These enthalpy changes are called the **ionisation energies**. Hence the enthalpy change necessary to change metallic elements into gaseous ions is a summation of the enthalpy of atomisation and the enthalpy of ionisation energies. For example, the enthalpy change $Na(s) \longrightarrow Na^+(g)$ can be represented as:

$$\Delta H = \Delta H_a^\ominus (Na) + \text{the \textit{1st ionisation energy}} \text{ of Na,}$$

whereas for the change $Al(s) \longrightarrow Al^{3+}(g)$ the enthalpy change:

$$\Delta H = \Delta H_a^\ominus (Al) + \text{the \textit{1st ionisation energy}} \text{ of Al} + \text{the \textit{2nd ionisation energy}} \text{ of Al} + \text{the \textit{3rd ionisation energy}} \text{ of Al.}$$

(b) Non-metallic elements
(iii) For changes involving non-metals into gaseous ions the enthalpy changes are the **enthalpy of atomisation** and the **enthalpies of electron affinities** necessary to produce a stable electronic configuration. For example, the enthalpy change $½F_2(g) \longrightarrow F^-(g)$ can be represented as:

$$\Delta H = \Delta H_a^\ominus (F) + \text{the \textit{1st electron affinity}} \text{ of F}$$

whereas the enthalpy change, $S(s) \longrightarrow S^{2-}(g)$ can be represented as:

$$\Delta H = \Delta H_a^\ominus (s) + \text{the \textit{1st electron affinity}} \text{ of S} + \text{the \textit{2nd electron affinity}} \text{ of S.}$$

(iv) **These are the energy changes which will bring about the formation of cations and anions in the gaseous state.**

Problem 2 Construct a Born–Haber cycle for the ionic solid CaO, calcium oxide.

The completed cycle is shown in *Fig 2*. The position of the **enthalpy datum position** represents the elements calcium and oxygen in their **standard states of zero enthalpy**. The enthalpy values shown above the datum line are **endothermic values** whereas those below are **exothermic values**. In this diagram, the enthalpy of formation of calcium oxide, the first electron affinity of oxygen, and the lattice energy of calcium oxide, are exothermic values, the remainder being endothermic values.

Problem 3 Calculate the enthalpy of formation of sodium chloride from the following data.

Enthalpy change	$\Delta H^\ominus$ atomisation of Na(s)	$\Delta H^\ominus$ ionisation energy of Na	$\Delta H^\ominus$ lattice energy NaCl	ΔH bond energy Cl–Cl	$\Delta H^\ominus$ electron affinity of Cl
kJ mol^{-1}	+108.4	+502.1	−772.8	+242.7	−370

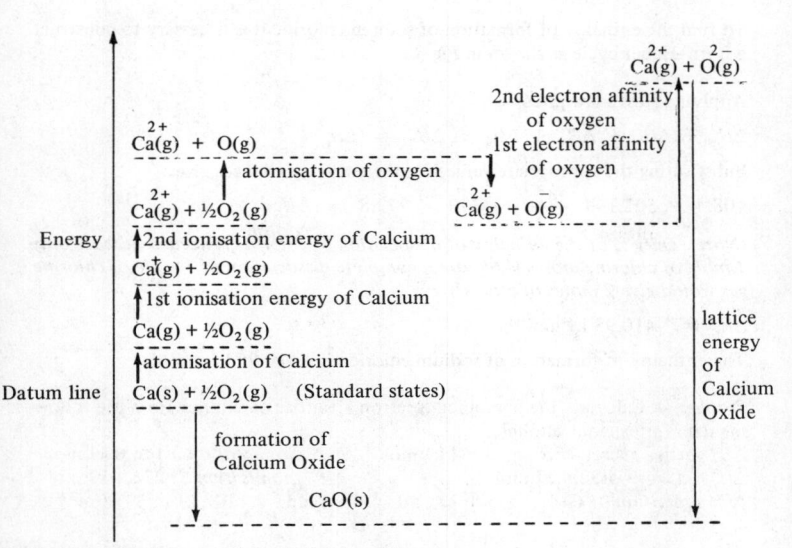

Fig 2 The Born-Haber cycle for calcium oxide

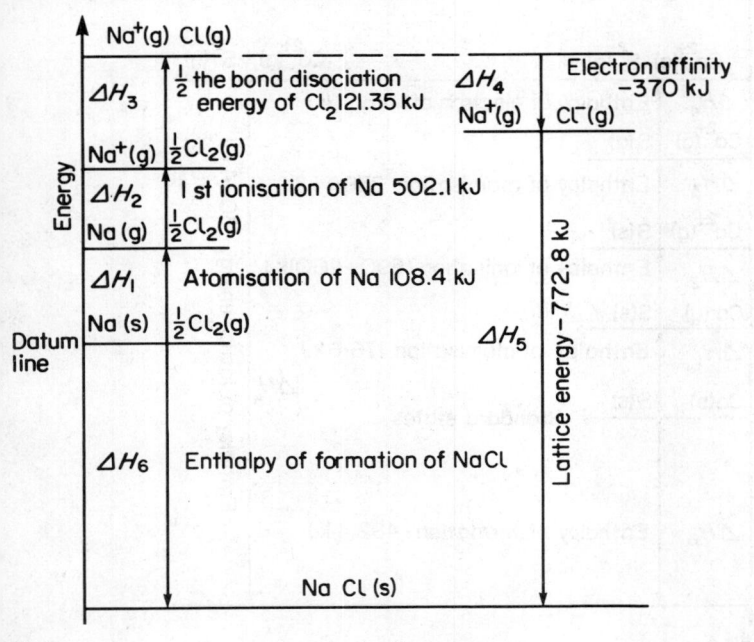

Fig 3

To find the enthalpy of formation of sodium chloride it is necessary to construct a Born–Haber cycle as shown in *Fig 3*.

Applying Hess's law gives

$$\Delta H_1 + \Delta H_2 + \Delta H_3 + \Delta H_4 + \Delta H_5 = \Delta H_6$$

Substituting the appropriate values for the enthalpy changes gives:

$$108.4 + 502.1 + \frac{242.7}{2} - 370 - 772.8 = \Delta H_6$$

(*Note: Only ½ of the enthalpy of dissociation of chlorine is needed because only 1 mole of chlorine atoms is required; complete dissociation of 1 mole of chlorine gas would give 2 moles of atoms.*)

$$\Delta H_6 = -410.95 \text{ kJ mol}^{-1}$$

The enthalpy of formation of sodium chloride is **−410.95 kJ mol⁻¹**.

Problem 4 Calculate the combined electron affinities of sulphur from the following data for calcium sulphide.
ΔH° lattice energy CaS = −3084 kJ mol⁻¹; ΔH° atomisation Ca 176.6 kJ mol⁻¹;
ΔH_f° CaS = −482.4 kJ mol⁻¹; ΔH° atomisation S 238.1 kJ mol⁻¹;
ΔH° ionisation of Ca 1st = 590 kJ mol⁻¹ (Ca⁺), 2nd = 1100 kJ mol⁻¹ (Ca²⁺)

Ca²⁺(g) S²⁻(g)		Ca²⁺(g) + S²⁻(g)
ΔH_4	Enthalpy of electron affinity X kJ	
Ca²⁺(g)	S(g)	
ΔH_3	Enthalpy of atomisation 238·1 kJ	
Ca²⁺(g)	S(s)	Enthalpy of lattice energy −3084 kJ
ΔH_2	Enthalpy of ionisation (590+1100)kJ	
Ca(g)	S(s)	
ΔH_1	Enthalpy of atomisation 176·6 kJ	
Ca(s)	S(s) Standard states	ΔH_5
ΔH_6	Enthalpy of formation −482.4 kJ	

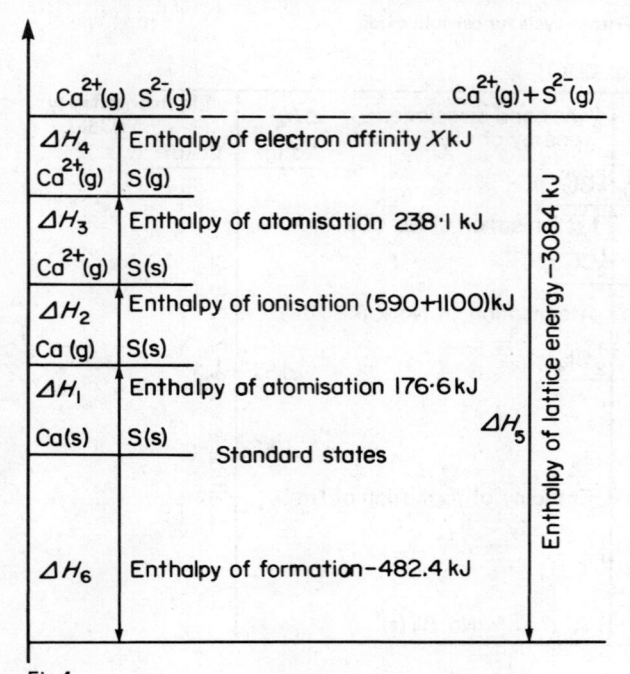

Fig 4

The electron affinities of sulphur can be found by constructing the Born–Haber cycle as in *Fig 4* and applying Hess's law to it. This gives the relationship

$$\Delta H_1 + \Delta H_2 + \Delta H_3 + \Delta H_4 + \Delta H_5 = \Delta H_6$$

Assuming that the electron affinities are X kJ mol^{-1} and substituting the other values into this equation gives

$176.6 + (590 + 1100) + 238.1 + X - 3084 = -482.4$
$X - 978.3 = -482.4$
$X = 496.9$ kJ mol^{-1}.

The sum of the electron affinities for the reaction S(g)→ S^{2-}(g) is **+496.9 kJ mol^{-1}**.

Problem 5 Explain what enthalpy changes occur in the formation of a covalently bonded molecule from elements in their standard states, using methane, CH$_4$(g) as an example.

The equation for the formation of methane can be written:

$$C(s) + 2H_2(g) \xrightarrow{\Delta H_1} CH_4(g),$$

where, by definition, ΔH_1 is the enthalpy of formation of methane. Before covalent bonds are formed by atoms of carbon and hydrogen, the carbon must be atomised and the hydrogen molecules dissociated into atoms. The enthalpies involved are ΔH_2 and ΔH_3 both of which are endothermic. Hence

$$C(s) \xrightarrow{\Delta H_2} C(g) \quad \text{and} \quad 2H_2(g) \xrightarrow{\Delta H_3} 4H(g)$$

ΔH_2 = the enthalpy of atomisation of carbon = $\Delta H_a^\ominus$ carbon

ΔH_3 = 2 × the bond dissociation enthalpy of hydrogen = $2 \times B.D._{H-H}$.

The next step involves the formation of four carbon to hydrogen single covalent bonds. Bond formation is an exothermic process and ΔH_4 in the equation:

$$C(g) + 4H(g) \xrightarrow{\Delta H_4} CH_4(g)$$

is 4 × the average bond dissociation energy of a C–H bond, i.e.

$\Delta H_4 = 4 \times E_{C-H}$.

By applying Hess's law of constant heat summation:

$\Delta H_1 = \Delta H_2 + \Delta H_3 + \Delta H_4$

or $\Delta H_f = \Delta H_a$ carbon $+ 2 \times B.D._{H-H} + 4 \times E_{C-H}$

Hence by knowing the required enthalpy values the enthalpy of formation can be calculated. These enthalpy changes are summarised in *Fig 5*.

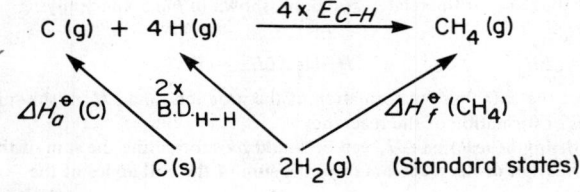

Fig 5

(It should be noted that for the use of an average bond dissociation energy the value ΔH_f is not the standard enthalpy of formation.)

Problem 6 Why is it possible to find the enthalpy of a reaction by a consideration of the enthalpies of formation of the reactants and products? Use the following reaction as an example.

$$C_2H_5OH(l) + PCl_5(s) \xrightarrow{\Delta H_1} C_2H_5Cl(l) + POCl_3(l) + HCl(g)$$

The standard enthalpy of formation is defined as the enthalpy change which occurs when 1 mole of a compound is formed from its elements in their standard states, measured under standard conditions (298 K and 101.325 kPa).
For the reactants, this corresponds to:

$$2C(s) + 3H_2(g) + P(s) + \tfrac{1}{2}O_2(g) + 2\tfrac{1}{2}Cl_2(g) \xrightarrow{\Delta H_2} C_2H_5OH(l) + PCl_5(s)$$

and **for the products**:

$$2C(s) + 3H_2(g) + P(s) + \tfrac{1}{2}O_2(g) + 2\tfrac{1}{2}Cl_2(g) \xrightarrow{\Delta H_3} C_2H_5Cl(l) + POCl_3(l) + HCl(g)$$

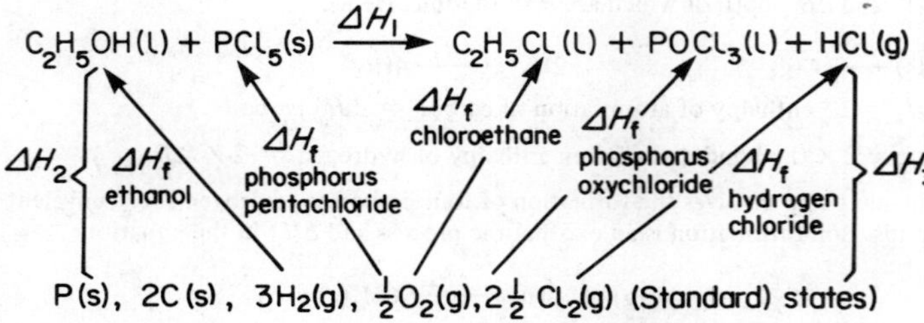

$$\Delta H_2 = \Delta H_f^\circ\, C_2H_5OH + \Delta H_f^\circ\, PCl_5 \quad \text{(Reactants)}$$

$$\Delta H_3 = \Delta H_f^\circ\, C_2H_5Cl + \Delta H_f^\circ\, POCl_3 + \Delta H_f^\circ\, HCl \quad \text{(Products)}$$

Fig 6

It is apparent that the same elements are involved in each case. Hence by constructing the enthalpy diagram for the related reactions, shown in *Fig 6* and applying Hess's law gives:

$$\Delta H_1 + \Delta H_2 = \Delta H_3 \quad \text{or} \quad \Delta H_1 = \Delta H_3 - \Delta H_2$$

ΔH_3 is the sum of the enthalpies of formation of the products, and ΔH_2 is the sum of the enthalpies of formation of the reactants.

Hence the enthalpy of reaction ΔH_1 can be found by subtracting the sum of the enthalpies of formation of the reactants from the sum of the enthalpies of the products.

Problem 7 Calculate the enthalpy of reaction for the conversion

$$C_2H_5OH(l) + PCl_5(l) \longrightarrow C_2H_5Cl(l) + POCl_3(l) + HCl(g)$$

from the following data:

Compound	C_2H_5OH	PCl_5	C_2H_5Cl	$POCl_3$	HCl
$\Delta H_f^{\ominus}$ kJ mol^{-1}	−277.7	−443.5	−136.5	−597.1	−92.3

The enthalpy change for a chemical reaction, can be found by considering the enthalpy of formation of the reactants and the enthalpy of the products, and taking the enthalpy of the reactants away from the enthalpy of the products.
Enthalpy of formation of the reactants = −277.7 + −(443.5) = −721.2
Enthalpy of formation of the products = −136.5 + −(597.1) −92.3 = −825.9
Enthalpy of reaction = Enthalpy of formation of products − Enthalpy of formation of reactants.

$$\Delta H = (-825.9) - (-721.2) = -104.7 \text{ kJ mol}^{-1}$$

The enthalpy of reaction is **−104.7 kJ mol^{-1}**.

Problem 8 Calculate the enthalpy of formation of ammonia, NH_3, from the following data:

Bond	H−H	N≡N	N−H
Mean bond enthalpy	436	945	388

The formation of ammonia from its element takes place according to the equation

$$N_2(g) + 3H_2(g) \longrightarrow 2NH_3(g)$$

To bring about this change, 1 mole of N_2 must be dissociated together with 3 moles of H_2, followed by the formation of 6 N−H bonds, 3 for each molecule.

$$N_2(g) + 3H_2(g) \xrightarrow{\Delta H_1} 2N(g) + 6H(g)$$

$$\Delta H_1 = 945 + 3 \times (436) = 2253 \text{ kJ}$$

$$2N(g) + 6H(g) \xrightarrow{\Delta H_2} 2NH_3(g)$$

$\Delta H_2 = 6 \times (-388)$ kJ (*Note. Negative because it is bond formation*).
= −2328 kJ.

The enthalpy of formation of $2NH_3(g) = \Delta H_1 + \Delta H_2$

$$\Delta H_f = 2253 - 2328 = -75 \text{ kJ}$$

For 1 mole of NH_3, $\Delta H_f = \dfrac{-75}{2} = -37.5$ kJ mol^{-1}

Thus the enthalpy of formation of ammonia is **−37.5 kJ mol^{-1}**.

Problem 9 Calculate the enthalpy of formation of butane using the following data.
Enthalpy of atomisation of carbon = 716 kJ mol^{-1}.
Bond dissociation energy of hydrogen = 436 kJ mol^{-1}.
$E_{C-C} = -342$ kJ mol^{-1}; $E_{C-H} = -413$ kJ mol^{-1}.

The enthalpy of formation of butane can be calculated by (i) considering the atomisation of carbon and hydrogen according to the equation:

$$4C(s) + 5H_2(g) \xrightarrow{\Delta H_1} 4C(g) + 10H(g).$$

and (ii) by considering the energy change when the following change occurs:

$$4C(g) + 10H(g) \xrightarrow{\Delta H_2} C_4H_{10}(g)$$

This involves the formation of 3 C–C bonds and 10 C–H bonds.

$\Delta H_1 = 4 \times (716) + 5 \times (436) = 5044$ kJ
$\Delta H_2 = 3 \times (-342) + 10 \times (-413) = -5156$ kJ

Hence, $\Delta H_1 + \Delta H_2 = 5044 - 5156 = -112$ kJ mol^{-1}
Thus the enthalpy of formation of butane, $\Delta H_f = -112$ **kJ mol^{-1}**.

Problem 10 (a) Calculate the standard enthalpy of formation of butane from the following data:

$C_4H_{10}(g) + 6\frac{1}{2}O_2(g) \longrightarrow 4CO_2(g) + 5H_2O(l)$ $\Delta H_c^\ominus = -2877.1$ kJ mol^{-1}.
$\Delta H_c^\ominus$ carbon = -393.4 kJ mol^{-1}; $\Delta H_c^\ominus$ hydrogen = -285.6 kJ mol^{-1}.

(b) Compare this value with that obtained in *Problem 9* and comment on any difference between them.

(a) The enthalpy diagram is constructed as shown in *Fig 7*.
Applying Hess's law gives:

$\Delta H_f^\ominus + \Delta H_c^\ominus = \Delta H_1 + \Delta H_2$

Substituting the values into the equation gives:

$\Delta H_f^\ominus - 2877.1 = 4 \times (-393.4) + 5 \times (-285.6) = -3001.6$ kJ mol^{-1},
$\Delta H_f^\ominus - 3001.6 + 2877.1 = -124.5$ kJ mol^{-1}.

Thus the standard enthalpy of formation of butane is **-124.5 kJ mol^{-1}**.

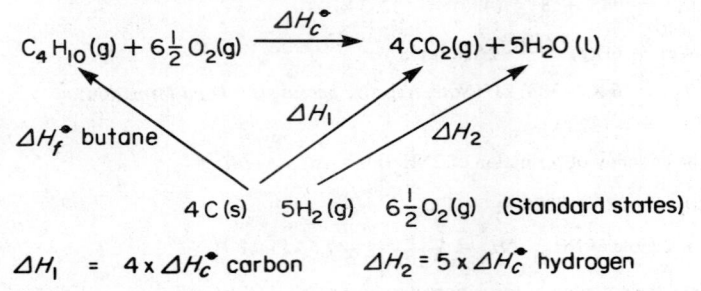

$C_4H_{10}(g) + 6\frac{1}{2}O_2(g) \xrightarrow{\Delta H_c^\ominus} 4CO_2(g) + 5H_2O(l)$

$\Delta H_f^\ominus$ butane ΔH_1 ΔH_2

          4 C (s)   5H$_2$(g)   6$\frac{1}{2}$O$_2$(g)   (Standard states)

$\Delta H_1 = 4 \times \Delta H_c^\ominus$ carbon $\Delta H_2 = 5 \times \Delta H_c^\ominus$ hydrogen
Fig 7

(b) The value obtained in *Problem 9* is **−112 kJ mol⁻¹**. *The difference in values is due to the use of average bond energies in the calculation of the enthalpy of formation in Problem 9, rather than the true values of the individual bonds.*

Problem 11 Calculate the enthalpy of atomisation of sulphur from the following data:

$B.D._{H-H}$ = 436 kJ mol⁻¹; $\Delta H_f^\ominus$ of H_2S = −20.6 kJ mol⁻¹
$B.D._{H-S}$ = 347 kJ mol⁻¹.

The equation of the formation reaction is

$$H_2(g) + S(s) \xrightarrow{\Delta H_f^\ominus} H_2S(g)$$

The enthalpy required for formation is a combination of two factors.
Firstly,

$$H_2(g) + S(s) \xrightarrow{\Delta H_2} 2H(g) + S(g),$$

and secondly,

$$2H(g) + S(g) \xrightarrow{\Delta H_3} H_2S(g)$$

ΔH_2 = Bond dissociation of H_2 + atomisation energy of sulphur
 = 436 kJ + X kJ, where X is the enthalpy of atomisation of sulphur.
ΔH_3 = 2 × formation of H−S bond = 2 × (−347) = −694 kJ

Applying Hess's law, $\Delta H_f^\ominus = \Delta H_2 + \Delta H_3$

Substituting in the appropriate values gives −20.6 = 436 + X − 694
Hence, X = 237.4 kJ mol⁻¹.
Thus the enthalpy of atomisation of sulphur is **237.4 kJ mol⁻¹**.

Problem 12 Calculate the enthalpy of reaction for the hydrogenation of ethene using the following data:

Bond	C−H	C=C	C−C	H−H
Mean bond energy kJ mol⁻¹	413	598	346	436

The equation of the reaction is:

$$C_2H_4(g) + H_2(g) = C_2H_6(g)$$

This can be considered as the breaking of all of the covalent bonds in the reactants and the formation of the covalent bonds in the products. This can be conveniently set out as follows:

Bonds broken	Total energy	Bonds formed	Total energy
4 × C−H	4 × 413 = +1652	6 × C−H	6 × 413 = −2478
1 × C=C	+598	1 × C−C	−346
1 × H−H	+436		
	+2686		−2824

11

The difference in enthalpy is 2686−2824 = −138 kJ.
The enthalpy of reaction, $\triangle H_h$ is −138 kJ mol^{-1}.

Problem 13 Calculate the enthalpy of atomisation of phosphorus from the following data:

E_{P-Cl} = 328 kJ mol^{-1}: $B.D._{Cl-Cl}$ = 242 kJ mol^{-1}; $\triangle H_f^\circ$ PCl$_3$ = −306 kJ mol^{-1}

The equation for the enthalpy of formation is:

$$P(s) + 1\tfrac{1}{2}Cl_2(g) \xrightarrow{\triangle H_1} PCl_3(l)$$

An alternative method is to form PCl$_3$ from individual atoms, that is,

$$P(s) + 1\tfrac{1}{2}Cl_2(g) \xrightarrow{\triangle H_2} P(g) + 3Cl(g) \xrightarrow{\triangle H_3} PCl_3(l)$$

By applying Hess's law, $\triangle H_1 = \triangle H_2 + \triangle H_3$

$\triangle H_1 = \triangle H_f(PCl_3) = -306$ kJ mol^{-1}.

$\triangle H_2 = \triangle H_a(P) + 1\tfrac{1}{2}B.D._{Cl-Cl} = \triangle H_a(P) + 363$ kJ mol^{-1}.

$\triangle H_3 = 3 \times E_{P-Cl} = -(3 \times 328) = -984$ kJ

Substituting these values into the equation gives:

$-306 = \triangle H_a(P) + 363 - 984$.

and $\triangle H_a(P) = -306 - 363 + 984 = 315$.

Thus the enthalpy of atomisation of phosphorus = **315 kJ mol^{-1}**.

C. FURTHER PROBLEMS ON THE ENERGETICS OF CHEMICAL REACTIONS

(a) SHORT ANSWER PROBLEMS

Fill in the missing words.

1. The law of constant heat summation is the law of . . . .

2. The enthalpy change which occurs when the most stable positive ion is formed from a metal atom is the . . . . of the . . . .

3. The enthalpy change which occurs when one mole of an ionic solid is formed from its constituent gaseous ions is called the . . . . of the ionic solid.

4. The interrelationship between all of the individual factors concerning the formation of an ionic solid from its elements in their standard states is called the . . . .

5. The difference between experimental and theoretical values of lattice energies can be explained as a result of the . . . . of the ionic bonds.

6. The enthalpy change which occurs when the bonds in a diatomic molecule are broken is called the . . . . enthalpy.

7. For covalently bonded molecules, containing several different types of covalent bonds, only the . . . . enthalpies can be found.

8. An estimation of the enthalpy of formation of covalent molecules can be made by

considering both the enthalpies of .... of the elements involved, together with the .... enthalpies of the bonds which are formed.

9 When covalent bonds are broken the enthalpy change is ...., whereas the enthalpy change when covalent bonds are formed is ....

10 The enthalpy change which occurs when an ionic solid is dissolved in water is called the enthalpy of ....

(b) MULTI-CHOICE PROBLEMS (answers on page 181)
Select the correct answer from those given
Problems 1 to 3 refer to Fig 8.

1 The enthalpy of formation of caesium iodide is represented by
(a) ΔH_3; (b) ΔH_4; (c) ΔH_5; (d) ΔH_6.

2 The lattice energy of caesium iodide is represented by
(a) ΔH_3; (b) ΔH_4; (c) ΔH_5; (d) ΔH_6.

3 The enthalpy of ionisation of caesium is represented by
(a) ΔH_1; (b) ΔH_2; (c) ΔH_3; (d) ΔH_4.

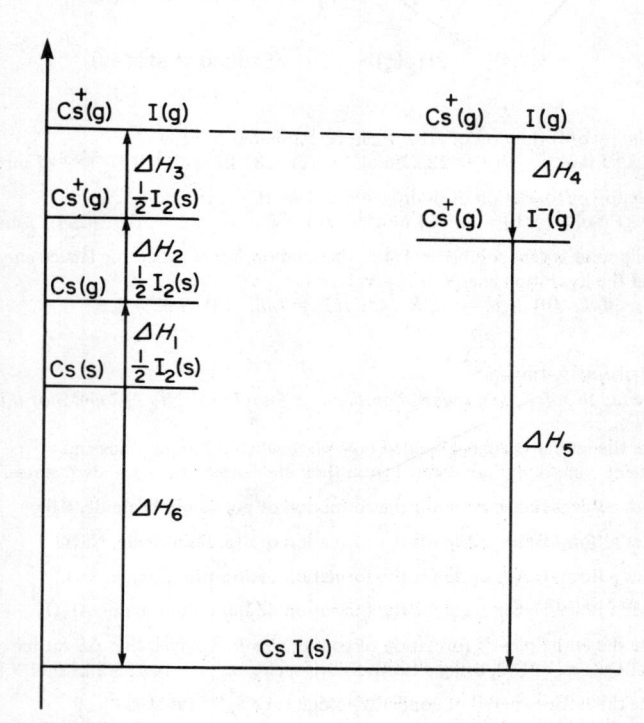

Fig 8

4   The values of the enthalpy changes for *Fig 8* are
    $\Delta H_a(Cs)$ 78.1 kJ, $\Delta H_a(I)$ 106.6 kJ, *1st I.E. of Cs* 380 kJ; *1st E.A. of I* −295.4 kJ.
    Lattice energy CsI = −582 kJ. The value of the enthalpy of formation is
    (a) +278.1 kJ mol^{-1}; (b) −366 kJ mol^{-1}; (c) +851.3 kJ mol^{-1};
    (d) −312.7 kJ mol^{-1}.
    Problems 5 to 9 require the use of Tables 1 and 2

5   The enthalpy of the reaction $CH_3-CH=CH_2(g) + H_2(g) \rightarrow CH_3-CH_2-CH_3(g)$ is
    (a) −123 kJ; (b) +123 kJ; (c) −559 kJ; (d) +559 kJ.

6   The enthalpy of the reaction $PCl_5(g) \rightarrow PCl_3(g) + Cl_2(g)$ is
    (a) +656 kJ; (b) −656 kJ; (c) −413 kJ; (d) +413 kJ.

7   The enthalpy of atomisation of silicon can be found using the enthalpy diagram in
    Fig 9. The value of this enthalpy change per mole is
    (a) +596 kJ; (b) −596 kJ; (c) −439 kJ; (d) +439 kJ.

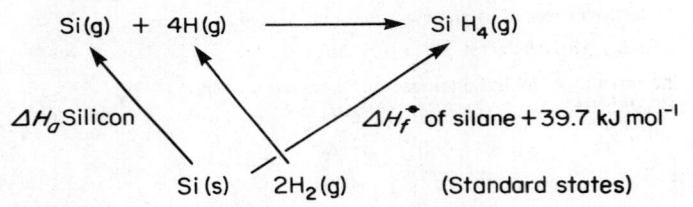

```
        Si(g)  +  4H(g)  ──────────────→   SiH₄(g)
            ↖                              ↗
             ↖                            ↗
         ΔHₐSilicon                  ΔH°f of silane +39.7 kJ mol⁻¹
                ↖                    ↗
                 Si(s)    2H₂(g)       (Standard states)
```

Fig 9

8   The enthalpy of formation of ethane can be estimated to be
    (a) −428 kJ mol^{-1}; (b) +428 kJ mol^{-1}; (c) −82 kJ mol^{-1}; (d) +82 kJ mol^{-1}

9   The enthalpy of formation of hydrogen peroxide H_2O_2 is
    (a) 139 kJ mol^{-1}; (b) −139 kJ mol^{-1}; (c) +141 kJ mol^{-1}; (d) −141 kJ mol^{-}

10 If an ionic solid is very soluble in water, the relationship between the lattice energy
    L.E., and the hydration energy *H.E.*, is
    (a) *H.E.* < *L.E.* (b) *H.E.* = −*L.E.* (c) *H.E.* = *L.E.* (d) *H.E.* > *L.E.*

(c) CONVENTIONAL PROBLEMS
The data needed to solve the numerical problems is found in Tables 1, 2 and 3 of this chapter.

1   Compare the enthalpy changes which take place when (a) ionic solids and
    (b) covalent compounds are formed from their elements in their standard states.

2   Construct a Born–Haber cycle for the formation of potassium bromide, KBr.

3   Construct a Born–Haber cycle for the formation of disodium oxide, Na_2O.

4   Construct a Born–Haber cycle for the formation of strontium oxide, SrO.

5   Construct a Born–Haber cycle for the formation of aluminium oxide, Al_2O_3.

6   Calculate the enthalpies of formation of copper (*II*) oxide given that ΔH lattice
    energy of CuO = −4142, using a Born–Haber cycle.   [−155.2 kJ mol^{-1}]

7   Calculate the lattice energy of copper (*I*) oxide Cu_2O given that $\Delta H_f^{\ominus}$ of
    $Cu_2O = -166.7$ kJ mol^{-1}.   [−3243 kJ mol^{-1}]

TABLE 3 Some enthalpy change for selected elements

$\Delta H_a^\ominus$ = molar enthalpy of atomisation
ΔH I.E. 1st. = molar enthalpy of the first ionisation energy
ΔH I.E. 2nd = molar enthalpy of the second ionisation energy
ΔH I.E. 3rd = molar enthalpy of the third ionisation energy
ΔH E.A. 1st = molar enthalpy of the first electron affinity
ΔH E.A. 2nd = molar enthalpy of the second electron affinity

Element	$\Delta H_a^\ominus$	ΔH I.E. 1st	ΔH I.E. 2nd	ΔH I.E. 3rd	ΔH E.A. 1st	ΔH E.A. 2nd
Hydrogen	218	1310			−72	
Lithium	161	520	7300	11800		
Sodium	108	500	4600	6900		
Potassium	89	420	3100	4400		
Rubidium	82	400	2700	3800		
Caesium	78	380	2400	3300		
Magnesium	149	740	1500	7700		
Calcium	177	590	1100	4900		
Strontium	164	550	1100	4200		
Barium	175	500	1000	4060		
Boron	590	800	2400	3700		
Aluminium	324	580	1800	2700		
Carbon (graphite)	714	1090	2400	4600		
Silicon	438	790	1600	3200		
Nitrogen	473	1400	2900	4600	0	
Phosphorus (red)	334	1010	1900	2900	−67	
Oxygen	249				−141	+791
Sulphur	238				−196	+649
Fluorine	79				−333	
Chlorine	121				−364	
Bromine	112				−342	
Iodine	107				−295	
Iron	418	760	1600	3000		
Copper	339	750	2000	3600		
Silver	286	730	2100	3400		
Lead	196	720	1500	3100 (4th 4100)		

8 Calculate the lattice energies of lead (*II*) oxide, PbO and lead (*IV*) oxide PbO$_2$, given that $\Delta H_f^\ominus$ are −217 and −277.4 kJ mol^{-1} respectively. [PbO −3556 kJ mol^{-1}. PbO$_2$ −11690.4 kJ mol^{-1}]

9 Calculate the enthalpy of hydrogenation for the reaction
$$CH_2=CH-CH=CH_2(g) + 2H_2(g) \longrightarrow CH_3-CH_2-CH_2-CH_3(g)$$
[−246 kJ mol^{-1}]

10 Calculate the enthalpy of formation of methanol, CH$_3$OH(l). [−239 kJ mol^{-1}]

11 Calculate the enthalpy of formation of tetrachloromethane CCl$_4$(l). [−156.6 kJ mol^{-1}]

12 Calculate the enthalpy of reaction for the bromination of ethene.
$$CH_2=CH_2(g) + Br_2(l) \longrightarrow CH_2Br-CH_2Br(l).$$
[−78.1 kJ mol^{-1}]

13 If the enthalpy of formation of iodine monochloride ICl(g) is +17.6 kJ mol^{-1}, calculate the bond dissociation enthalpy of the I–Cl bond. [179.25 kJ mol^{-1}]

14 Using the bond dissociation enthalpy value found in *Problem 13*, calculate the enthalpy of formation of iodine trichloride, ICl$_3$, using the structure Cl–I–Cl .
                                                                                Cl
[−98.25 kJ mol^{-1}]

15 Calculate the mean bond dissociation of the B–Cl bond given that $\Delta H_f^\ominus = -427.2$ kJ mol^{-1} for BCl$_3$(l). [460.4 kJ mol^{-1}]

16 Why is there such a large discrepancy between the experimental and theoretical values of the lattice energies of the silver halides whereas there is close agreement for the potassium halides, as shown below.

Compound	KCl	KBr	KI	AgCl	AgBr	AgI
Theoretical value	692	667	631	769	759	736
Experimental value	698	672	632	916	908	865

17 Calculate the enthalpy of reaction for the following reactions using the data in *Table 4*.
  (i) Fe$_2$O$_3$(s) + 3CO(g) = 2Fe(s) + 3CO$_2$(g)   [−582.9 kJ mol^{-1}]
 (ii) Fe$_2$O$_3$(s) + 3C(s) = 2Fe(s) + 3CO(g).   [−64.7 kJ mol^{-1}]

18 Calculate the enthalpy of reaction for the following reactions using *Table 4*.
   (i) MgO(s) + H$_2$(g) = Mg(s) + H$_2$O(g).   [+354.9 kJ mol^{-1}]
  (ii) CaO(s) + H$_2$(g) = Ca(s) + H$_2$O(g).   [+393.8 kJ mol^{-1}]
 (iii) SrO(s) + C(s) = Sr(s) + CO(g).   [+480 kJ mol^{-1}]
 (iv) 2BaO(s) + C(s) = 2Ba(s) + CO$_2$(g).   [+722.2 kJ mol^{-1}]

19 Calculate the enthalpy of reaction for the following reactions using *Table 4*.
   (i) Al$_2$O$_3$(s) + 3Mg(s) = 3MgO(s) + 2Al(s).   [−130 kJ mol^{-1}]
  (ii) Fe$_2$O$_3$(s) + 3Ca(s) = 3CaO(s) + 2Fe(s).   [−1639.5 kJ mol^{-1}]
 (iii) MgO(s) + Ca(s) = Mg(s) + CaO(s) .   [−33.5 kJ mol^{-1}]
 (iv) ZnO(s) + Mg(s) = MgO(s) + Zn(s).   [−254 kJ mol^{-1}]

20 Calculate the enthalpy of reaction for the following reactions using *Table 4*.
   (i) CH$_4$(g) = C(g) + 2H$_2$(g).   [+74.8 kJ mol^{-1}]
  (ii) NH$_3$(g) = ½N$_2$(g) + 1½H$_2$(g).   [+124.7 kJ mol^{-1}]
 (iii) H$_2$O(g) = H$_2$(g) + ½O$_2$(g).   [+241.7 kJ mol^{-1}]
 (iv) HF(g) = ½H(g) + ½F$_2$(g).   [+271 kJ mol^{-1}]

TABLE 4 Some standard enthalpies of formation

Compound	CO(g)	CO$_2$(g)	CH$_4$(g)	NH$_3$(g)	H$_2$O(g)	HF(g)
$\Delta H_f^\ominus$ (kJ mol^{-1})	−110.5	−393.8	−74.8	−124.7	−241.7	−271

Compound	Al$_2$O$_3$(s)	Fe$_2$O$_3$(s)	ZnO(s)
$\Delta H_f^\ominus$ (kJ mol^{-1})	−1676	−267	−348

Compound	MgO(s)	CaO(s)	SrO(s)	BaO(s)
$\Delta H_f^\ominus$ (kJ mol^{-1})	−602	−635.5	−590.5	−558

2 Gaseous equilibria

A. MAIN POINTS CONCERNING GASEOUS EQUILIBRIA

1. (i) The **ideal gas law** relates the **pressure, temperature, volume** and **number of moles** of an ideal gas by the equation $PV = nRT$ where P = pressure V = volume, n = number of moles of gas, R = the gas constant and T = the absolute temperature.
   (ii) At a **constant volume** and **temperature**, the **pressure** of the gas is **proportional to the number of moles of that gas.** By rearranging, the ideal gas law, $PV = nRT$ can be written as

   $$P = n\frac{RT}{V} \quad \text{or} \quad P = \text{a constant} \times n$$

   that is, $P \propto n$.

2. (i) When a mixture of gases occupy a given volume at a constant temperature the pressure of the individual gases are called the **partial pressures** and the **total pressure** of the mixture is **the sum of the partial pressures.**
   (ii) The partial pressure of a gas is defined as **the mole fraction of the gas multiplied by the total pressure.**

3. When a gaseous reaction forms an equilibrium mixture, the total pressure of the mixture of gases is equal to the sum of the partial pressures. Since the partial pressure of a gas is proportional to the number of moles of that gas, **the relative numbers of moles of the gases are proportional to their partial pressures.** Thus, the **composition of an equilibrium mixture** can be expressed in terms of the partial pressures of the gases.

4. For the general equilibrium equation

   $$w\text{A(g)} + x\text{B(g)} \rightleftharpoons y\text{C(g)} + z\text{D(g)}.$$

   the equilibrium constant in terms of partial pressures is

   $$K_p = \frac{(p\text{C})^Y \times (p\text{D})^Z}{(p\text{A})^W \times (p\text{B})^X}$$

   where $p\text{A}, p\text{B}, p\text{C}$ and $p\text{D}$ are the partial pressures of the gases A, B, C and D respectively.

5. The effect of **increasing the pressure** on a gaseous equilibrium is equivalent to **reducing the volume** available to the gaseous mixture. If possible, the composition

of the equilibrium will change to allow the mixture of gases to exist in the smallest possible volume. (The effects are summarised in *Problems 5 and 6*.)

6 (i) The effect of temperature on a gaseous equilibrium can be found by using the equation

$$\log_{10} \frac{K_p^1}{K_p^2} = -\frac{\Delta H^\circ}{2.303R} \left(\frac{1}{T_1} - \frac{1}{T_2}\right)$$

where K_p^1 is the equilibrium constant at temperature T_1 and K_p^2 is the equilibrium constant at temperature T_2, ΔH° is the standard enthalpy of the reaction and R is the gas constant (8.31 JK^{-1} mol^{-1}). The effects are shown for an exothermic and an endothermic reaction in *Table 1*.

TABLE 1

	ΔH (kJ mol^{-1})	T (K)	K_p (Pa)
Exothermic reaction $2SO_2 + O_2(g) \rightleftharpoons 2SO_3(g)$	-19.7	298	4×10^{24}
		500	2.5×10^{10}
		700	3.0×10^4
		1100	1.3×10^{-1}
Endothermic reaction $N_2(g) + O_2(g) \rightleftharpoons 2NO(g)$	180	298	4×10^{-31}
		700	5×10^{-13}
		1100	4×10^{-8}
		1500	1×10^{-5}

(ii) For an **exothermic** reaction, an **increase in temperature decreases the amount of the products**, whereas for an **endothermic** reaction an **increase in temperature increases the concentration of the products**.

B. WORKED PROBLEMS ON GASEOUS EQUILIBRIA

Problem 1 What is the mole fraction of hydrogen in a mixture of hydrogen and oxygen in which the partial pressure of oxygen is 10 Pa and the total pressure is 100 Pa.

The pressure of a mixture of gases is the sum of the partial pressures. Let P be the total pressure, pH_2, the partial pressure of hydrogen and pO_2 the partial pressure of oxygen. Then:

$P = pH_2 + pO_2$ or $pH_2 = P - pO_2$

Hence, $pH_2 = 100 - 10 = 90$ Pa.

The partial pressure of a gas is the mole fraction of the gas multiplied by the total pressure. Let n^1H_2 = the number of moles of H_2 and n^2O_2 = the number of moles of O_2. Then:

Total number of molecules = $n^1H_2 + n^2O_2$

The mole fraction of hydrogen $= \dfrac{n^1 H_2}{n^1 H_2 + n^2 O_2}$

Since $pH_2 = \dfrac{n^1 H_2}{n^1 H_2 + n^2 O_2} \times P$

then $\dfrac{n^1 H_2}{n^1 H_2 + n^2 O_2} = \dfrac{pH_2}{P} = \dfrac{90}{100} = 0.9$

i.e. the mole fraction of hydrogen is **0.9**.

Problem 2 A mixture of gases containing 3 moles of gas A and 5 moles of gas B is contained at a pressure of 10 kPa in a 1 dm³ volume. What are the partial pressures of the two gases?

The partial pressure of a gas is the mole fraction of the gas multiplied by the total pressure. Let pA be the partial pressure of gas A, and pB be the partial pressure of gas B then

$pA + pB$ = Total pressure = 10 kPa.

The total number of moles of gas = 3 + 5 = 8.

The mole fraction of gas A $= \dfrac{\text{Number of moles A}}{\text{Total number of moles of gas}}$

i.e. the mole fraction of A $= \dfrac{3}{8}$.

Hence, the partial pressure $pA = \dfrac{3}{8} \times 10 = \dfrac{30}{8} = 3\dfrac{3}{4}$ kPa.

The mole fraction of B $= \dfrac{\text{Number of moles of B}}{\text{Total number of moles of gas}} = \dfrac{5}{8}$

Hence, the partial pressure of B $= \dfrac{5}{8} \times 10 = \dfrac{50}{8} = 6\dfrac{1}{4}$ kPa.

Hence the partial pressure of A is 3.75 kPa, and that of B is 6.25 kPa.

Problem 3 What are the units of K_p for the reaction

$$2SO_2(g) + O_2(g) \rightleftharpoons 2SO_3(g)$$

The value of Kp for this reaction can be found from the equation:

$$K_p = \dfrac{(pSO_3)^2}{(pSO_2)^2(pO_2)}$$

Since the units of partial pressure are Pa, considering only the units gives

$$K_p = \dfrac{(Pa)^2}{(Pa)^2 \times (Pa)} = \dfrac{1}{Pa} = Pa^{-1}.$$

Thus the units of K_p for the given reaction are Pa^{-1}.

Problem 4 Why are there no units for K_p the equilibrium constant of the reaction

$$CO(g) + H_2O(g) \rightleftharpoons CO_2(g) + H_2(g).$$

The equilibrium constant K_p can be found using the equation

$$K_p = \frac{(pCO_2) \times (pH_2)}{(pCO) \times (pH_2O)}$$

Since the partial pressures have the units of Pa, considering only the units for K_p gives

$$K_p = \frac{(Pa) \times (Pa)}{(Pa) \times (Pa)} = 1$$

Hence K_p for the reaction has no units.

Problem 5 Explain why an increase in pressure does not alter the composition of the equilibrium

$$H_2O(g) + CO(g) \rightleftharpoons H_2(g) + CO_2(g)$$

Assume that 1 mole of H_2 and 1 mole of CO_2 react at equilibrium to produce X moles of H_2O and X moles of CO. Let the pressure be 100 kPa. The partial pressures of the gases at equilibrium are

$$pH_2 = \frac{1-X}{2} \times 100 \text{ kPa} \quad \text{and} \quad pCO_2 = \frac{1-X}{2} \times 100 \text{ kPa}$$

$$pH_2O = \frac{X}{2} \times 100 \text{ kPa} \quad\quad pCO = \frac{X}{2} \times 100 \text{ kPa}$$

$$K_p = \frac{(pH_2) \times (pCO_2)}{(pH_2O) \times (pCO)} = \frac{(50(1-X)) \times (50(1-X))}{(50X) \quad \times \quad (50X)}$$

or $K_p = \frac{(1-X)^2}{(X)^2}$

Let the pressure be increased to 200 kPa and let Y moles each of H_2O and CO be formed at equilibrium.
The partial pressures of the gases at equilibrium are

$$pH_2 = \frac{1-Y}{2} \times 200 \text{ kPa} \quad\quad pCO_2 = \frac{1-Y}{2} \times 200 \text{ kPa}$$

$$pH_2O = \frac{Y}{2} \times 200 \text{ kPa} \quad\quad pCO = \frac{Y}{2} \times 200 \text{ kPa}$$

$$K_p = \frac{(pH_2) \times (pCO_2)}{(pH_2O) \times (pCO)} = \frac{(100(1-Y)) \times (100(1-Y))}{(100Y) \quad \times \quad (100Y)}$$

$$K_p = \frac{(1-Y^2)}{Y^2}$$

Thus X must be equal to Y. **The effect of increasing the pressure on this equilibrium does not change the composition of the equilibrium** mixture because the number of components on the reactants side of the equilibrium is equal to the number of components on the products side of the equilibrium.

Problem 6 At 350 K and a pressure of 200 kPa, 1 mole of dinitrogen tetroxide reaches an equilibrium which contains 0.14 moles of nitrogen dioxide. What would be the number of moles of nitrogen dioxide if 1 mole of N_2O_4 reached equilibrium at 350 K and 100 kPa pressure.

First it is necessary to calculate K_p for the reaction

$$N_2O_4(g) \rightleftharpoons 2NO_2(g) \quad \text{using} \quad K_p = \frac{(pNO_2)^2}{(pN_2O_4)}$$

Since 1 mole of N_2O_4 produces 2 moles of NO_2 on complete reaction, the production of 0.14 moles of NO_2 requires 0.07 moles of N_2O_4. The total number of moles at equilibrium is $(1-0.07) + 0.14 = 1.07$ moles. The mole fractions and partial pressures can be expressed as

Gas	Mole fraction	Partial pressure
N_2O_4	$\dfrac{0.93}{1.07}$	$\dfrac{0.93}{1.07} \times 200$ kPa
NO_2	$\dfrac{0.14}{1.07}$	$\dfrac{0.14}{1.07} \times 200$ kPa

Substituting into the equilibrium expression

$$K_p = \frac{\left(\dfrac{0.14}{1.07} \times 200\right)^2}{\dfrac{0.93}{1.07} \times 200} = \frac{684.78}{173.83} = 3.94$$

Hence $K_p = 3.94$ kPa.

At 100 kNm^{-2} pressure, let X moles of N_2O_4 be used up at equilibrium. The constitution of the equilibrium mixture can be expressed as

	$N_2O_4(g)$	$2NO_2(g)$	
Initially	1	0	moles
At equilibrium	$1-X$	$2X$	moles.

The total number of moles at equilibrium is $(1-X) + 2X = (1+X)$ moles. The mole fractions and partial pressures can be expressed as

Gas	Mole fraction	Partial pressure
N_2O_4	$\dfrac{1-X}{1+X}$	$\dfrac{(1-X)}{(1+X)} \times 100$ kPa
NO_2	$\dfrac{2X}{(1+X)}$	$\dfrac{2X}{(1+X)} \times 100$ kPa

Substituting these values into the expression for K_p and using $K_p = 3.94$ gives

$$3.94 = \frac{\left(\dfrac{2X}{1+X} \times 100\right)^2}{\dfrac{1-X}{1+X} \times 100} = \frac{400X^2}{(1+X)(1-X)} = \frac{400X^2}{1-X^2}$$

Solving for X gives

$$3.94(1-X^2) = 400X^2, \quad 3.94 = 403.94X^2, \quad X = \frac{3.94}{403.94} = 0.099$$

Thus 0.099 moles of N_2O_4 are used up at equilibrium to produce $2 \times 0.099 = 0.198$ moles of NO_2.

By halving the pressure the number of moles of nitrogen dioxide increases from 0.14 moles to 0.198 moles.

Problem 7 Derive an expression for the equilibrium constant K_p for the synthesis of ammonia according to the equation

$$N_2(g) + 3H_2(g) \rightleftharpoons 2NH_3(g)$$

if 1 mole of nitrogen and 3 moles of hydrogen were mixed together and achieved an equilibrium pressure of P Pa. (Assume that X moles of nitrogen are used up at equilibrium.)

The equation of the reaction $N_2(g) + 3H_2(g) \rightleftharpoons 2NH_3(g)$ shows that at equilibrium three gases are present. These gases give rise to the total pressure of P Pa. Assuming that X moles of nitrogen are used up to form ammonia at equilibrium, then

	$N_2(g)$	+	$3H_2(g)$	$2NH_3(g)$	
Initially	1		3	0	moles
At equilibrium	$1-X$		$3-3X$	$2X$	moles

At equilibrium the total number of moles is

$$(1-X) + (3-3X) + 2X = (4-2X) \text{ moles}$$

Since the partial pressure of a gas in a mixture is defined as

Partial pressure of a gas = Mole fraction of the gas × Total pressure

Then,

$$pN_2 = \frac{1-X}{4-2X} \times P \text{ Pa}$$

$$pH_2 = \frac{3-3X}{4-2X} \times P \text{ Pa}$$

$$pNH_3 = \frac{2X}{4-2X} \times P \text{ Pa}$$

Substituting these values in the equation for Kp gives

$$Kp = \frac{\left(\frac{2X}{4-2X}\right)^2 \times P^2}{\left(\frac{1-X}{4-2X}\right) \times \left(\frac{3-3X}{4-2X}\right)^3 \times P^4} = \frac{\left(\frac{4X^2}{(4-2X)^2}\right) \times P^2}{\frac{(1-X)(3-3X)^3}{(4-2X)^4} \times P^4}$$

$$\frac{4X^2(4-2X)^2}{(1-X)\,3^3\,(1-X)^3\,P^2} = \frac{4X^2\,2^2(2-X)^2}{(1-X)^4\,27\,P^2}$$

Hence, $\quad K_p = \dfrac{16X^2(2-X)^2}{27(1-X)^4\,P^2}$

Problem 8 Calculate the value of K_p for the equilibrium formed when 1 mole of nitrogen and 3 moles of hydrogen react to produce 0.5 moles of ammonia at a pressure of 15 kPa.

The equation of the reaction is

$$N_2(g) + 3H_2(g) \rightleftharpoons 2NH_3(g)$$

The equilibrium equation in terms of partial pressures is

$$K_p = \frac{(p\text{NH}_3)^2}{(p\text{N}_2)(p\text{H}_2)^3}$$

Let X moles of nitrogen be used up at equilibrium. This means that X moles of N_2 react with $3X$ moles of H_2 to form $2X$ moles of ammonia. The equation of the reaction is

$$\text{N}_2(g) + 3\text{H}_2(g) \quad 2\text{NH}_3(g)$$

At equilibrium $1-X$ $3-3X$ $2X$ moles
(Since in this problem $2X = 0.5$ moles or $X = 0.25$)

Then   0.75   2.25   0.5   moles are present

The total number of moles at equilibrium $= 0.75 + 2.25 + 0.5 = 3.5$.

Hence, the mole fraction of $N_2 = \dfrac{0.75}{3.5}$, and

the partial pressure $= \dfrac{0.75}{3.5} \times 15$ kPa.

the mole fraction of $H_2 = \dfrac{2.25}{3.5}$ and

the partial pressure $= \dfrac{2.25}{3.5} \times 15$ kPa

and the mole fraction of $NH_3 = \dfrac{0.5}{3.5}$ and

the partial pressure $= \dfrac{0.5}{3.5} \times 15$ kPa

Substituting these partial pressure values into the equilibrium equation gives

$$K_p = \frac{\left(\dfrac{0.5}{3.5} \times 15\right)^2}{\dfrac{0.75}{3.5} \times 15 \left(\dfrac{2.25}{3.5} \times 15\right)^3} \quad \text{kPa}^{-2}$$

Hence, $K_p = \dfrac{4.6}{3.2 \times 896.6} = 1.6 \times 10^{-3}$ kPa^{-2}

The value of K_p is 1.6×10^{-3} kPa^{-2}.

Problem 9 Calculate the number of moles of nitrogen oxide in the equilibrium mixture formed when 2 moles of nitrogen react with 1 mole of oxygen at a temperature of 1500 K, and a pressure of 150 kPa. K_p for the reaction at 1500 K is 1×10^{-5}.

The equation of the reaction is

$$\text{N}_2(g) + \text{O}_2(g) \rightleftharpoons 2\text{NO}(g)$$

and the equilibrium equation is

$$K_p = \frac{(p\text{NO})^2}{(p\text{N}_2) \times (p\text{O}_2)}$$

Let X moles of oxygen be used up at equilibrium

$$N_2(g) + O_2(g) \rightleftharpoons 2NO(g)$$

Initially	2	1	0	moles
At equilibrium	$2-X$	$1-X$	$2X$	moles

The total number of moles at equilibrium is

$(2-X) + (1-X) + 2X = 3-2X + 2X = 3$.

The partial pressure of any gas = (the mole fraction of the gas) × (the total pressure of the gas mixture)

The values of the mole fractions and partial pressures of N_2, O_2 and NO are conveniently tabulated as follows:

Gas	Mole fraction	Partial pressure
N_2	$\dfrac{2-X}{3}$	$\dfrac{2-X}{3} \times 150$
O_2	$\dfrac{1-X}{3}$	$\dfrac{1-X}{3} \times 150$
NO	$\dfrac{2X}{3}$	$\dfrac{2X}{3} \times 150$

Substituting these values into the equilibrium equation gives

$$K_p = \frac{\left(\dfrac{2X}{3} \times 150\right)^2}{\left(\dfrac{2-X}{3} \times 150\right) \times \left(\dfrac{1-X}{3} \times 150\right)} = \frac{(50 \times 2X)^2}{(50(2-X)) \times (50(1-X))}$$

Simplifying the equation and substituting the value of K_p gives

$$1 \times 10^{-5} = \frac{4X^2}{(2-X)(1-X)} = \frac{4X^2}{2-3X+X^2}$$

Then, $1 \times 10^{-5}(2-3X+X^2) = 4X^2$
$2-3X+X^2 = 400000X^2$
$399999X^2 + 3X - 2 = 0$

Solving for X using the quadratic formula

$$X = \frac{-b \pm \sqrt{b^2 - 4ac}}{2a}$$

where, $a = 399999$ $b = 3$ and $c = -2$

$$X = \frac{-3 \pm \sqrt{9 + 3199992}}{799998}$$

Hence $X = \dfrac{-3 - 1788.85}{799998}$ or $X = \dfrac{-3 + 1788.85}{799998}$

Since X cannot be negative, $X = \dfrac{1785.85}{799998} = 0.0022$

Thus 0.0022 moles of oxygen are used up at equilibrium which must give $2 \times 0.0022 = 0.0044$ moles of nitrogen oxide.

Hence the number of moles of nitrogen oxide at equilibrium is **4.4×10^{-3}**.

Problem 10 Calculate the number of moles of iodine which must be added to 3 moles of hydrogen to produce 1.98 moles of hydrogen iodide at 500 K, when K_p for the reaction is 160.

The equation of the reaction is

$$H_2(g) + I_2(g) \rightleftharpoons 2HI(g)$$

The equilibrium equation is

$$Kp = \frac{(pHI)^2}{(pH_2)(pI_2)}$$

Let the pressure of the system be P Pa and let X moles of iodine be the amount added. The concentrations of the reactants and products can be expressed as

	H_2	+	I_2	$\rightleftharpoons$	2HI	
Initially	3		X		0	moles
At equilibrium	3−0.99		(X−0.99)		1.98	moles

The total number of moles at equilibrium is

$$3 - 0.99 + (X - 0.99) + 1.98 = 3 + X$$

The mole fractions of H_2, I_2 and HI can be expressed conveniently as

Gas	Mole fraction	Partial pressure
H_2	$\dfrac{2.01}{3+X}$	$\dfrac{2.01}{3+X} \times P$, Pa
I_2	$\dfrac{X-0.99}{3+X}$	$\dfrac{X-0.99}{3+X} \times P$, Pa
HI	$\dfrac{1.98}{3+X}$	$\dfrac{1.98}{3+X} \times P$, Pa

Substituting these partial pressures into the equilibrium equation, and using $K_p = 160$ gives

$$160 = \frac{\left(\dfrac{1.98}{3+X} \times P\right)^2}{\dfrac{2.01}{3+X} \times P \quad \dfrac{X-0.99}{3+X} \times P} = \frac{1.98^2}{2.01(X-0.99)}$$

Simplifying this equation gives

$$160 \times 2.01(X-0.99) = 1.98^2 = 3.92$$
$$321.6X - 0.99 \times 321.6 = 3.92$$
$$321.6X = 318.38 + 3.92 = 322.3$$
$$X = \frac{322.3}{321.6} = 1.002$$

The number of moles of iodine to be added are **1.002**.

Problem 11 When phosphorus pentachloride is heated to 450 K it undergoes thermal dissociation to phosphorus trichloride and chlorine. If the relative density of the vapour at this temperature is 75, calculate the degree of dissociation of the PCl_5.

The equation of the reaction is

$$PCl_5(g) \rightleftharpoons PCl_3(g) + Cl_2(g).$$

Consider 1 mole of PCl_5 and assume that X moles are used up to form PCl_3 and Cl_2

$$PCl_5(g) \rightleftharpoons PCl_3(g) + Cl_2(g)$$

	PCl_5	PCl_3	Cl_2	
Initially	1	0	0	moles
At equilibrium	$1-X$	X	X	moles

The total number of moles of gas at equilibrium is

$(1-X) + X + X = 1 + X$ moles

The relative density of a gas is equal to half the molecular mass, i.e.
i.e. **Relative density = ½ (molecular mass)**.
The molecular mass of PCl_5 = 208.5 and hence its relative density should be 104.25
The number of moles of a gas in a given volume is proportional to the reciprocal of the relative density of the gas.

Hence 1 mole $\propto \dfrac{1}{104.25}$ (1)

and $1 + X$ moles $\propto \dfrac{1}{75}$ (2)

Dividing (2) by (1) gives $\dfrac{1+X}{1} = \dfrac{104.25}{75} = 1.39$

Thus $1+X = 1.39$, $X = 0.39$.
At 450 K, PCl_5 is 0.39 dissociated into PCl_3 and Cl_2, or 39% dissociated

---

Problem 12 Calculate the value of K_p at 1100 K if K_p at 700 K is 3×10^4 Pa^{-1} and $\Delta H^\ominus$ for the reaction is -19.7 kJ mol^{-1}.

The required equation is

$$\log \frac{K_p^1}{K_p^2} = \frac{-\Delta H^\ominus}{2.303 R} \left(\frac{1}{T_1} - \frac{1}{T_2}\right)$$

where K_p^1 is unknown, T_1 is 1100 K, K_p^2 is 3×10^4 Pa^{-1}, T_2 is 700 K, ΔH is -19.7 kJ mol^{-1} and R is 0.0083 kJ K^{-1} mol^{-1}.
Substituting these values into the equation gives

$$\log \frac{K_p^1}{3 \times 10^4} = \frac{19.7}{2.303 \times 0.0083} \times \left(\frac{1}{1100} - \frac{1}{700}\right)$$

$$\log K_p^1 - \log(3 \times 10^4) = \frac{19.7}{2.303 \times 0.0083} \times \left(\frac{7-11}{7700}\right)$$

$$\log K_p^1 - 4.4771 = \frac{19.7 \times (-4)}{2.303 \times 0.0083 \times 7700} = -0.5354$$

$\log K_p^1 = -0.5354 + 4.4771 = 3.9417$

Taking antilogs of both sides

K_p^1 = antilog 3.9417 = 8.744×10^3 Pa^{-1}

Thus **the value of K_p at 1100 K is 8.744×10^3 Pa^{-1}**.

C. FURTHER PROBLEMS ON GASEOUS EQUILIBRIA

(a) SHORT ANSWER PROBLEMS

Fill in the missing words

1 The equation $PV = nRT$ represents the .... equation.

2 The partial pressure of a gas in a mixture of gases is dependent on the .... of the gas and the .... of the gaseous mixture.

3 The partial pressure of a gas in a mixture of gases can be considered to be proportional to the .... of the gas.

4 For a gaseous equilibrium reaction the equilibrium constant K_p can be expressed in terms of the .... of the constituents of the mixture.

5 For an exothermic equilibrium reaction, an increase in temperature would shift the position of equilibrium towards the ....

6 If a decrease in temperature causes a shift in the position of the equilibrium towards the reactants, the reaction must be an .... reaction.

7 For the equilibrium mixture, $2A(g) + B(g) \rightleftharpoons C(g)$, an increase in pressure on the equilibrium mixture will cause a shift towards the ....

8 In order to predict the formation of the highest yield of products in an equilibrium reaction both the .... and .... of the reaction must be considered.

9 For the equilibrium mixture $A + B \rightleftharpoons C$ the units of the equilibrium constant K_p are ....

10 If a number of values of the equilibrium constant K_p are determined at different temperatures for an equilibrium reaction then the equation which relates the values can be used to find the .... of the reaction.

(b) MULTI-CHOICE PROBLEMS (answers on page 181)

Select the correct answer from those given

1 When three gases, A, B and C, are mixed together in the molar ratio of 1:2:3 the mole fraction of B is

(a) $\frac{1}{3}$; (b) $\frac{1}{2}$; (c) $\frac{1}{6}$; (d) $\frac{2}{3}$.

2 When 1 mole of nitrogen and 2 moles of oxygen are mixed together at a pressure of 300 kPa the partial pressure of oxygen is

(a) 50 kPa; (b) 100 kPa; (c) 150 kPa; (d) 200 kPa.

3 The equilibrium constant for the reaction $2NO(g) + O_2(g) \rightleftharpoons 2NO_2(g)$ can be written as

(a) $K_p = \dfrac{(pNO)^2 \times (pO_2)}{(pNO_2)^2}$; (b) $K_p = \dfrac{(pNO_2)^2}{(pNO)^2 \times (pO_2)}$

(c) $K_p = \dfrac{(2pNO_2)}{(2pNO) \times (pO_2)}$; (d) $K_p = \dfrac{(2pNO) \times (pO_2)}{(2pNO_2)}$

4 The units for the equilibrium constant K_p of the reaction

$N_2(g) + 3H_2(g) \rightleftharpoons 2NH_3(g)$ are

(a) Pa^{-2}; (b) Pa^{-1}; (c) Pa; (d) Pa^2.

5. For which of the following equilibria would an increase in pressure improve the yield of the products?
   (a) $N_2O_4(g) \rightleftharpoons 2NO_2(g)$;
   (b) $N_2(g) + O_2(g) \rightleftharpoons 2NO(g)$;
   (c) $2SO_2(g) + O_2(g) \rightleftharpoons 2SO_3(g)$;
   (d) $H_2(g) + I_2(g) \rightleftharpoons 2HI(g)$.

6. The equation which relates the equilibrium constants K_1 and K_2 of a reaction at different temperatures T_1 and T_2 is
   (a) $\dfrac{K_1}{K_2} = \dfrac{-\Delta H}{R}\left(\dfrac{1}{T_1} - \dfrac{1}{T_2}\right)$;
   (b) $\dfrac{K_1}{K_2} = \dfrac{-\Delta H}{R}\left(\dfrac{1}{T_2} - \dfrac{1}{T_1}\right)$
   (c) $\log\dfrac{K_1}{K_2} = \dfrac{-\Delta H}{2.303R}\left(\dfrac{1}{T_1} - \dfrac{1}{T_2}\right)$;
   (d) $\log\dfrac{K_1}{K_2} = \dfrac{-\Delta H}{2.303R}\left(\dfrac{1}{T_2} - \dfrac{1}{T_1}\right)$

7. The effect of increasing the temperature of the reaction
   $H_2O(g) + CO(g) \rightleftharpoons CO_2(g) + H_2(g)$, ΔH – ve would be
   (a) to increase the amounts of H_2O and CO;
   (b) to increase the amounts of CO_2 and H_2;
   (c) to achieve the same equilibrium more quickly;
   (d) to increase the value of K_p.

8. If the relative density of dinitrogen tetroxide N_2O_4 is 23.5 at 400 K, the degree of dissociation is
   (a) 0.48; (b) 0.68; (c) 0.88; (d) 0.98.

9. For an equilibrium reaction, K_p is found to be 10^{-3} Pa at 300 K, and 10^{-4} Pa at 500 K. The enthalpy of the reaction is
   (a) -14.37 kJ mol^{-1};
   (b) $+14.37$ kJ mol^{-1};
   (c) -0.0696 kJ mol^{-1};
   (d) $+0.0696$ kJ mol^{-1}.
   (Use $R = 8.3 \times 10^{-3}$ kJ K^{-1} mol^{-1})

10. To optimise the yield of products in the equilibrium
    $2A(g) + B(g) \rightleftharpoons C(g) + D(g)$ ΔH + ve
    the conditions affecting the reaction should be
    (a) high pressure and high temperature;
    (b) low pressure and low temperature;
    (c) high pressure and low temperature;
    (d) low pressure and high temperature.

(c) CONVENTIONAL PROBLEMS

1. Explain why partial pressures can be used to express the equilibrium constant of a gaseous reaction.

2. Calculate the partial pressures of 1.5 moles of carbon monoxide and 3.5 moles of nitrogen which combine to give a pressure of 180 kPa.
   [pCO = 54 kPa. pH$_2$ = 126 kPa]

3. Calculate the mole fraction of neon in a mixture of helium and neon at a pressure of 250 kPa if the partial pressure of helium is 90 kPa. [0.56]

4. Derive an expression for the equilibrium constant K_p for the reaction
   $2SO_2(g) + O_2(g) \rightleftharpoons 2SO_3(g)$ formed by mixing a moles of sulphur dioxide

and b moles of oxygen at 300 K and P Pa pressure, if c moles of SO_3 are formed at equilibrium.

5. Calculate the number of molecules of hydrogen iodide present in the equilibrium mixture formed when 1 mole of hydrogen and 2 moles of iodine react to equilibrium at 700 K. K_p for the reaction is 54. [1.877]

6. When 1 mole of hydrogen and 3 moles of carbon dioxide are reacted to equilibrium at 1000 K and 500 kPa pressure, 0.25 moles of hydrogen are present. Calculate K_p for this reaction at this temperature, given $H_2(g) + CO_2(g) \rightleftharpoons H_2O(g) + CO(g)$
[$K_p = 1$]

7. Calculate the number of moles of dinitrogen tetroxide which are needed to produce an equilibrium mixture containing 2 moles of nitrogen dioxide at a pressure of 100 kPa and a temperature of 350 K, if K_p is 3.89 kPa. [10.19]

8. When ammonia is maintained at 750 K and a pressure of 100 kPa it reaches an equilibrium which contains 20% by volume of ammonia. Calculate the degree of dissociation of the equilibrium reaction. [66.67%]

9. When 1 mole of O_2 and 2 moles of SO_2 are converted into SO_3 at a constant temperature and a pressure of 1000 kPa, one fifth of the SO_2 is present at equilibrium. Calculate the value of the equilibrium constant, K_p. [0.176 kPa^{-1}]

10. When 1 mole of nitrogen dioxide is heated to equilibrium in a closed vessel 0.8 moles of NO_2 are present in the equilibrium mixture, $2NO_2(g) \rightleftharpoons 2NO(g) + O_2(g)$. If $K_p = 7 \times 10^{-4}$ kPa^{-1} at this temperature, calculate the pressure at which the mixture is maintained. [0.1344 kPa]

11. Calculate the value of the equilibrium constant for the reaction $H_2(g) + I_2(g) \rightleftharpoons 2HI(g)$ at 1000 K, given that at 730 K, $K_p = 49$ and ΔH for the reaction is +26.5 kJ mol^{-1}. (Use $R = 8.31$ J K^{-1} mol^{-1}) [15.06]

12. Calculate the enthalpy of the reaction

$$N_2O_4(g) \rightleftharpoons 2NO_2(g)$$

if $K_p = 3.89$ Pa and 293 Pa at 350 K and 600 K respectively.
[+46.23 kJ mol^{-1}]

3 Ionic equilibria

A. MAIN POINTS CONCERNING IONIC EQUILIBRIA

1. (i) The **Brönsted-Lowry theory** defines **an acid** as a molecule which can **donate a proton** to another molecule. For example, the general acid HA dissociates or ionises according to the equation

    $$\underset{Acid}{HA} \rightleftharpoons \underset{Proton}{H^+} + \underset{Base}{A^-}$$

    (ii) The Brönsted-Lowry theory defines **a base** as a molecule which can **accept a proton** from another molecule. Using the general equation given above,

    $$\underset{Base}{A^-} + \underset{Proton}{H^+} \rightleftharpoons \underset{Acid}{HA}$$

    (iii) For any acid to behave as an acid it must have a base to which a proton can be donated, and for any base to behave as a base it must have an acid from which it can accept a proton.

2. When an acid and a base react together they produce another acid and base. For example

    $$\underset{Acid\ 1}{HNO_3} + \underset{Base\ 2}{H_2O} \rightleftharpoons \underset{Acid\ 2}{H_3{}^+O} + \underset{Base\ 1}{NO_3{}^-}$$

    The base produced by the loss of a proton is called the **conjugate base of the acid**, and the acid and base are called a **conjugate acid base pair**. For the example shown, the loss of a proton from nitric acid, HNO_3, gives the nitrate ion, $NO_3{}^-$, thus nitric acid and the nitrate ion are a conjugate acid base pair. Similarly, when the water molecule accepts a proton, it becomes the hydrated hydrogen ion $H_3{}^+O$, and hence, **water is the base and the hydrogen ion is the acid of a conjugate acid base pair**. (Further examples are given in *Problem 1*.)

3. (i) All acid reactions can be written as equilibrium reactions. For the general reaction of an acid HA with water, the equation is

    $$HA + H_2O \rightleftharpoons H_3{}^+O + A^-$$

    The equilibrium constant for this reaction is given by

    $$K_c = \frac{[H_3{}^+O][A^-]}{[HA][H_2O]}$$

In this equilibrium, the **concentration of water is considered to be constant** and the equilibrium constant is called the **dissociation or ionisation constant**, K_a, of the acid.

i.e. $$K_a = \frac{[H_3^+O][A^-]}{[HA]}$$

(ii) For a base in solution, for example,

$$BOH + H_2O \rightleftharpoons B^+ + OH^-$$

the equilibrium constant K_b is called **the dissociation constant (ionisation constant) of the base.**

i.e. $$K_b = \frac{[B^+][OH^-]}{[BOH]}$$

(iii) The numerical value of both K_a and K_b is a measure of the **degree of dissociation (or ionisation)** of the acid or base.

(iv) For large values of K_a and K_b the acids and bases are considered to be completely dissociated and represented by a suitable equation. For example

for an acid $\quad HCl + H_2O = H_3^+O + Cl$
or, for a base, $\quad NaOH + H_2O = Na^+ + OH^-$.

These acids and bases are called **strong acids and bases.**

(v) For small numerical values of K_a and K_b the acids and bases are only **partially dissociated** and are called **weak acids** and **weak bases**. These are represented by **equilibrium equations**.

4 The degree of dissociation (or ionisation) is given the symbol α and expressed either as a fraction of unity or as a percentage.

5 (i) The degree of dissociation, α, is used to calculate the concentration of hydrogen ions for weak acids according to the expression

$$[H_3^+O]_{(Equil)} = [HA]_{(Initial)} \times \alpha$$

(ii) The concentration of hydroxide ions for weak bases is given by the expression

$$[OH^-]_{(Equil)} = [BOH]_{(Initial)} \times \alpha$$

(See *Problems 7 to 14*.)

6 The dissociation constant, K_a, the degree of dissociation α, and the concentration of the acid, expressed as the number of litres, V, containing 1 mole of the weak acid, are related by the expression

$$K_a = \frac{\alpha^2}{V(1-\alpha)}$$

which is called the **Ostwald Dilution Law**.

7 The concentration of hydrogen ions for weak acids are conveniently expressed on the **pH scale**, where

$$pH = \log_{10} \frac{1}{[H_3^+O]} \quad \text{or} \quad -\log_{10} [H_3^+O]$$

Similarly, the concentration of hydroxide ions for weak bases are conveniently expressed on the *pOH* scale, where

$$pOH = \log_{10} \frac{1}{[OH^-]} \quad \text{or} \quad -\log_{10} [OH^-]$$

8 The dissociation constants of weak acids K_a and weak bases K_b are numerically small and are expressed more conveniently as pK_a or pK_b values where

$$pK_a = \log_{10} \frac{1}{K_a} \quad \text{or} \quad -\log_{10} K_a$$

$$\text{and } pK_b = \log_{10} \frac{1}{K_b} \quad \text{or} \quad -\log_{10} K_b$$

9 **Buffer solutions** can be prepared by (i) dissolving the salt of a weak acid in a solution of the weak acid or (ii) dissolving the salt of a weak base in a solution of the weak base.

10 The **pH value of a buffer solution** is given by the equation

$$pH = pK_a + \log_{10} \frac{\text{concentration of the salt}}{\text{concentration of the acid}}$$

The *pOH* value of a buffer solution is given by the equation

$$pOH = pK_b + \log_{10} \frac{\text{concentration of the salt}}{\text{concentration of the base}}$$

(See *Problems 15 to 19*.)

B. WORKED PROBLEMS ON IONIC EQUILIBRIA

Problem 1 Write down the conjugate acids of the following bases.
(a) OH^-; (b) NH_3; (c) $C_6H_5NH_2$; (d) CH_3COO^-; (e) NH_2^-; (f) Cl^-; (g) H_2O.

The conjugate of any base can be obtained by adding a proton (H^+) to each of the bases.

(a) OH^- + H^+ $\rightleftharpoons$ H_2O
      base   proton   conjugate acid

(b) NH_3 + H^+ $\rightleftharpoons$ NH_4^+

(c) $C_6H_5NH_2$ + H^+ $\rightleftharpoons$ $C_6H_5NH_3^+$

(d) CH_3COO^- + H^+ $\rightleftharpoons$ CH_3COOH

(e) NH_2^- + H^+ $\rightleftharpoons$ NH_3

(f) Cl^- + H^+ $\rightleftharpoons$ HCl

(g) H_2O + H^+ $\rightleftharpoons$ H_3^+O

Problem 2 Write down the conjugate bases of the following acids.
(a) H_3^+O; (b) NH_4^+; (c) $HCOOH$; (d) HNO_3; (e) H_2SO_4; (f) H_2O.

The conjugate base of any acid can be written by removing a proton (H^+) from that acid.

(a) H_3^+O − H^+ ⇌ H_2O
    acid   proton   conjugate base
(b) NH_4^+ − H^+ ⇌ NH_3
(c) $HCOOH$ − H^+ ⇌ $HCOO^-$
(d) HNO_3 − H^+ ⇌ NO_3^-
(e) H_2SO_4 − H^+ ⇌ HSO_4^-
(f) H_2O − H^+ ⇌ OH^-

Problem 3 Complete the following equations and hence write down the conjugate acid base pairs.

(a) $CH_3COOH + H_2O$ (b) $HCl + H_2O$
(c) $NH_3 + H_2O$ (d) $H_2O + H_2O$
(e) $NH_3 + NH_3$

(a) $\quad CH_3COOH + H_2O \rightleftharpoons CH_3COO^- + H_3^+O$
    Conjugate acid base pairs $\quad CH_3COOH : CH_3COO^-, H_3^+O : H_2O$

(b) $\quad HCl + H_2O \rightleftharpoons H_3^+O + Cl^-$
    Conjugate acid base pairs $\quad HCl : Cl^-, H_3^+O : H_2O$

(c) $\quad NH_3 + H_2O \rightleftharpoons NH_4^+ + OH^-$
    Conjugate acid base pairs $\quad NH_4^+ : NH_3, H_2O : {}^-OH$

(d) $\quad H_2O + H_2O \rightleftharpoons H_3^+O + OH^-$
    Conjugate acid base pairs $\quad H_2O : {}^-OH, H_3^+O : H_2O$

(e) $\quad NH_3 + NH_3 \rightleftharpoons NH_4^+ + NH_2^-$
    Conjugate acid base pairs $\quad NH_3 : NH_2^-, NH_4^+ : NH_3$

Problem 4 Explain the terms (i) *pH*; (ii) *pOH*; (iii) *pK$_a$* and (iv) *pK$_b$*.

(i) The *pH* of a solution is defined as the logarithm of the reciprocal of the hydrogen ion concentration of the solution,

i.e. $pH = \log_{10} \dfrac{1}{[H_3^+O]} = -\log_{10} [H_3^+O]$

(ii) The *pOH* of a solution is defined as the logarithm of the reciprocal of the hydroxide ion of the solution,

i.e. $pOH = \log_{10} \dfrac{1}{[{}^-OH]} = -\log_{10} [{}^-OH]$

(iii) The *pK$_a$* of a solution is the logarithm of the reciprocal of the acid dissociation constant of that acidic solution.

i.e. $pK_a = \log_{10} \dfrac{1}{K_a} = -\log_{10} K_a$

(iv) The *pK$_b$* of a solution is the logarithm of the reciprocal of the basic dissociation constant of the basic solution.

i.e. $pK_b = \log_{10} \dfrac{1}{K_b} = -\log_{10} K_b$

> **Problem 5** Convert the following K_a values into pK_a values,
> (i) $K_a = 10^{-6}$ mol dm^{-3}; (ii) $K_a = 3.5 \times 10^{-7}$ mol dm^{-3}.

(i) If $K_a = 10^{-6}$ mol dm^{-3} then $pK_a = \log_{10} \frac{1}{(10^{-6})} = -\log_{10}(10^{-6}) = -(-6) = 6$

Hence, $pK_a = 6$ mol^{-1} dm^3.

(ii) If $K_a = 3.5 \times 10^{-7}$ mol dm^{-3}

then $pK_a = \log_{10} \frac{1}{(3.5 \times 10^{-7})} = -\log_{10}(3.5 \times 10^{-7})$

Hence, $pK_a = -(\log_{10} 3.5 + \log_{10} 10^{-7})$
$= -(0.544 - 7) = 6.456$

The pK_a value is 6.456 mol^{-1} dm^3.

> **Problem 6** Find the hydrogen ion concentration of a 0.1 M monobasic acid which is 15% ionised at 298 K.

Let the monobasic acid be HA. In solution it will ionise according to the equation

$$HA + H_2O \rightleftharpoons H_3O^+ + A^-$$

Since the concentration of the acid is 0.1 M, if the acid was completely ionised the concentration of hydrogen ions would be 0.1 mol dm^{-3}.
However the acid is only 15% ionised hence the hydrogen ion concentration is
$0.1 \times \frac{15}{100}$ or 0.015 mol dm^{-3}.
i.e. $[H_3^+O] = 0.015$ mol dm^{-3}.

> **Problem 7** Calculate the pH of a 0.05 M solution of nitrous acid, HNO_2, for which the degree of dissociation is 0.097.

The equation of the reaction is

$$HNO_2(aq) + H_2O(l) \rightleftharpoons H_3^+O(aq) + NO_2^-(aq)$$

Using the relationship

$[H_3^+O] = \alpha \times [HNO_2]$ mol dm^{-3}

gives

$[H_3^+O] = 0.097 \times 0.05$ mol dm^{-3}

$[H_3^+O] = 0.00485$ mol dm^{-3} or 4.85×10^{-3} mol dm^{-3}

The pH of a solution is given by the expression

$pH = -\log_{10}[H_3^+O]$.

Thus $pH = -\log_{10}(4.85 \times 10^{-3}) = -\log_{10} 4.85 - \log_{10} 10^{-3}$

i.e. $pH = -0.686 - (-3) = 3 - 0.686 = 2.31$

Thus the pH of a 0.05 M solution of nitrous acid is 2.31.

Problem 8 Find the degree of ionisation of a 0.5 M monobasic acid if its hydrogen ion concentration is 0.1 mol dm^{-3}.

Let the monobasic acid be HA which ionises according to the equation

$$HA + H_2O \rightleftharpoons H_3O^+ + A^-$$

Assuming complete ionisation [HA] = 0.05 mol dm^{-3}
However [H$_3^+$O] = 0.1 mol dm^{-3}

Using the relationship for a weak acid,

[H$_3^+$O] = $\alpha \times$ [HA], where α = the degree of ionisation, and substituting [H$_3^+$O] = 0.1 and [HA] = 0.5 mol dm^{-3} gives

0.1 mol dm^{-3} = $\alpha \times$ 0.5 mol dm^{-3}

Thus $\quad \alpha = \dfrac{0.1 \text{ mol dm}^{-3}}{0.5 \text{ mol dm}^{-3}} = 0.2$

(*Note: α has no units*)
Thus the degree of ionisation is **0.2 or the acid is 20% ionised.**

Problem 9 Derive an expression relating the dissociation constant K_a, the degree of dissociation, α, and the concentration of a monobasic acid.

Let the formula of the monobasic acid be HA, then the equation of the equilibrium is

$$HA(aq) + H_2O(l) \rightleftharpoons H_3^+O(aq) + A^-(aq)$$

and the equilibrium constant is given by

$$K_a = \frac{[H_3^+O][A^-]}{[HA]} \quad \text{(Note, water is omitted because it is assumed to be constant)}$$

Assuming that 1 mole of the acid is contained in V dm^3 of solution, the concentration of the acid before dissociation is $1/V$ mol dm^{-3}.
At equilibrium the concentration of hydrogen ions is given by

$$[H_3^+O] = \alpha \times [HA] = \alpha \times \frac{1}{V} \text{ mol dm}^{-3}$$

It can be deduced that [A$^-$] is also $\alpha \times \dfrac{1}{V}$ mol dm^{-3} and that at equilibrium

[HA] = $\dfrac{1}{V} - \dfrac{\alpha}{V}$ mol dm^{-3}. Substituting these values into the expression for

the equilibrium constant gives

$$K_a = \frac{\dfrac{\alpha}{V} \times \dfrac{\alpha}{V}}{\dfrac{1}{V} - \dfrac{\alpha}{V}} \text{ mol dm}^{-3}$$

i.e. $K_a = \dfrac{\dfrac{\alpha^2}{V^2}}{\dfrac{1-\alpha}{V}} = \dfrac{\alpha^2}{V^2} \times \dfrac{V}{1-\alpha} = \dfrac{\alpha^2}{V(1-\alpha)}$ mol dm^{-3}

Thus, for a monobasic acid, K_a, α and the concentration $\frac{1}{V}$ are related by the equation $K_a = \frac{\alpha^2}{V(1-\alpha)}$, this expression being known as the **Ostwald Dilution Law**.

Problem 10 Use the Ostwald dilution law to find the degree of dissociation of a 0.01 M solution of methanoic acid for which $K_a = 1.6 \times 10^{-4}$ mol dm^{-3}.

The equation of the reaction is

$$HCOOH(aq) + H_2O(l) \rightleftharpoons HCOO^-(aq) + H_3^+O(aq).$$

since the concentration of the methanoic acid is 0.01 mol dm^{-3}, 1 mole of the acid will be contained in 100 dm^3 of solution. Ostwald's dilution law states that

$$K_a = \frac{\alpha^2}{V(1-\alpha)}$$

Since $K_a = 1.6 \times 10^{-4}$ mol dm^{-3} and $V = 100$ dm^3 then

$$1.6 \times 10^{-4} = \frac{\alpha^2}{100(1-\alpha)}$$

Simplifying the equation gives

$1.6 \times 10^{-4}(100 - 100\alpha) = \alpha^2$
$1.6 \times 10^{-2} - (1.6 \times 10^{-2})\alpha = \alpha^2$
or $100\alpha^2 + 1.6\alpha - 1.6 = 0$

Solving this quadratic equation using the quadratic formula

$$\alpha = \frac{-b \pm \sqrt{(b^2 - 4ac)}}{2a}, \text{ where } a = 100, \ b = 1.6 \text{ and } c = -1.6$$

gives $\alpha = \frac{-1.6 \pm \sqrt{(2.56 + 640)}}{200}$

and $\alpha = \frac{-1.6 + 25.35}{200}$ or $\alpha = \frac{-1.6 - 25.35}{200}$

Since α cannot be negative,

$$\alpha = \frac{23.75}{200} = 0.1188$$

Hence the degree of dissociation of 0.01 M methanoic acid is **0.119**.

Problem 11 Calculate the degree of ionisation of a 0.4 M solution of propanoic acid, CH_3CH_2COOH, which has a K_a value of 1.3×10^{-5} mol dm^{-3}.

The equation of the reaction is

$$CH_3CH_2COOH(aq) + H_2O(l) \rightleftharpoons CH_3CH_2COO^-(aq) + H_3^+O(aq)$$

Assume the degree of ionisation is α.
At equilibrium the concentration of hydrogen ions for a weak acid is given by

$[H_3^+O] = \alpha \times [CH_3CH_2COOH]$
Hence, $[H_3^+O] = \alpha \times 0.4$ mol dm^{-3}

It can be seen from the equation that

$$[CH_3CH_2COO^-] = \alpha \times 0.4 \text{ mol dm}^{-3}$$

The value of $[CH_3CH_2COOH]$ at equilibrium is

$$[CH_3CH_2COOH] = (0.4 - 0.4\alpha) \text{ mol dm}^{-3}$$

since 0.4α mol dm^{-3} have been ionised.
The equilibrium law applied to the equation gives

$$K_a = \frac{[CH_3CH_2COO^-][H_3^+O]}{[CH_3CH_2COOH]}$$

Substituting into this equation the values of K_a and the concentrations in terms of α gives

$$1.3 \times 10^{-5} = \frac{(0.4\alpha)(0.4\alpha)}{(0.4 - 0.4\alpha)}$$

Solving for α gives

$$1.3 \times 10^{-5}(0.4 - 0.4\alpha) = (0.4\alpha)^2$$

$$(5.2 \times 10^{-6}) - (5.2 \times 10^{-6})\alpha = 0.16\alpha^2$$

or $160000\alpha^2 + 5.2\alpha - 5.2 = 0$

Using the quadratic formula, $= \frac{-b \pm \sqrt{(b^2 - 4ac)}}{2a}$

where $a = 160000$, $b = 5.2$ and $c = -5.2$ gives

$$\alpha = \frac{-5.2 \pm \sqrt{(27.04 + 3328000)}}{320,000}$$

$$\alpha = \frac{-5.2 + 3328027.04}{320,000} \quad \text{or} \quad \frac{-5.2 - 3328027.04}{320,000}$$

Since α cannot be negative, then

$$\alpha = \frac{-5.2 + 1824.29}{320,000} = 0.0057$$

Hence, the degree of ionisation of 0.4 M propanoic acid is **0.0057**.

Problem 12 What is the *pH* of a 0.3 M solution of chloroethanoic acid for which $K_a = 1.3 \times 10^{-3}$ mol dm^{-3}.

The equation for the reaction is

$$CH_2ClCOOH(aq) + H_2O(l) \rightleftharpoons CH_2ClCOO^-(aq) + H_3^+O(aq)$$

Since the concentration of the solution is 0.3 M, 1 mole of the acid is contained in $3\frac{1}{3}$ dm^3. Applying the Ostwald law

$$K_a = \frac{\alpha^2}{V(1-\alpha)}$$

where $K_a = 1.3 \times 10^{-3}$ mol dm^{-3}, and $V = 3\frac{1}{3}$ dm^3.
Substituting in these values gives

$$1.3 \times 10^{-3} = \frac{\alpha^2}{3\frac{1}{3}(1-\alpha)}$$

Simplifying this equation gives

$(1.3 \times 10^{-3})(3\frac{1}{3} - 3\frac{1}{3}\alpha) = \alpha^2$

$4.33 \times 10^{-3} - (4.33 \times 10^{-3})\alpha = \alpha^2$

or $1000\alpha^2 + 4.33\alpha - 4.33 = 0$

Hence, $\alpha = \dfrac{-4.33 \pm \sqrt{(18.78 + 17333)}}{2000} = \dfrac{-4.33 \pm 131.93}{2000} = 0.064$ or -0.068

Since α cannot be negative $\alpha = 0.064$
Using the relationship $[H_3^+O] = \alpha \times (0.3)$ mol dm^{-3},

$[H_3^+O] = 0.064 \times 0.3 = 0.019$ mol dm^{-3}

The *pH* of the solution is found using the expression

$pH = -\log_{10}[H_3^+O]$.

Thus $pH = -\log_{10}(0.019) = -\log_{10}(1.9 \times 10^{-2})$

$pH = -\log_{10} 1.9 - \log_{10} 10^{-2} = -0.279 - (-2) = 1.72$

Thus the *pH* of a 0.3 M solution of chloroethanoic acid is 1.72.

Problem 13 Calculate the ionisation constant (K_a) of ethanoic acid which is 0.2 M and 0.94% ionised.

The equation of equilibrium is

$$CH_3COOH(aq) + H_2O(l) \rightleftharpoons CH_3COO^-(aq) + H_3^+O(aq)$$

Applying the equilibrium law to this equation gives

$K_a = \dfrac{[CH_3COO^-][H_3^+O]}{[CH_3COOH][H_2O]}$

Since water is a solvent, its concentration is considered to be constant and the equilibrium expression can be rewritten as

$K_a = \dfrac{[CH_3COO^-][H_3^+O]}{[CH_3COOH]}$

where K_a is the ionisation (or dissociation) constant of the acid. Since the original concentration of the ethanoic acid is 0.2 M and $\alpha = 0.0094$.
Using the relationship $[H_3^+O] = \alpha \times CH_3COOH$ gives

$[H_3^+O] = 0.0094 \times 0.2 = 0.00188$ or 1.88×10^{-3} mol dm^{-3}

Since $[H_3^+O] = 1.88 \times 10^{-3}$ mol dm^{-3}, from the equation of the reaction $[CH_3COO^-] = 1.88 \times 10^{-3}$ mol dm^{-3}. Since 1.88×10^{-3} mol dm^{-3} of the acid has been dissociated the concentration of the acid at equilibrium is given by

$[CH_3COOH]$ = Initial concentration − Equilibrium concentration, that is, $0.2 - (1.88 \times 10^{-3})$ mol dm^{-3} = 0.198 mol dm^{-3}.

Substituting the concentration values in the equation gives

$K_a = \dfrac{(1.88 \times 10^{-3}) \text{ mol dm}^{-3} \times (1.88 \times 10^{-3}) \text{ mol dm}^{-3}}{0.198 \text{ mol dm}^{-3}}$

$= \dfrac{3.534 \times 10^{-6}}{0.198} = 1.78 \times 10^{-5}$ mol dm^{-3}

Hence the ionisation (or dissociation) constant of ethanoic acid is
1.78 × 10⁻⁵ mol dm⁻³

Problem 14 What concentration of a solution of benzoic acid, for which $K_a = 6.4 \times 10^{-5}$ mol dm⁻³, would give a degree of dissociation of 0.025.

The equation of the equilibrium is

$$C_6H_5COOH(aq) + H_2O(l) \rightleftharpoons C_6H_5COO^-(aq) + H_3^+O(aq)$$

Assuming the concentration of benzoic acid is X mol dm⁻³, then the concentration of hydrogen ions at equilibrium is given by the expression

$[H_3^+O] = \alpha \times [C_6H_5COOH]$

or $[H_3^+O] = 0.025 \times (X)$ mol dm⁻³

It can be deduced that $[C_6H_5COO^-] = 0.025 \times (X)$ mol dm⁻³
and $[C_6H_5COOH] = (X - 0.025X)$ mol dm⁻³

The dissociation constant for the equilibrium is given by,

$$K_a = \frac{[C_6H_5COO^-][H_3^+O]}{[C_6H_5COOH]}$$

Substituting the known values into this equation gives

$$6.4 \times 10^{-5} = \frac{(0.025X)(0.025X)}{(X - 0.025X)}$$

Simplifying this equation gives

$(6.4 \times 10^{-5})(X - 0.025X) = (0.025X)^2$
$(6.4 \times 10^{-5})X - (0.16 \times 10^{-5})X + (62.5 \times 10^{-5})X^2$
$(6.24 \times 10^{-5})X + (62.5 \times 10^{-5})X^2$
Hence $62.5 \times 10^{-5}X^2 - 6.24 \times 10^{-5}X = 0$
i.e. $10^{-5}(62.5X - 6.24)X = 0$
Hence either $X = 0$ or $62.5X - 6.24 = 0$ from which

$$X = \frac{6.24}{62.5} = 0.0998 \text{ mol dm}^{-3}$$

Thus the concentration of benzoic acid is **0.0998 mol dm⁻³**.

Problem 15 Derive an expression for the *pH* of a buffer solution obtained by dissolving a weak acid (HA) in a solution of the sodium salt of that acid (NaA), assuming K_a is the dissociation constant of the acid.

The equation of the weak acid in water is

$$HA(aq) + H_2O(l) \rightleftharpoons H_3^+O(aq) + A^-(aq)$$

and the equilibrium law applied to the equation gives

$K_a = \dfrac{[H_3^+O][A^-]}{[HA]}$, assuming that $[H_2O]$ is constant

Rearranging, this equation becomes

$$K_a = [H_3^+O] \times \frac{[A^-]}{[HA]}$$

or $-[H_3^+O] = -K_a \times \dfrac{[A^-]}{[HA]}$

Taking logarithms of both sides of this equation gives

$-\log [H_3^+O] = -\log K_a + \log \dfrac{[A^-]}{[HA]}$

Since $-\log [H_3^+O] = pH$ and $-\log K_a = pK_a$

then $pH = pK_a + \log \dfrac{[A^-]}{[HA]}$

Problem 16 Calculate the *pH* of an equimolar solution of potassium ethanoate and ethanoic acid, for which $K_a = 1.8 \times 10^{-5}$ mol dm^{-3}.

The equation for the *pH* of a buffer solution is given by

$pH = pK_a + \log \dfrac{[salt]}{[acid]}$ (from *Problem 15*)

For this buffer solution, $pH = pK_a + \log \dfrac{[\text{potassium ethanoate}]}{[\text{ethanoic acid}]}$

Since the solution is equimolar then

$\dfrac{[\text{potassium ethanoate}]}{[\text{ethanoic acid}]} = 1$

$pK_a = -\log(1.8 \times 10^{-5}) = -\log 1.8 - \log 10^{-5}$
$= -0.255 - (-5) = 4.745$

Substituting these values into the equation gives

$pH = 4.745 + \log 1 = 4.745$

Thus the *pH* of the solution is 4.745 which is equal to the pK_a value of ethanoic acid.

Problem 17 Calculate the ratio of the compositions of the buffer solution composed of ethanoic acid, $K_a = 1.8 \times 10^{-5}$ mol dm^{-3}, and sodium ethanoate, which would give solution *pH* of 5.

The equation relating *pH*, K_a and composition is

$pH = pK_a + \log \dfrac{[A^-]}{[HA]}$, (see *Problem 15*)

and [HA] is the concentration of the acid.
For this problem the equation becomes

$pH = pK_a + \log \dfrac{[CH_3COO^-]}{[CH_3COOH]}$

For this equation, $pH = 5$ and $pK_a = -\log_{10}(1.8 \times 10^{-5})$,
hence $pK_a = 4.745$ (from *Problem 16*).

Substituting these values into the equation gives

$$5 = 4.745 + \log \frac{[CH_3COO^-]}{[CH_3COOH]} \quad \text{hence} \quad \log \frac{[CH_3COO^-]}{[CH_3COOH]} = 0.255$$

Taking antilogarithms of both sides gives

$$\frac{[CH_3COO^-]}{[CH_3COOH]} = \text{antilog } 0.255 = 1.80$$

Hence the ratio of the concentrations of sodium ethanoate to ethanoic acid is 1.80 : 1.
Thus, if the concentration of ethanoic acid is 0.1 M, then that of sodium ethanoate will be **0.18 M.**
Alternatively, if the concentration ethanoic acid is 0.02 M then that of the sodium ethanoate will be

$0.02 \times 1.80 = 0.036$ M.

Problem 18 Calculate the number of moles of sodium propanoate, C_2H_5COONa, which must be added to 1 dm^3 of a 0.04 M solution of propanoic acid for which K_a is 1.3×10^{-5} mol dm^{-3} to give a *pH* of 4.6.

The equation for the *pH* of a buffer solution is

$$pH = pK_a + \log \frac{[salt]}{[acid]}$$

In this equation, $pH = 4.6$, and $pK_a = -\log_{10}(1.3 \times 10^{-5})$
Hence $pK_a = -\log 1.3 - \log 10^{-5} = -0.1139 - (-5) = 4.89$
Substituting these values into the equation gives

$$4.6 = 4.89 + \log \frac{[salt]}{[acid]} \quad \text{or} \quad -0.29 = \log \frac{[salt]}{[acid]}$$

Using the laws of logarithms, this equation becomes

$$-0.29 = -\log \frac{[acid]}{[salt]} \quad \text{i.e.} \quad 0.29 = \log \frac{[acid]}{[salt]}$$

Taking antilogs of both sides gives

$$\text{antilog } 0.29 = \frac{[acid]}{[salt]} \quad \text{or} \quad \frac{[acid]}{[salt]} = 1.95$$

Hence the ratio propanoic acid : sodium propanoate = 1.95 : 1

The concentration of propanoic acid is 0.04 M.

thus the concentration of sodium propanoate = $0.04 \times \frac{1}{1.95}$ mol dm^{-3}
= 0.0205 mol dm^{-3}.

Thus the number of moles of sodium propanoate to be added is **0.0205 moles.**

Problem 19 Calculate the hydrogen ion concentration of a solution containing 0.5 moles of ammonium chloride dissolved in 0.2 M ammonia solution, for which $K_b = 1.8 \times 10^{-5}$.

Since this is a basic buffer solution, the hydroxide ion concentration must be found first. The equation for the pOH of a basic buffer solution is

$$pOH = pK_b + \log \frac{[salt]}{[base]},$$

which for this buffer becomes

$$pOH = pK_b + \log \frac{[ammonium\ chloride]}{[ammonia\ solution]}$$

Substituting in the known values gives

$$pOH = -\log(1.8 \times 10^{-5}) + \log \frac{(0.5)}{(0.2)}$$

$$= -\log 1.8 - \log 10^{-5} + \log 2.5 = -0.2553 + 5 + 0.3979$$

Hence $pOH = 5.143$ or $-\log_{10}[^-OH] = 5.143$
Changing signs and taking antilogs gives

$$[^-OH] = \text{antilog}(-5.143) = \text{antilog}(-6 + 0.857)$$
$$= \text{antilog}(-6) \times \text{antilog}\ 0.857$$

Hence $[^-OH] = 10^{-6} \times 7.194\ mol\ dm^{-3}$
using the expression $[H_3^+O][^-OH] = 10^{-14}\ mol^2\ dm^{-6}$ for any aqueous solution gives

$$[H_3^+O](7.194 \times 10^{-6}) = 10^{-14}\ mol\ dm^{-3}$$

Hence $[H_3^+O] = \dfrac{10^{-14}}{7.194 \times 10^{-6}} = 1.39 \times 10^{-9}\ mol\ dm^{-3}$

Thus the hydrogen ion concentration of the buffer solution is
$1.39 \times 10^{-9}\ mol\ dm^{-3}$.

C. FURTHER PROBLEMS ON IONIC EQUILIBRIA

(a) SHORT ANSWER PROBLEMS

Fill in the missing words

1   The Brönsted–Lowry definition of an acid states that it is a compound which acts as a........ ....

2   The Brönsted–Lowry definition of a base states that it is a compound which acts as a........ ....

3   The chemical species HCl(aq) and Cl⁻(aq) are classified as a........ .... pair.

4   The conjugate base of the water molecule is the....... ion.

5   The pH of any solution is defined as the............ .... of the hydrogen ion concentration of the solution.

6   The pK_b of a solution can be defined as the negative logarithm to the base ten of the........ ....

7   The concentration of hydrogen ions for a weak acid, HA, is found by multiplying the concentration of the acid by its ....

8   The degree of dissociation of a weak acid or weak base is a measure of the extent of the .... of the acid.

9   The value of the dissociation constant for a weak base is only constant at ....

10 The pH of a buffer solution depends upon the .... of the weak acid or weak base and the ratio of the .... to the ....

(b) MULTI-CHOICE PROBLEMS (answers on page 181)

Select the correct answer from those given.

1   The Brönsted—Lowry theory defines an acid as a molecule which
    (a) contains replaceable hydrogen;   (c) donates a proton;
    (b) releases hydrogen in a reaction with metals;   (d) accepts a proton.

2   In the following equation
    $$CH_3COOH + H_2O \rightleftharpoons CH_3COO^- + H_3^+O$$
    a conjugate acid and base pair is
    (a) CH_3COOH and H_2O;   (b) CH_3COOH and CH_3COO^-;
    (c) CH_3COOH and H_3^+O;   (d) CH_3COO^- and H_3^+O.

3   The pK_a of a weak acid is defined as
    (a) $\log_{10} K_a$; (b) $\dfrac{1}{\log_{10} K_a}$; (c) $\log_{10} \dfrac{1}{K_a}$; (d) $-\log_{10} \dfrac{1}{K_a}$.

4   If the concentration of a base BOH is 0.2 M and the concentration of hydroxide ions at equilibrium is 0.005 M, the degree of dissociation α is
    (a) 0.025; (b) 0.25; (c) 0.05; (d) 0.5.

5   The Ostwald Dilution law can be written as
    (a) $K_a = \dfrac{\alpha^2}{V}$; (b) $K_a = \dfrac{\alpha}{V(1-\alpha)}$; (c) $K_a = \dfrac{\alpha^2}{V(\alpha-1)}$; (d) $K_a = \dfrac{\alpha^2}{V(1-\alpha)}$.

6   pK_a for butanoic acid is 4.8. The acid dissociation constant is
    (a) 4.8×10^{-5} mol dm^{-5};   (b) 1.5×10^{-5} mol dm^{-3};
    (c) 4.8×10^{-2} mol dm^{-3};   (d) 1.5×10^{-3} mol dm^{-3}.

7   For an acid HA the pK_a value is negative. This indicates that the acid is
    (a) completely dissociated;   (b) partially dissociated;
    (c) 50% dissociated;   (d) not dissociated at all.

8   The equation for the pH of a buffer solution can be represented by
    $$pH = X + \log \dfrac{[salt]}{[acid]}$$
    X in this equation is
    (a) K_a; (b) $-K_a$; (c) pK_a; (d) $-pK_a$.

9   For a basic buffer solution, the pH is 9.3. The pH can be increased by
    (a) increasing the concentration of the salt;
    (b) increasing the concentration of the acid;
    (c) decreasing the concentration of the acid;
    (d) decreasing the K_b value of the base.

10 The pOH value of a buffer solution is related to the pH of that solution by the equation
(a) $pH + pOH = 10^{14}$;
(b) $pH + pOH = 10^{-14}$;
(c) $pH + pOH = 14$;
(d) $(pH) \times (pOH) = 14$.

(c) CONVENTIONAL PROBLEMS

1 How are acids and bases defined by the Brönsted–Lowry theory?
Using the definitions, select the acid and base conjugate pairs from the following list
$$H_2SO_4, \ HCl, \ NH_3, \ OH^-, \ H_2O, \ HSO_4^-, \ NH_4^+, \ Cl^-$$

2 Calculate the degree of dissociation of a 0.05 M solution of methanoic acid if hydrogen ion concentration of the solution is 1.5×10^{-4} mol dm^{-3} at 298 K.
[0.003]

3 Calculate the hydroxide ion concentration of a 0.02 M solution of hydroxylamine which dissociates according to the reaction $NH_2OH + H_2O \rightleftharpoons NH_3OH^+ + OH^-$ and has a degree of dissociation of 5.8×10^{-4} at 298 K. [1.16×10^{-5}]

4 Calculate (a) the hydrogen ion concentration and (b) the pH value of a 0.04 M solution of butanoic acid for which $K_a = 1.5 \times 10^{-5}$ mol dm^{-3} at 298 K.
[(a) 1.92×10^{-2} mol dm^{-3}; (b) 1.72]

5 Calculate the value of the acid dissociation constant of ethanoic acid if α for a 0.01 M solution of the acid is 4.2×10^{-2} mol dm^3 at 298 K.
[1.84×10^{-5} mol dm^{-3}]

6 Calculate the degree of dissociation of a 0.05 M solution of nitrous acid which has a K_a value of 4.7×10^{-4} mol dm^{-3} at 298 K. [0.0924]

7 Calculate the pK_b value of a 0.2 M solution of aqueous ammonia which is 0.95% dissociated at 298 K. [4.74]

8 The dissociation constant of propanoic acid is 1.3×10^{-5} mol dm^{-3} at 298 K. Calculate the concentration of the acid which will produce a pH value of 3.94.
[0.001 M]

9 Silver hydroxide has a pK_b value of 4. Calculate the concentration of a solution which is 10% dissociated. [9×10^{-4} M]

10 Calculate the pH of a 0.02 M aqueous ammonia solution which has a pK_b value of 4.8 at 298 K. [10.75]

11 Hydroxylamine, NH_2OH, dissociates in water according to the equation
$$NH_2OH + H_2O \rightleftharpoons NH_3OH^+ + OH^-$$
and a 0.03 M solution has a pH of 9.8.
Calculate the K_b value of hydroxylamine. [1.33×10^{-7}]

12 Derive an expression for the pH of a buffer solution obtained by dissolving the chloride of a weak base, BCl, in a solution of the weak base BOH for which the base dissociation constant is K_b.

13 A 0.01 M solution of hydrofluoric acid, for which K_a is 5.6×10^{-4} mol dm^{-3}, has a hydrogen ion concentration of 2.37×10^{-4} mol dm^{-3}. Calculate the pK_a and pH values for this solution of the acid. [$pK_a = 3.25, pH = 3.62$]

14 When phosphoric (V) acid dissociates according to the equation
$$H_3PO_4 + H_2O \rightleftharpoons H_3^+O + H_2PO_4^-$$
the *pH* of a 0.1 M solution is 1.56. Calculate the acid dissociation constant K_a for the acid acting in this way. [7.9×10^{-3}]

15 What is the Ostwald Dilution law? Use the law to find the value of K_b for a monoacidic weak base, for which a 0.001 M solution is 0.15% dissociated. [2.3×10^{-9}]

16 Calculate the *pH* of the buffer solution formed when 0.1 moles of sodium ethanoate are added to 1 dm³ of a 0.2 M solution of ethanoic acid for which $K_a = 1.8 \times 10^{-5}$ at 298 K. [4.439]

17 Calculate the number of moles of sodium propanoate which must be added to 2 dm³ of 0.1 M propanoic acid ($K_a = 1.3 \times 10^{-5}$ mol dm^{-3}) to give a *pH* value of 4. [0.026]

18 Calculate the *pH* of the buffer solution formed when 0.02 moles of ammonium chloride are added to a 0.05 M solution of aqueous ammonia. ($K_b = 1.8 \times 10^{-5}$ mol dm^{-3}). [4.34]

19 Calculate the concentration of phenylamine, $C_6H_5NH_2$ (pK_b is 9.4 at 298 K) containing 0.01 moles of phenylamine hydrochloride, $C_6H_5NH_3Cl$, to give a *pH* value of 12. [4×10^{-8} M]

20 Calculate the *pH* value of the solution of 500 cm³ of 0.25 M ethanoic acid ($K_a = 1.8 \times 10^{-5}$ mol dm^{-3} at 298 K) to which 100 cm³ of 0.1 M potassium hydroxide has been added. [3.68]

4 Heterogeneous equilibria

A. MAIN POINTS CONCERNING HETEROGENEOUS EQUILIBRIA

1 A **heterogeneous reaction** is one in which different phases are involved. For example the equilibrium

$$A(s) \rightleftharpoons B(s) + C(g)$$

involves **solid** and **gas** phases. A further example is given by the equilibrium

$$A(aq) + B(aq) \rightleftharpoons C(s) + D(aq)$$

which involves **aqueous solutions** and the **solid** phase.

2 A heterogeneous equilibrium reaction can be considered as two separate reactions. For example

$$A(s) \rightleftharpoons B(s) + C(g)$$

can be considered as

$$A(s) \longrightarrow B(s) + C(g) \tag{1}$$

and $\quad C(g) + B(s) \longrightarrow A(s) \tag{2}$

The rates of reactions (1) and (2) can be written as

Rate of reaction $(1) = k_1 [A]$, where k_1 = the velocity constant of reaction (1) and

Rate of reaction $(2) = k_2 [B][C]$, where k_2 = the velocity constant of reaction (2).

[A], [B] and [C] are the **active masses** of the compounds. Though the **concentrations** of liquids, solutions and gases can be calculated and **approximated** to the active masses, **this does not apply to solids**. However, for an elementary treatment of heterogeneous equilibria involving solids, the **active mass of a solid is assumed to be constant**.

3 Applying the equilibrium law to the equation

$$A(s) + B(g) \rightleftharpoons C(s) + D(g), \text{ gives, a constant } = \frac{[C_s][D_g]}{[A_s][B_g]}$$

Assuming $[C_s]$ and $[D_s]$ are constant, then, a constant $= \dfrac{[D_g]}{[B_g]}$

or for a gaseous equilibrium

a constant $= \dfrac{pD}{pB}$ where, pD and pB are the **partial pressures** of the gases. This constant is assigned as the **equilibrium constant** relating the non-solid components of the equilibrium reaction, and in the case of gases is symbolised K_p or for solutions or liquids K_c. Some examples of heterogeneous equilibria are shown in *Table 1*.

TABLE 1 Some examples of heterogeneous equilibria

Equation	Phases
$C + H_2O \rightleftharpoons CO + H_2$	Solid and gas
$CaCO_3 \rightleftharpoons CaO + CO_2$	Solid and gas
$3Fe + 4H_2O \rightleftharpoons Fe_3O_4 + 4H_2$	Solid and gas
$2Ag^+ + Cu \rightleftharpoons 2Ag + Cu^{2+}$	Solid and solution
$Cu^{2+} + Zn \rightleftharpoons Cu + Zn^{2+}$	Solid and solution

4 (i) When a **solute** dissolves without association or dissociation in two different **immiscible solvents**, the solute is **distributed** according to the **relative solubility** of the solute in those solvents. This is shown diagrammatically in *Fig 1*, in which (a) is any solution and (b) is a supersaturated solution.

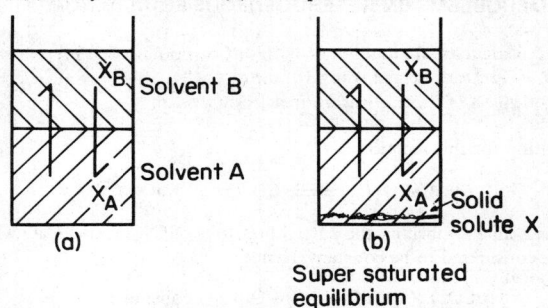

Fig 1 The distribution of a solute between two immiscible liquids

(ii) It has been found that when such a solute is distributed between two liquids, the **ratio of the concentrations** in each immiscible layer **is a constant**. For example, for the solute S and the immiscible solvents A and B then

$$\dfrac{\text{The concentration of S in solvent A}}{\text{The concentration of S in solvent B}} = \text{a constant}$$

This constant is symbolised K, and is called the **partition (or distribution) coefficient**.

(iii) Since the distribution of the solute in two immiscible liquids is a constant, the system can be regarded as a type of heterogeneous equilibrium.

5 (i) When **ionic solids** crystallise from an aqueous solution, they usually contain **water of crystallisation** which is a result of the metal ions being hydrated in solution. The crystalline solid in contact with the atmosphere is consequently in contact with **water vapour** which varies with the **humidity** of the atmosphere.

(ii) When the water vapour pressure exerted by a crystalline solid is **greater** than the water vapour pressure of the atmosphere, the solid **loses water to the atmosphere**, an example being

$$Na_2CO_3 \cdot 10H_2O(s) \rightleftharpoons NaCO_3 \cdot xH_2O(s) + (10-x)H_2O(l)$$

This type of behaviour is called **efflorescence**. Thus depending on the water vapour pressure above the solid it may lose some or all of its water of crystallisation. In a closed system an equilibrium will be reached between the solid and water vapour.

(iii) When the water vapour exerted by a crystalline solid is **lower** than the water vapour pressure of the atmosphere, the solid **absorbs water vapour from the atmosphere** resulting in the solid eventually **dissolving** to form a solution, an example being

$$CaCl_2 \cdot H_2O(s) + H_2O(l) \rightleftharpoons CaCl_2(aq)$$

This type of behaviour is called **deliquescence**. If this type of solid is held in a **closed vessel** an equilibrium will be formed between the solid and the water vapour pressure.

B. WORKED PROBLEMS ON HETEROGENEOUS EQUILIBRIUM

Problem 1 Calculate the number of moles of carbon dioxide present in the equilibrium reaction formed when 1 mole of $CaCO_3$ is heated at 1200 K under a pressure of 200 kPa (take K_p as 4), in a 1 dm³ vessel.

The equation for this reaction is

$$CaCO_3(s) \rightleftharpoons CO_2(g) + CaO(s)$$

Since this is an equilibrium, the partial pressures of $CaCO_3$ and CaO which are solids are considered to be constant. Hence

$$a\ constant = \frac{(pCO_2) \times (pCaO)}{(pCaCO_3)} = \frac{(pCO_2) \times a\ constant}{a\ constant}$$

Hence (pCO_2) is a constant and equal to K_p, that is,

$K_p = pCO_2 = 4$.

Since the partial pressure = the mole fraction × the total pressure then
4 = mole fraction × 200.
Since CO_2 is the only gas present the mole fraction = number of moles.

Thus the number of moles = $\frac{4}{200}$ = **0.02 moles**.

Problem 2 Calculate the equilibrium constant K_p for the reaction

$$3Fe(s) + 4H_2O(g) \rightleftharpoons Fe_3O_4(s) + 4H_2(g)$$

If at equilibrium at 470 K the partial pressure of steam is 613.3 Pa and that of hydrogen 12745.6 Pa.

Since this is a heterogeneous equilibrium, the equilibrium constant may be written as

$$\text{a constant} = \frac{(p\text{Fe}_3\text{O}_4) \times (p\text{H}_2)^4}{(p\text{Fe})^3 \times (p\text{H}_2\text{O})^4}$$

The partial pressures of Fe_3O_4 and Fe are assumed to be constant and the expression becomes

$$\text{a constant} = \frac{\text{a constant} \times (p\text{H}_2)^4}{\text{a constant} \times (p\text{H}_2\text{O})^4}$$

or $\quad K_p = \dfrac{(p\text{H}_2)^4}{(p\text{H}_2\text{O})^4}$

Substituting the values for the partial pressures into equilibrium expression gives

$$K_p = \frac{(12745.6)^4}{(613.3)^4} = 186530.25$$

Thus K_p for the reaction is **186530.25**

Problem 3 Calculate the number of moles of carbon monoxide present in the equilibrium mixture

$$\text{H}_2\text{O(g)} + \text{C(s)} \rightleftharpoons \text{H}_2\text{(g)} + \text{CO(g)}$$

which are formed when 2 moles of steam react with 1 mole of carbon at a temperature of 1000 K and a pressure of 100 Pa, if $K_p = 3.72$ Pa.

Since this is a heterogeneous equilibrium, by assuming that the partial pressure of solid carbon is constant the equilibrium expression can be written as

$$K_p = \frac{(p\text{H}_2)(p\text{CO})}{(p\text{H}_2\text{O})}$$

Let the number of moles of carbon monoxide be X, then at equilibrium the number of moles of each component can be represented as

	$\text{H}_2\text{O(g)}$	+ C(s)	$\rightleftharpoons$ $\text{H}_2\text{(g)}$	+ CO(g)	
Initially	2		0	0	moles
At equilibrium	2−X		X	X	moles

The total number of moles at equilibrium is

$2 - X + X + X = 2 + X$ moles

The mole fractions and partial pressures are conveniently expressed in tabular form as follows:

Gas	Mole fraction	Partial pressure
H_2O	$\dfrac{2-X}{2+X}$	$\dfrac{2-X}{2+X} \times 100$ kPa
H_2	$\dfrac{X}{2+X}$	$\dfrac{X}{2+X} \times 100$ kPa
CO	$\dfrac{X}{2+X}$	$\dfrac{X}{2+X} \times 100$ kPa

Substituting these values into the equilibrium equation and using $K_p = 3.72$ gives

$$3.72 = \frac{\frac{X}{(2+X)} \times 100 \; \frac{X}{(2+X)} \times 100}{\frac{(2-X)}{(2+X)} \times 100}$$

Simplifying this equation gives

$$3.72 = \frac{X^2 \times 100}{(2+X)(2-X)} = \frac{100X^2}{4-X^2}$$

$$3.72(4-X^2) = 100X^2 \text{ or } 103.72X^2 = 14.88$$

$$X^2 = \frac{14.88}{103.72} = 0.379$$

Thus the number of moles of carbon monoxide is **0.379**.

Problem 4 Calculate the concentration of iron (*III*) ions in the equilibrium

$$Ag^+(aq) + Fe^{2+}(aq) \rightleftharpoons Fe^{3+}(aq) + Ag(s)$$

if 1 mole of silver ions are added to 1 mole of iron (*II*) ions in a total volume of 1 dm^3, and K_c for the equilibrium reaction is 3.4 mol^{-1} dm^3 at 298 K.

This is a heterogeneous equilibrium, and in this equilibrium the concentration of the solid, silver, is assumed to be constant. The expression for the equilibrium can be written as

$$K_c = \frac{[Fe^{3+}]}{[Ag^+][Fe^{2+}]}$$

Assume that X moles of Ag^+(aq) are reacted to form Fe^{3+}(aq) at equilibrium. The concentrations of the ions at equilibrium are conveniently found as follows

$$Ag^+(aq) + Fe^{2+}(aq) \rightleftharpoons Fe^{3+}(aq) + Ag(s)$$

Initial concentration	1	1	0	0 mol dm^{-3}
At equilibrium	1−X	1−X	X	constant mol dm^{-3}

Substituting these values into the equilibrium equation gives

$$K_c = \frac{X}{(1-X)(1-X)} = 3.4$$

Solving for X gives $\quad 3.4(1-2X+X^2) = X$
hence $\quad 3.4X^2 - 7.8X + 3.4 = 0$

Using $X = \frac{-b \pm \sqrt{(b^2-4ac)}}{2a}$, where $a = 3.4$, $b = -7.8$ and $c = 3.4$ gives

$$X = \frac{-(-7.8) \pm \sqrt{(-7.8)^2 - 4 \times 3.4 \times 3.4}}{2 \times 3.4}$$

$$X = \frac{7.8 \pm \sqrt{14.6}}{6.8} = \frac{7.8+3.82}{6.8} \text{ or } \frac{7.8-3.82}{6.8}$$

The first value of X is greater than 1 which is impossible.

Thus, $X = \frac{3.98}{6.8} = 0.585$

Hence the number of moles of iron (*III*) ions is 0.585 in 1 dm³ of the equilibrium solution.

Problem 5 Calculate the partition coefficient of iodine in carbon disulphide, CS_2, and water, if 10 cm³ of carbon disulphide extracts 0.0878 g of iodine from a solution containing 0.09 g of iodine in water.

The partition coefficient = $\frac{\text{the concentration of iodine in carbon disulphide}}{\text{the concentration of iodine in water}}$

Thus, the partition coefficient = $\dfrac{\frac{0.0878}{10}}{\frac{0.09-0.0878}{10}} = \frac{0.0878}{10} \times \frac{100}{0.0022}$

$= \frac{8.78}{0.022} = 399.1$

Thus the partition coefficient of iodine in CS_2 and H_2O is **399.1**

Problem 6 The following data refers to the distribution of butan −1, 4−dioc acid $(CH_2COOH)_2$ in ether and water. Show that the data is in agreement with the distribution law and find the partition (or distribution) coefficient.

Concentration of acid in ether, mol dm⁻³	1.91×10^{-4}	9.56×10^{-3}	1.43×10^{-2}	1.91×10^{-2}
Concentration of acid in water, mol dm⁻³	1×10^{-3}	5×10^{-2}	7.5×10^{-2}	1×10^{-1}

Let the concentration of acid in ether be C_1 and the concentration of acid in water be C_2.

By definition, the partition coefficient, $K = \dfrac{C_1}{C_2}$.

Calculating K for each pair of concentration values gives

$K_1 = \dfrac{1.91 \times 10^{-4}}{1 \times 10^{-3}} = 0.191$ $\qquad K_2 = \dfrac{9.56 \times 10^{-3}}{5 \times 10^{-2}} = 0.191$

$K^3 = \dfrac{1.43 \times 10^{-2}}{7.5 \times 10^{-2}} = 0.191$ $\qquad K^4 = \dfrac{1.91 \times 10^{-2}}{1 \times 10^{-1}} = 0.191$

Hence the ratio of the concentration of the acid in ether and water is constant and in agreement with the distribution law. **The value of the partition coefficient is 0.191.**

Problem 7 An aqueous solution of an organic compound, R, has a concentration of 5 g dm^{-3}. Calculate the weight of R which will be extracted from 200 cm^3 of this solution by 40 cm^3 of ether if the partition coefficient,

$$\frac{C\,ether}{C\,water} = 20.$$

The partition coefficient is defined as $\dfrac{\text{the concentration of } R \text{ in ether}}{\text{the concentration of } R \text{ in water}}$

200 cm^3 of solution contains 1 g of R.

Let X g of R be extracted by 40 cm^3 of ether.

Then, $\dfrac{\text{the concentration of } R \text{ in ether}}{\text{the concentration of } R \text{ in water}} = \dfrac{\dfrac{X}{40}\text{ g cm}^{-3}}{\dfrac{(1-X)}{200}\text{ g cm}^{-3}} = 20$

Hence $20 = \dfrac{X}{40} \times \dfrac{200}{(1-X)} = \dfrac{5X}{(1-X)}$

Solving for X gives $\quad 20(1-X) = 5X$
$\qquad\qquad\qquad\qquad 20 - 20X = 5x$
$\qquad\qquad\qquad\qquad 20 \quad\quad\; = 25X$ and,
$\qquad\qquad\qquad\qquad X \quad\quad\; = \dfrac{20}{25} = 0.8$

Thus the weight of R extracted is 0.8 g.

Problem 8 The partition coefficient of ammonia between trichloromethane and water at a particular temperature is 24. Calculate (a) the weight of ammonia that would be extracted from 500 cm^3 of a 5 M solution of aqueous ammonia by 100 cm^3 of trichloromethane, and (b) by using two consecutive aliquots of 50 cm^3 of trichloromethane.

(a) A 5 M solution contains **5 moles of ammonia in 1000 cm^3** hence 500 cm^3 contain 2½ moles of ammonia. The molecular weight of ammonia, NH_3, is $14 + (3 \times 1) = 17$ g, hence the weight of 2½ moles of NH_3 is $2½ \times 17 = 42.5$ g. Let X g of ammonia be extracted by 100 cm^3 of trichloromethane, then since

Partition coefficient = $\dfrac{\text{the concentration of } NH_3 \text{ in trichloromethane}}{\text{the concentration of } NH_3 \text{ in water}}$

then $24 = \dfrac{\dfrac{X}{100}}{\dfrac{(42.5-X)}{500}} = \dfrac{X}{100} \times \dfrac{500}{(42.5-X)} = \dfrac{5X}{(42.5-X)}$

Solving for X gives $24\,(42.5-X) = 5X$
$1020 - 24X = 5X$
$1020 \quad\quad\; = 29X$

and $X \quad\quad\; = \dfrac{1020}{29} = 35.17$ g

Hence 35.17 g of ammonia are extracted by 100 cm^3 of $CHCl_3$.

(b) Let Y g be extracted by 50 cm³ of CHCl$_3$, then

$$24 = \frac{\frac{Y}{50}}{\frac{(42.5-Y)}{500}} = \frac{Y}{50} \times \frac{500}{(42.5-Y)} = \frac{10Y}{(42.5-Y)}$$

Solving for Y gives

$24(42.5-Y) = 10Y$
$1020-24Y = 10Y$

and $Y = \dfrac{1020}{34} = 30$ g

When 30 g of ammonia are extracted by 50 cm³ of CHCl$_3$ (42.5−30) g **remain in the 500 cm³ of solution**, that is 12.5 g in 500 cm³ of solution.
Let Z g be extracted by the second 50 cm³ of trichloromethane then, applying the partition coefficient expression gives

$$24 = \frac{\frac{Z}{50}}{\frac{(12.5-Z)}{500}}$$

Solving for Z gives

$24(12.5-Z) = 10Z$
$300-24Z = 10Z$

and $Z = \dfrac{300}{34} = 8.82$ g

When a second 50 cm³ of trichloromethane are added to the ammonia solution 8.82 g are extracted.
The total extracted by the two aliquots is $Y + Z = 30 + 8.82 = 38.82$ g.
Thus the use of two consecutive aliquots of 50 cm³ extracts 38.82 g of ammonia, whereas one extraction with 100 cm³ extracts 35.17 g

C. FURTHER PROBLEMS ON HETEROGENEOUS EQUILIBRIA

(a) SHORT ANSWER PROBLEMS

Fill in the missing words.

1 A heterogeneous equilibrium is one which contains more than .... for the constituents.

2 For equilibrium systems which are heterogeneous, solid constituents are assumed to have a constant .... value.

3 Immiscible solvents are solvents which are .... in each other.

4 When a solute is distributed between two immiscible solvents, the ratio dissolved in each solvent is a constant value which is called the ....

5 If a solvent is used to extract a solute from another solvent, the most efficient extraction can be achieved by using .... of the solvent.

6 The absorption of water from the atmosphere by an ionic solid is called ....
and occurs when atmospheric vapour pressure is .... than the water vapour
pressure of the solid.

7 The release of water vapour from an ionic solid to the atmosphere is called ....,
and occurs when the atmospheric vapour pressure is .... than the water
vapour pressure of the solid.

(b) MULTI-CHOICE PROBLEMS (answers on page 181)

Select the correct answer from those given

1 The equilibrium constant in terms of partial pressures for the reaction

$$wA(s) + xB(g) \rightleftharpoons yC(g) + zD(s)$$

can be written as

(a) $K_p = \dfrac{(pC)^y \times (pD)^z}{(pA)^w \times (pB)^x}$;

(b) $K_p = \dfrac{(pC)^y}{(pB)^x}$;

(c) $K_p = \dfrac{(pA)^w}{(pD)^z}$;

(d) $K_p = \dfrac{(pA)^w \times (pB)^x}{(pC)^y \times (pD)^z}$.

2 When silver carbonate is heated, it dissociates into silver oxide and carbon dioxide. The amount of carbon dioxide released is
   (a) proportional to the concentration of silver carbonate;
   (b) proportional to the concentration of silver oxide;
   (c) independent of the concentration of silver carbonate;
   (d) proportional to the ratio of silver oxide to silver carbonate.

3 The partition or distribution law relates
   (a) the ratio of the concentrations of a solute in two immiscible liquids;
   (b) the ratio of the concentrations of a solute in two miscible liquids;
   (c) the concentrations of a solute distributed in a solvent;
   (d) the partition of two insoluble solvents.

4 If 0.8 g of a solute are dissolved in a solvent A and 0.2 g in an equal volume of solvent B the partition coefficient of solvent A to solvent B is
   (a) 0.16; (b) 0.6; (c) 0.25; (d) 4.

5 A solid undergoes efflorescence if
   (a) the water vapour pressure of the solid is less than atmospheric water vapour pressure;
   (b) the water vapour pressure of the solid is greater than atmospheric vapour pressure;
   (c) the solid is very soluble in water;
   (d) the solid is only sparingly soluble in water.

(c) CONVENTIONAL PROBLEMS

1 Explain what is meant by the terms
   (a) homogeneous equilibrium; (b) heterogeneous equilibrium.

2 What assumptions are made when an expression for the equilibrium constant of a heterogeneous equilibrium is derived?

3 Why is the partial pressure of carbon dioxide in the equilibrium reaction

$$CaCO_3(s) \rightleftharpoons CaO(s) + CO_2(g)$$

a measure of the degree of dissociation of the calcium carbonate.

4 Calculate the partial pressure of hydrogen in the equilibrium reaction

$$3Fe(s) + 4H_2O(g) \rightleftharpoons Fe_3O_4(s) + 4H_2(g)$$

if the partial pressure of steam is 481 Pa at 470 K and $K_p = 1.86 \times 10^5$.

[9989 Pa]

5 Calculate the pressure of carbon dioxide produced in a 1 dm³ vessel if 0.06 moles of carbon dioxide are produced at 1200 K from 1 mole of calcium carbonate. ($K_p = 4$). [66.67]

6 Calculate the number of moles of hydrogen formed when 1 mole of steam reacts with 2 moles of carbon at 1000 K and a pressure of 200 Pa if $K_p = 3.72$ Pa.

[0.135 moles]

7 For the reaction

$$Fe^{2+}(aq) + Ag^+(aq) \rightleftharpoons Fe^{3+}(aq) + Ag(s)$$

the value of K_c is 3.11 mol⁻¹ dm³ at 298 K. Calculate the concentration of Fe^{3+} ions in the equilibrium mixture formed when 2 moles of Fe^{2+} ions are added to 1 mole of Ag^+ ions in a volume of 1 dm³. [0.79 moles]

8 Calculate the partition coefficient for the equilibrium mixture which contains 0.5 moles of a solute X in 500 cm³ of ether and 0.02 moles of the solute X in 750 cm³ of water. [37.45]

9 The partition coefficient of iodine between carbon disulphide CS_2 and water is 588 at a certain temperature. Calculate what weight of iodine will be extracted from 1 dm³ of aqueous iodine containing 1 g of iodine if it is extracted with 100 cm³ of carbon disulphide. [0.983 g]

10 When 10 cm³ of CCl_4 are added to 100 cm³ of water containing 1 g of phenol, 0.76 g of phenol are extracted. Calculate the weight of phenol remaining in the water layer if another extraction is made with 20 cm³ of CCl_4. [0.033 g]

5 The lattice crystal structures of some inorganic compounds

A. MAIN POINTS CONCERNING THE LATTICE CRYSTAL STRUCTURES OF SOME INORGANIC COMPOUNDS

1. In the solid state, the external appearance of inorganic compounds shows clearly that different crystal shapes are possible for different compounds. The **external shape** of the crystal **does not give any information about the internal structure** of the crystal lattice.

TABLE 1

Lattice type	Examples
Sodium chloride or Rock-salt structure 6:6 co-ordination	LiF NaF KF MgO CaO LiCl NaCl KCl RbCl SrO BaO LiBr NaBr KBr RbBr MnO NiO LiI NaI KI RbI NH_4I
Caesium chloride structure 8:8 co-ordination	CsCl RbF NH_4Cl CsBr NH_4Br CsI
Zinc blende structure 4:4 co-ordination	ZnS AgI CuBr HgS
Wurtzite structure 4:4 co-ordination	ZnS NH_4F ZnO
Fluorite structure 8:4 co-ordination	CaF_2 $SrCl_2$ SrF_2 CdF_2 BaF_2 PbF_2
Rutile structure 6:3 co-ordination	TiO_2 ZnF_2 MnF_2 CoF_2 SnO_2 MnO_2
β-Cristobalite structure 4:2 co-ordination	SiO_2 Cu_2O Ag_2O
Cadmium iodide structure layer structure	CdI_2

TABLE 2 Radius ratios and crystal lattice structures

		AB TYPE	
	Tetrahedral	*Octahedral*	*Cubic*
	Zinc blende	Sodium chloride	Caesium chloride
$\dfrac{r_c}{r_a}$	0.225 to 0.414	0.414 to 0.732	0.732 to 1

	AB_2 TYPE	
	Fluorite	*Rutile*
$\dfrac{r_c}{r_a}$	0.65 to 1	0.5 to 0.65

2 The composition of inorganic solids has been shown by **X-ray crystallographic methods** devised by Sir William Bragg and his son Sir William L Bragg to exist in **regular arrangements** of particles. The techniques of X-ray crystallography are discussed in *Problem 1*.

3 The majority of inorganic solids can be **sub-divided** into those which are **ionic in structure** and those which are **covalent in structure**. In ionic solids the particles mentioned in para. 2 are ions, whereas in covalent solids the particles are atoms or groups of atoms.

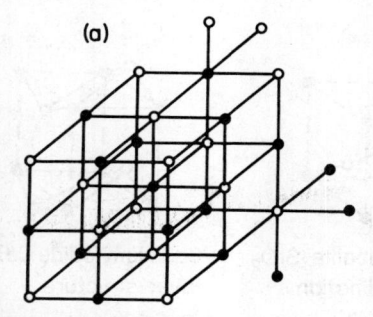

(a) Sodium chloride, NaCl
6:6 coordination
● = Na⁺ ○ = Cl⁻

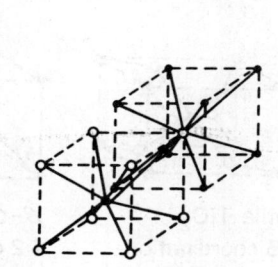

(b) Caesium chloride CsCl
8:8 coordination
● = Cs⁺ ○ = Cl⁻

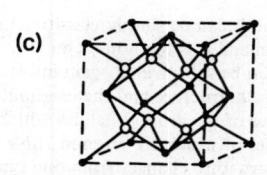

(c) Fluorite CaF₂
8:4 coordination
● = Ca²⁺ ○ = F⁻

Fig 1

Zinc blende ZnS
4:4 coordination
● = Zn   ○ = S

Wurtzite ZnS
4:4 coordination
● = Zn   ○ = S

(a)

(b)

Rutile TiO$_2$
6:3 coordination
● = Ti   ○ = O
(c)

β-Cristobalite SiO$_2$
4:2 coordination
● = Si   ○ = O
(d)

Cadmium iodide CdI$_2$
layer structure
● = Cd
(e)

Fig 2

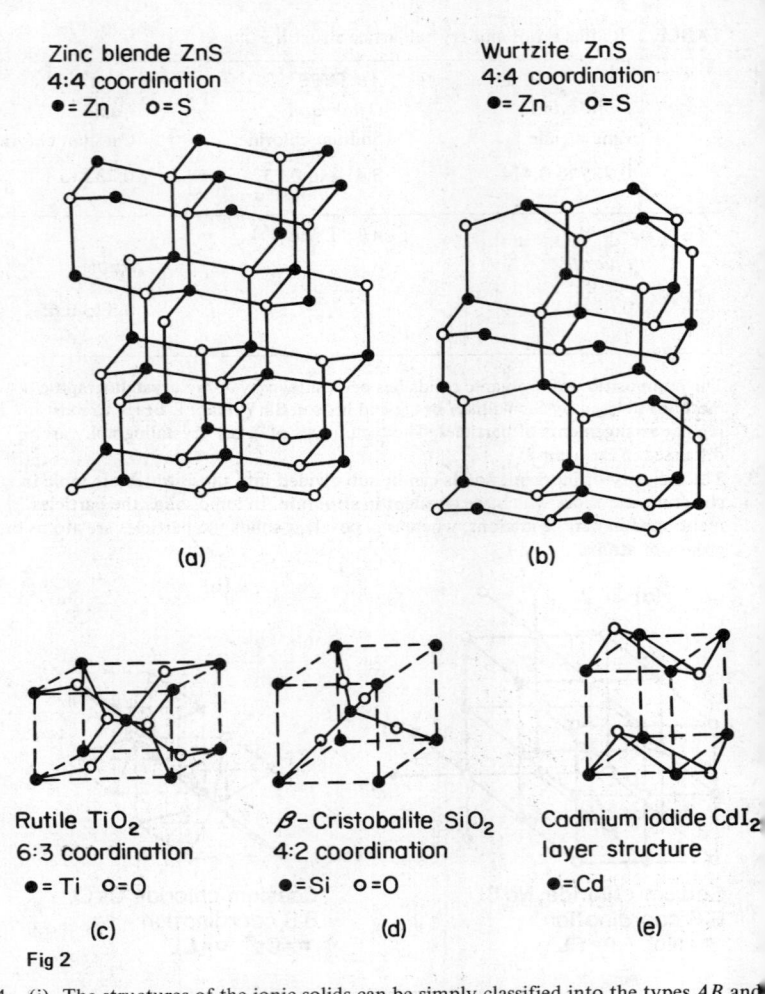

4 (i) The structures of the ionic solids can be simply classified into the types AB and AB_2, where A is the metal ion and B is the non-metal ion.

(ii) Ionic solids of the type AB can be sub-divided again into two main types, the **sodium chloride** or **rock salt structure** and the **caesium chloride structure**. These are the lattice structures of the group I halides which are shown in *Figs 1(a) and (b)* and examples of which are given in *Table 1*.

(iii) The reasons why the lattice structure changes from one type of ionic solid to another are considered to be due to the **ratio of the size of the cation and the anion**, some values of which are given in *Table 2* and discussed in *Problem 2*.

(iv) Ionic solids of the type AB_2 can be considered to be the **fluorite structure** of calcium fluoride CaF$_2$. The change in lattice structure in this case is due to both the **radius ratio** and also the **ratio of one cation to two anions**. The lattice structure is shown in *Fig 1(c)* and examples of the structure are given in *Table 1*.

5   All **ionic solids** in the **molten state** will be **electrolytes** and in general the solids will have high melting points and boiling points and will be conducting solutions if soluble in water.

6   (i) The inorganic compounds which have covalently bonded lattice structures can also be **sub-divided** into the types AB and AB_2.
   (ii) Covalent solids of the type AB can be considered to be the **zinc blende lattice structure** and the **wurtzite lattice structure** of the compound with the same formula ZnS. These structures are shown in *Figs 2(a) and (b)* and examples given in *Table 1*.
   (iii) Covalent solids of the type AB_2 can be classified into three types, **the rutile or titanium dioxide structure**, the **β-cristobalite structure** of SiO_2 and the **cadmium iodide layer structure**. These are shown in *Figs 2(c) to (e)* with examples given in *Table 1*.

7   Covalent solids which exist as crystal lattice structures are equally as rigid as ionic crystals and have high melting and high boiling points. However **covalent solids** are **not conductors** in the **molten state** and are not usually soluble in water.

8   The concept of **coordination number** is used to express the **number of different nearest neighbours** associated with an atom or ion. The number refers to the total number of near neighbours both in the same plane and above and below the particle under consideration. The coordination numbers associated with the different lattice crystal structures are shown in *Figs 1 and 2* and also in *Table 1*. (See *Problem 5*.)

B. WORKED PROBLEMS ON THE LATTICE CRYSTAL STRUCTURES OF SOME INORGANIC COMPOUNDS

Problem 1 Explain why X-ray diffraction measurements can be used to give information about the structure of crystal lattices.

The **diffraction** of light through a **diffraction grating** produces a series of bands of intensified light interspersed with bands of darkness. This is interpreted, using the wave theory of light, as the reinforcement of **two waves in phase**, (see *Fig 3(ii)*), to explain the **intensified bands**, and the **cancellation** of light as a result of **two wave forms out of phase** (see *Fig 3 (iii)*).

The ability of a diffraction grating to produce diffraction patterns depends on the wavelength of the type of light used. Since visible light is one type of electromagnetic radiation, other forms of radiation should be capable of diffraction if a suitable diffraction grating can be found.

Sir William Bragg and his son discovered that crystal lattices were able to form diffraction patterns using X-rays. The existence of diffraction patterns was very good evidence in support of the theory that in the solid state the particles are arranged in a regular pattern which could be resolved into layers depending on the way in which the crystal lattice is viewed.

If a set of planes are considered as shown in *Fig 3(i)*, the wave labelled AXD which is incident onto the surface of the crystal at an angle θ, strikes the surface particle at X and is reflected at an angle of θ. The second wave BZF meets the surface at a position where no particle is present and passes through the lattice structure until it strikes a particle at Z and is diffracted back through the crystal

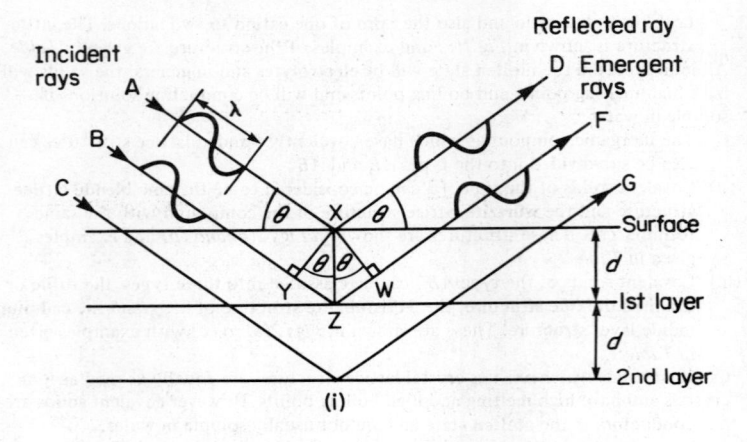

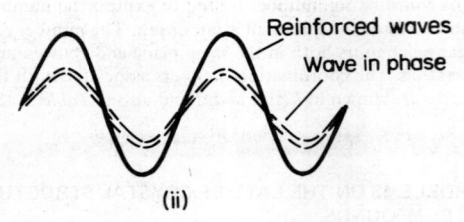

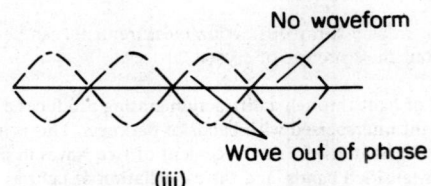

Fig 3

(i) Diagram showing incident rays A, B, C reflecting from lattice surface with emergent rays D, F, G at angle θ, with layers separated by distance d, and points X, Y, Z, W marked.

(ii) Reinforced waves / Wave in phase

(iii) No waveform / Wave out of phase

lattice surface. The waves are **in phase** when they are incident to the lattice surface but the wave BZF must travel a **longer path** than the wave AXD. For the **emergent waves to be in phase**, the extra distance travelled by the wave BZF must be equal to a whole number of wavelengths.

Bragg found that by varying the incident angle θ, regions of intense radiation could be detected, followed by regions where no radiation could be detected. For a fixed wavelength of X-radiation, λ, Bragg related the extra distance travelled by the second wave as

$$YZ + ZW = n\lambda, \quad \text{where } n = 1, 2 \text{ etc.}$$

Using trigonometry

$$YZ = ZW = d \sin \theta$$

Hence, $\mathbf{YZ + ZW} = \mathbf{2d \sin \theta} = \mathbf{n\lambda}$

This equation is called the Bragg equation and for varying values of n and θ the interplanar distance d can be found. A knowledge of these interplanar distances correspond to the distances between ions or atoms, (single or in groups) and the lattice crystal can be discovered by constructing models of them.

Problem 2 Explain why the coordination numbers of sodium chloride, caesium chloride and calcium flouride are 6:6, 8:8 and 8:4 respectively.

(i) When ions of different charges are incorporated into a crystal lattice, the arrangement of the ions depends on three main properties. Firstly the difference in charge, secondly the relative sizes of cations and anions and thirdly the ratio of cations to anions.

(ii) Since cations are positively charged and anions are negatively charged, any crystal lattice will experience repulsive forces between identical cations and identical anions of identical charge, whereas it will experience forces of attraction between oppositely charged cations and anions. The arrangement of ions must be such that electrical neutrality exists in the structure. This is achieved by a cation surrounding itself with anions, and by an anion surrounding itself with cations.

A simple application of this principle would lead to the same lattice structure for all ionic solids, but the ability of cations and anions to pack together also depends on the relative sizes of these particles. Cations are much smaller than anions and it is easier to view the positioning of anions about a cation than vice versa.

(iii) For the sodium chloride crystal lattice, (*Fig 1(a)*), each Na^+ ion has six Cl^- ions as near neighbours. This is because the ionic radius of the sodium ion is small enough to fit into such a site within the lattice. Geometrical calculations (see *Problems 3 and 4*) show that for the six Cl^- ions to touch the Na^+ ion, the ratio $\frac{\text{cation radius}}{\text{anion radius}} \frac{r_c}{r_a}$ is 0.414. Since the ionic radius of Na^+ is 0.98A and that of Cl^- is 1.81A then, $\frac{r_c}{r_a} = 0.541$. This means that in sodium chloride the ions are not touching but are dispersed about the central Na^+ ion.

(iv) As the radius ratio increases the positioning of a cation in such a site causes the anions to be moved farther and farther apart. This results in a change of site for the cation when the radius ratio reaches 0.732. This crystal lattice structure is shown by caesium chloride, (*Fig 1(b)*), where instead of six near neighbours each Cs^+ ion is surrounded by eight Cl^- ions and each Cl^- ion is surrounded by eight Cs^+ ions. The ionic radii of Cs^+ and Cl^- are 1.65A and 1.81A giving a value of $\frac{r_c}{r_a} = 0.912$. The size of the radius ratio is responsible for a change in coordination number from 6:6 to 8:8.

(v) In calcium fluoride, CaF_2, the cation has a charge of +2, and each anion −1, and for electrical neutrality there must be twice as many anions as cations. The structure of this crystal lattice is such that each Ca^{2+} ion is surrounded by eight F^- ions and each F^- ion is surrounded by four Ca^{2+} ions and this results in a coordination number of 8:4.

Problem 3 What is the maximum sized particle which can fit into the triangular site AXY shown in *Fig 4*.

In *Fig 4* the three larger spheres represent anions or non-metals, whereas the smaller sphere represents a metal ion or atom. The radii of the large and small spheres are r_a and r_c respectively. Joining the centres of the three spheres produces an equilateral triangle AXY, and the triangle ABC is a right angled triangle in which BAC = 30°.

Using trigonometry,

$$\cos 30° = \frac{AB}{AC} = \frac{r_a}{r_a + r_c}$$

Using this relationship

$$\frac{r_a}{r_a + r_c} = 0.866.$$

Rearranging this expression gives

$$\frac{1}{0.866} = \frac{r_a + r_c}{r_a}$$

or $\quad 1.1547 = 1 + \frac{r_c}{r_a}$

This gives the value of $\frac{r_c}{r_a}$ as $1.1547 - 1$ ot 0.1547.

This value is called the radius ratio of this structure. The range of this ratio of $\frac{r_c}{r_a}$ is from 0.155 to 0.225 for a triangular site.

Fig 4

Problem 4 Calculate the radius ratio for the arrangement of particles representing an octahedral site in a lattice structure, shown in *Fig 5*.

In order to find the radius ratio for this arrangement the triangle ABC is constructed which is a right angled triangle in which $C\hat{A}B = A\hat{B}C = 45°$.
Using trigonometry

$$\frac{AC}{AB} = \cos 45°$$

Using the identity, $\cos 45° = \frac{1}{\sqrt{2}}$ gives

$$\frac{AC}{AB} = \frac{r_a + r_c}{2r_a} = \frac{1}{\sqrt{2}}$$

Rearranging this expression gives

$$\frac{r_a + r_c}{r_a} = \frac{2}{\sqrt{2}} = \sqrt{2}$$

Simplifying gives $1 + \frac{r_c}{r_a} = \sqrt{2}$

or $\quad \frac{r_c}{r_a} = \sqrt{2} - 1 = 0.414$

Hence for an octahedral site the radius ratio for touching contact is **0.414**.

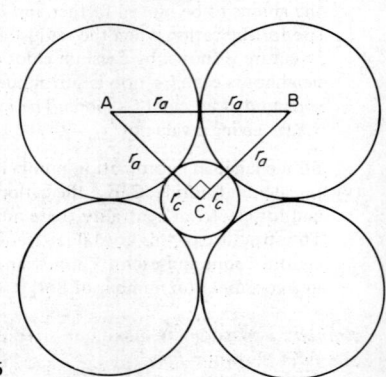

Fig 5

62

Problem 5 Explain the coordination numbers of 4:4 for the zinc blende crystal lattice and 4:2 for β-cristobalite shown in *Fig 2(a) and (d)*.

In *Fig 2(a)* the zinc atoms in the **zinc blende structure** are represented by ● and the sulphur atoms by ○. By considering a single silicon atom and the oxygen atoms surrounding it shown in *Fig 6(iii)*, it can be seen that **four oxygen atoms** are distributed **tetrahedrally** about the **silicon atom**. Also included in *Fig 6(iii)* are the

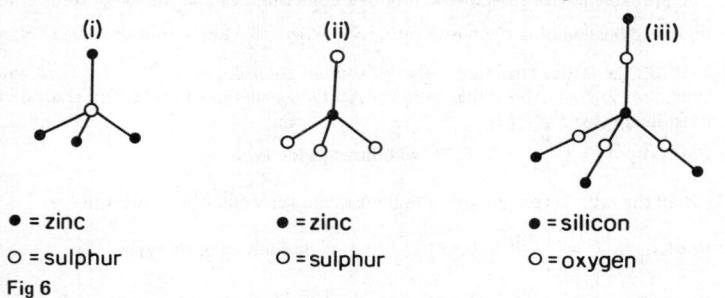

(i)   (ii)   (iii)

● = zinc   ● = zinc   ● = silicon
○ = sulphur   ○ = sulphur   ○ = oxygen

Fig 6

oxygen atoms which are **shared linearly between two silicon atoms**. Hence because each silicon atom has four oxygen atoms surrounding it and each oxygen is shared by two silicon atoms, **the coordination number is 4:2**.

Problem 6 Using the unit cell of caesium chloride explain (a) how the empirical formula for caesium chloride can be found and (b) how the crystal lattice maintains electrical neutrality.

(a) Consider the unit cell of caesium chloride in which one Cs^+ ion is surrounded by eight Cl^- ions as shown in *Fig 7*.

The unit cell is the smallest part of a crystal lattice of which the whole lattice is constructed. It can be seen from *Fig 7* that each Cl^- ion is at a corner, which means that it will be shared with eight other unit cells. Thus the contribution of each chloride ion to the unit cell, is only one eighth, and since there are eight Cl^- ions the total contribution is $8 \times \frac{1}{8} Cl^-$ or one Cl^- ion. The Cs^+ ion is within the unit cell and not shared with any other cell. Consequently each unit cell contains one Cl^- ion and one Cs^+ ion, giving an empirical formula of caesium chloride of CsCl.

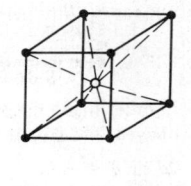

● = Cl^- ○ = Cs^+

Fig 7 The unit cell of caesium chloride

(b) Since the electrical charges are equal within each unit cell, any compilation of unit cells into a crystal lattice will also be electrically neutral.

Problem 7 Using the ionic radii given below, assign the probable lattice structure of the solids NaF, KI, RbF, NH_4Cl, and NH_4I.

Ion	Na^+	K^+	Rb^+	NH_4^+	F^-	Cl^-	I^-
Ionic size Å	0.98	1.33	1.49	1.48	1.33	1.81	2.29

The probable lattice crystal structure of a compound can be found for some compounds by calculating the radius ratio $\frac{r_c}{r_a}$. When $\frac{r_c}{r_a}$ lies within the range 0.414 to 0.732 the lattice structure is that of sodium chloride, i.e. of the 6:6 coordination type, see *Fig 1(a)*. Above that ratio for AB type structures the caesium chloride is most likely (see *Fig 1(b)*).

For NaF, $\frac{r_c}{r_a} = \frac{0.98}{1.33} = 0.737$ **sodium chloride type**

(when the ratio is very close to the limit the lower value type is most likely).

For KI, $\frac{r_c}{r_a} = \frac{1.33}{2.29} = 0.581$ **Sodium chloride type**

For RbF, $\frac{r_c}{r_a} = \frac{1.49}{1.33} = 1.120$ **Caesium chloride type**

For NH_4Cl, $\frac{r_c}{r_a} = \frac{1.48}{1.81} = 0.818$ **Caesium chloride type**

For NH_4I, $\frac{r_c}{r_a} = \frac{1.48}{2.29} = 0.646$ **Sodium chloride type**

Thus calculation of the radius ratio $\frac{r_c}{r_a}$ can give an indication of the lattice crystal structure of an ionic solid

Problem 8 When a crystal of sodium chloride is held in a certain orientation and X-radiation of wavelength 0.0597 nm is allowed to fall upon it, regions of radiation can be detected when the angle of incident radiation is 12.25° and 25.1°.
(a) What is the interplanar distance between the planes of ions in this orientation, and
(b) Why is there more than one value for which radiation can be detected.

(a) In order that a region of radiation is detected the Bragg equation must be obeyed. The equation is

$$2d \sin \theta = n\lambda$$

where d is the interplanar distance, θ is the angle of incidence, n is an integer and λ is the wavelength. (See *Problem 1*.) Assuming $n = 1$, and using $\theta = 12.25$ and $\lambda = 0.0597$ nm and substituting these values into the equation gives

$$2d \sin 12.25° = 1 \times 0.9597 \text{ nm.}$$

Rearranging this expression gives

$$d = \frac{1 \times 0.0597}{2 \times \sin 12.25} = \frac{0.0597}{2 \times 0.2122} = 0.1407 \text{ nm.}$$

Hence the interplanar distance is **0.1407 nm**.

For the second value of $\theta = 25.1$, the substitution of the appropriate values into the Bragg equation assuming that $n = 2$ gives

$$2d \sin 25.1 = 2 \times 0.0597 \text{ n.m.}$$

Rearranging this expression gives

$$d = \frac{2 \times 0.0597}{2 \times \sin 25.1} = \frac{0.1194}{2 \times 4242} = 0.1407 \text{ n.m.}$$

Again the interplanar distance is 0.1407 n.m.

(b) The reason why more than one value of θ for which intensified radiation can be detected is because for the emergent waves to be in phase the extra distance travelled through the crystal can be any number of complete wavelengths.

C. FURTHER PROBLEMS ON THE LATTICE CRYSTAL STRUCTURES OF SOME INORGANIC COMPOUNDS

(a) SHORT ANSWER PROBLEMS

Fill in the missing words

1. The technique which has been of most importance in identifying crystal lattice structures is ....

2. The Bragg equation in crystallographic use, relates the angle of incident X-radiation θ, to the distance between the .... of the lattice structure and the .... of the electromagnetic radiation.

3. The existence of regions of intensified and diminished radiation are caused by the ability of ionic solids to .... the radiation incident on the ....

4. Ionic solids of the AB type exist in two main types which are called the .... structure and the .... structure.

5. The most probable structure of an AB type of ionic solid can be predicted by finding the .... of the constituent ....

6. For the fluorite crystal lattice the coordination numbers of the ions are ...., ... refers to calcium ions, and .... refers to fluoride ions.

7. Zinc sulphide exists in two forms both of which are of .... coordination number. The different forms are called the .... structure and the .... structure.

8. For the AB_2 type of covalent crystal lattice, the three main crystal lattices are the .... structure, the .... structure and the .... structure.

9. For the covalent crystal lattices of the type AB_2, the coordination numbers can be .... or ....

10. The main difference in properties between ionic and covalent crystal structure is the .... of the compounds.

(b) MULTI-CHOICE PROBLEMS (answers on page 181)

Select the correct answer from those given

1. The Bragg equation is usually represented as
   (a) $d \sin \theta = 2n\lambda$;
   (b) $d \sin 2\theta = n\lambda$;
   (c) $2d \sin \theta = n\lambda$;
   (d) $2\lambda \sin \theta = nd$.

Problems 2 to 7 refer to the following structures:
P = the sodium chloride structure; Q = the caesium chloride structure;
R = the fluorite structure; S = the rutile structure; T = the zinc blende structure
and U = the β-cristobalite structure.
Select the appropriate letter for the correct answer.

2. The crystal lattice which shows 6:3 coordination is
   (a) P; (b) R; (c) S; (d) U.

3. The crystal lattice which shows 4:2 coordination is
   (a) R; (b) S; (c) T; (d) U.

4. For an ionic solid with a radius ratio $\dfrac{r_c}{r_a}$ of 0.55 the most probable structure is
   (a) P; (b) Q; (c) R; (d) S.

5. For an ionic solid with the radius ratio $\dfrac{r_c}{r_a}$ of 0.94 the most probable structure is
   (a) P; (b) Q; (c) T; (d) U.

6. The ionic radii of Ca^{2+} and O^{2-} are 1.06 Å and 1.32 Å respectively. The most likely crystal lattice structure will be of the type
   (a) P; (b) Q; (c) R; (d) S.

7. The crystal lattice which shows 4:4 coordination is
   (a) P; (b) Q; (c) T; (d) U.

8. For the unit cell shown in *Fig 8* the empirical formula of the solid is
   (a) MA; (b) M_2A; (c) MA_2; (d) MA_3.

9. The coordination number of the metal, M in the structure shown in *Fig 8* is
   (a) 2, (b) 4, (c) 6; (d) 8.

10. The coordination number of the non-metal, A in the structure in *Fig 8* is (a) 2; (b) 4, (c) 6; (d) 8.

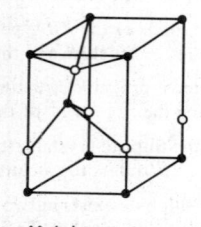

● = Metal
○ = Non metal

Fig 8

(c) CONVENTIONAL PROBLEMS

1. Explain the results of defracting electromagnetic radiation with a suitable diffraction grating.

2. What is meant by the terms (a) in phase, and (b) out of phase, applied to X-rays. Draw diagrams to illustrate your answer.

3. State the Bragg equation, explaining what each term in the equation means.

4. Using a powder of sodium chloride, three values for the angle of incidence θ

produced regions of intensified radiation using X-radiation of wavelength 0.0597 nm.
These angles were as follows

θ_1	12.25°	24.5°	36.75°
θ_2	16.6°	33.2°	
θ_3	10.75°	21.5°	32.25°

What information can be found about the crystal lattice using this data?
$$[d_1 = 0.1407 \text{ nm}; d_2 = 0.1045 \text{ nm}; d_3 = 0.1600 \text{ nm}]$$

5   The ionic radii of Mg^{2+} and O^{2-} are 0.78 Å and 1.32 Å respectively.
What is the most probable structure of magnesium oxide? Draw a diagram of the crystal lattice structure you have chosen. [Sodium chloride type]

6   The ionic radii of Rb^+ and Cl^- are 1.49 Å and 1.81 Å respectively.
What is the most probable structure of rubidium chloride? Draw a diagram of the crystal lattice structure you have chosen. [Caesium chloride]

7   Discuss the types of crystal lattice structures exhibited by inorganic solids with the formula of the type MA_2, where M is the metal and A the non-metal.

8   What similarities are there between the lattice crystal structures of diamond, silver iodide, and copper(I) oxide?

9   What similarities are there between the lattice crystal structures of graphite and cadmium iodide?

10 Discuss the factors which affect the crystal lattice structure adopted by inorganic solid compounds.

TABLE 3   The ionic radii of selections ions (Å)

Li^+	0.78				
Na^+	0.98	Mg^{2+}	0.78	Zn^{2+}	0.83
K^+	1.33	Ca^{2+}	1.06	Fe^{2+}	0.83
Rb^+	1.49	Sr^{2+}	1.27	Ni^{2+}	0.78
Cs^+	1.65	Ba^{2+}	1.43	Co^{2+}	0.82
NH_4^+	1.48				
F^-	1.33	O^{2-}	1.32		
Cl^-	1.81	S^{2-}	1.74		
Br^-	1.96				
I^-	2.29				

11 Using *Tables 2 and 3* assign the most probable crystal lattices for the following compounds.
(a) LiBr; (b) NaI; (c) RbF; (d) MgO; (e) SrO; (f) RbI; (g) NH_4Cl.
[a, b, d, e, f NaCl type; c, g, CsCl type]

12 Using *Tables 2 and 3* assign the most probable crystal lattices for the following compounds
(a) SrF_2; (b) NiF_2; (c) BaF_2; (d) FeF_2 [a, c, fluorite, b, d, rutile]

13 Manganese fluoride has the rutile structure. By drawing a diagram of the unit cell, find the empirical formula of the compound by calculating the contributions of the constituent ions to the unit cell. [MnF_2]

14 The perovskite structure contains calcium, titanium and oxygen. Using the diagram of the unit cell shown in *Fig 9* find the empirical formula of the compound. [$CaTiO_3$]

15 Construct a table to compare the physical properties of (a) ionic lattices, (b) covalent lattices and (c) layer lattices.

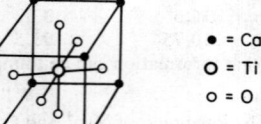

Fig 9

o at each face of the unit cell

● = Ca
O = Ti
o = O

6 The inorganic chemistry of some elements

A. MAIN POINTS CONCERNING THE INORGANIC CHEMISTRY OF SOME ELEMENTS

1. The study of inorganic chemistry is a wide ranging topic which can be undertaken from three main approaches:
   (a) the study of an **individual element** and all of its compounds;
   (b) a comparative study of the elements within their **groups in the periodic table**; or
   (c) a comparative study of the elements in **blocks of elements**, i.e. the s-block, p-block and d-block elements, (see *Table 1*), the method used in this text is a combination of approaches (b) and (c).

2. The assignment of the elements into groups, periods and blocks within the periodic table has been covered in *Chemistry 2 Checkbook*, and certain tables are reproduced here for the convenience of the reader.

3. In this chapter the **general trends** in properties of the s, p and d-block elements will be discussed together with a more extensive comparative study of the elements of group IV and V. The comparative study is to illustrate the trends in properties of groups midway across the periodic table, shown in *Table 1*.

4. The electronic configuration of the elements is shown in *Table 2*. Consideration of this table shows that s, p and d-block elements contain electrons in s, p or d orbitals as their **highest energy electrons**.

5. The elements are compared in terms of their **metallic** or **non-metallic character**. The metallic characteristics of the elements are shown by both **physical** and **chemical** properties as discussed in *Problem 1*.

6. The main properties of the s-block elements are given in *Table 3* and some physical properties of the elements in *Table 4*. These properties are also dealt with in *Problem 2*.

7. The main properties of the p-block elements are given in *Table 5*, together with some physical properties in *Table 6*. These properties are also dealt with in *Problem 3*.

8. The main properties of the d-block elements are given in *Table 7* and some physical properties in *Table 8*. These properties are also dealt with in *Problem 4*.

9. The elements in group IV of the periodic table are **carbon, silicon germanium, tin and lead.** The first of these elements, carbon, is clearly **non-metallic**, whereas the final element, lead, is **metallic** in character. The elements can be compared by a consideration of the structures of **the elements**, also **the chlorides, the oxides, the hydrides** and **the oxidation states** of the elements. These factors are summarised

TABLE 1

s block

1s	^{1}H 1.008		^{2}He 4.00
2s	^{3}Li 6.94	^{4}Be 9.01	
3s	^{11}Na 23.0	^{12}Mg 24.3	
4s	^{19}K 39.1	^{20}Ca 40.1	
5s	^{37}Rb 85.5	^{38}Sr 87.6	
6s	^{55}Cs 132.9	^{56}Ba 137.3	
7s	^{87}Fr (223)	^{88}Ra (226)	

d block

3d	^{21}Sc 45.0	^{22}Ti 47.9	^{23}V 50.9	^{24}Cr 52.0	^{25}Mn 54.9	^{26}Fe 55.9	^{27}Co 58.9	^{28}Ni 58.7	^{29}Cu 63.5	^{30}Zn 65.4
4d	^{39}Y 88.9	^{40}Zr 91.2	^{41}Nb 92.9	^{42}Mo 95.9	^{43}Tc 99	^{44}Ru 101.1	^{45}Rh 102.9	^{46}Pd 106.4	^{47}Ag 107.9	^{48}Cd 112.4
5d	^{72}Hf 178.5	^{73}Ta 181.0	^{74}W 183.9	^{75}Re 186.2	^{76}Os 190.2	^{77}Ir 192.2	^{78}Pt 195.1	^{79}Au 197	^{80}Hg 200.6

p block

2p	^{5}B 10.8	^{6}C 12.01	^{7}N 14.01	^{8}O 16.00	^{9}F 19.0	^{10}Ne 20.2
3p	^{13}Al 27.0	^{14}Si 28.1	^{15}P 31.0	^{16}S 32.1	^{17}Cl 35.5	^{18}Ar 39.9
4p	^{31}Ga 69.7	^{32}Ge 72.6	^{33}As 74.9	^{34}Se 79	^{35}Br 79.9	^{36}Kr 83.6
5p	^{49}In 114.8	^{50}Sn 118.7	^{51}Sb 121.8	^{52}Te 127.6	^{53}I 126.9	^{54}Xe 131.3
6p	^{81}Tl 204.4	^{82}Pb 207.2	^{83}Bi 209	^{84}Po (210)	^{85}At (210)	^{86}Rn (222)

- 1st short period
- 2nd short period
- 3rd short period
- 1st long period
- 2nd long period
- 3rd long period

TABLE 2

Element	At No (Z)	K	L	M	N	O	P	1s	2s	2p	3s	3p	4s	3d	4p	5s	4d	5p	6s
		\multicolumn{6}{l	}{Shell Structure}	\multicolumn{13}{l	}{Orbital structure}
Hydrogen	1	1						1											
Helium	2	2						2											
Lithium	3	2	1					2	1										
Beryllium	4	2	2					2	2										
Boron	5	2	3					2	2	1									
Carbon	6	2	4					2	2	2									
Nitrogen	7	2	5					2	2	3									
Oxygen	8	2	6					2	2	4									
Fluorine	9	2	7					2	2	5									
Neon	10	2	8					2	2	6									
Sodium	11	2	8	1				2	2	6	1								
Magnesium	12	2	8	2				2	2	6	2								
Aluminium	13	2	8	3				2	2	6	2	1							
Silicon	14	2	8	4				2	2	6	2	2							
Phosphorus	15	2	8	5				2	2	6	2	3							
Sulphur	16	2	8	6				2	2	6	2	4							
Chlorine	17	2	8	7				2	2	6	2	5							
Argon	18	2	8	8				2	2	6	2	6							
Potassium	19	2	8	8	1			2	2	6	2	6	1						
Calcium	20	2	8	8	2			2	2	6	2	6	2						
Scandium	21	2	8	9	2			2	2	6	2	6	2	1					
Titanium	22	2	8	10	2			2	2	6	2	6	2	2					
Vanadium	23	2	8	11	2			2	2	6	2	6	2	3					
Chromium	24	2	8	13	1			2	2	6	2	6	1	5					
Manganese	25	2	8	13	2			2	2	6	2	6	2	5					
Iron	26	2	8	14	2			2	2	6	2	6	2	6					
Cobalt	27	2	8	15	2			2	2	6	2	6	2	7					
Nickel	28	2	8	16	2			2	2	6	2	6	2	8					
Copper	29	2	8	18	1			2	2	6	2	6	1	10					
Zinc	30	2	8	18	2			2	2	6	2	6	2	10					
Gallium	31	2	8	18	3			2	2	6	2	6	2	10	1				
Germanium	32	2	8	18	4			2	2	6	2	6	2	10	2				
Arsenic	33	2	8	18	5			2	2	6	2	6	2	10	3				
Selenium	34	2	8	18	6			2	2	6	2	6	2	10	4				
Bromine	35	2	8	18	7			2	2	6	2	6	2	10	5				
Krypton	36	2	8	18	8			2	2	6	2	6	2	10	6				
Rubidium	37	2	8	18	8	1		2	2	6	2	6	2	10	6	1			
Strontium	38	2	8	18	8	2		2	2	6	2	6	2	10	6	2			
Iodine	53	2	8	18	18	7		2	2	6	2	6	2	10	6	2	10	5	
Xenon	54	2	8	18	18	8		2	2	6	2	6	2	10	6	2	10	6	
Caesium	55	2	8	18	18	8	1	2	2	6	2	6	2	10	6	2	10	6	1
Barium	56	2	8	18	18	8	2	2	2	6	2	6	2	10	6	2	10	6	2

TABLE 3 The properties of the *s*-block elements

	Property	Exceptions
1	All *s*-block elements display metallic bonding in the solid state, usually as body centred cubic structures.	Be and Mg are hexagonal close packed Ca and Sr are cubic close packed
2	The halides of Group I are ionic in character displaying the sodium chloride or caesium chloride structure.	Lithium halides display some covalent character
	The halides of Group II are ionic in character, usually as fluorite or rutile.	$BeCl_2$ is a covalent polmeric solid
3	The oxides are basic, dissolving to differing extents in water to form hydroxides.	BeO is covalent and insoluble in water
4	The hydrides are ionic, and react with water to form hydrogen gas.	Be and Mg form metallic hydrides. LiH is insoluble
5	The relative thermal stabilities of the nitrates of Group I are greater than those of Group II, which all decompose to the oxide.	$4LiNO_3 \rightarrow 2Li_2O + 2N_2O_4 + O_2$
6	The relative thermal stabilities of the carbonates of Group I are greater than those of Group II which all decompose to the oxide.	$Li_2CO_3 \rightarrow Li_2O + CO_2$
7	The elements show a valency of +1 and +2 for Group I and Group II in all of their compounds.	None
8	The elements undergo many direct combination reactions due to their high relative reactivity.	

TABLE 4 Some physical properties of the *s*-block elements

Group		Covalent radius, nm	Ionic radius, nm	1st I.E. kJ	2nd I.E. kJ	3rd I.E.
	Li	0.123	0.068	520	7300	11800
	Na	0.157	0.098	500	4600	6900
I	K	0.203	0.133	420	3100	4400
	Rb	0.216	0.148	400	2400	3800
	Cs	0.235	0.167	380	2400	3300
	Be	0.106	0.030	900	1800	14800
	Mg	0.140	0.065	740	1500	7700
II	Ca	0.174	0.094	590	1100	4900
	Sr	0.191	0.110	550	1100	5500
	Ba	0.198	0.134	500	1000	5300

TABLE 5 The properties of the *p*-block elements (Table 6 elements only)

	Property	Exceptions
1	The elements can exist as solids, liquids or gases, showing a variety of structures, including giant lattices, layer lattices, molecular crystals and simple molecules.	None
2	The elements can form ionic and covalent compounds	B covalent only C, Si covalent only
3	The elements can exhibit variable oxidation states.	B, Al, C, F
4	The elements form covalent chlorides if chlorides can be formed.	$GeCl_2$
5	The elements form acidic oxides if oxides can be formed.	Al_2O_3 amphoteric Ga_2O_3 amphoteric
6	The elements form covalent hydrides.	None
7	The elements form oxyacids.	Al, O, F

TABLE 6 The physical properties of some *p*-block elements

Group		r_a (nm)	r_i (nm)	Cations	Anions	Oxidation states	Melting point, (°K)
III	B	0.088	0.016	—	—	+3	2300
	Al	0.126	0.045	Al^{3+}	—	+3	2720
	Ga	0.126	0.062	Ga^{3+}	—	+3, +1	303
IV	C	0.077	0.016	—	—	+4, −4	4000
	Si	0.177	0.038	—	—	+4, −4	2950
	Ge	0.122	0.093	Ge^{2+}	—	+2, +4	1210
V	N	0.070	0.171	—	N^{3-}	+3, +4, +5, −3, −2, −1, +1, +2,	63
	P	0.110	0.212	—	P^{3-}	−3, −2, −1 +1, +2, +3, +4, +5	317
	As	0.121	0.069	—	—	+3, +5	886[†]
VI	O	0.066	0.146	—	O^{2-}, O_2^{2-}	−2, −1	54
	S	0.104	0.190	—	S^{2-}, S_2^{2-}	−2, −1 +2, +3, +4, +5, +6	392
	Se	0.117	0.198	—	—	+2, +4, +6	490
VII	F	0.064	0.133	—	F^-	−1	53
	Cl	0.099	0.181	—	Cl^-	−1, +1, +3, +4, +5, +6, +7	172
	Br	0.111	0.196	—	Br^-	−1, +1, +4, +5, +6	266
	I	0.128	0.219	—	I^-	−1, +1, +3, +5, +7	397
O	Ne	0.160	—	—	—	—	25
	Ar	0.192	—	—	—	—	84
	Kr	0.197	—	—	—	+2, +4	116

[†]Sublimation

TABLE 7 The properties of the d-block elements

	Property	Exceptions
1	The elements are metallic in structure but more dense than other metals	
2	The elements are of similar atomic and ionic radii	Sc, Zn
3	The elements form coloured compounds	Sc, Zn
4	The elements form magnetic compounds	Sc, Zn
5	The elements form interstitial compounds	Sc, Cu, Zn
6	The elements exhibit variable valency states	Sc, Zn
7	The elements form complex ions and complex compounds	Sc
8	The elements form basic oxides and acidic oxides	
9	The elements form ionic and covalent chlorides	

TABLE 8 Some properties of the d-block elements

Element	Atomic radius, nm	Valency states	Ions	Paramagnetism	Colour
Scandium	0.161	3	Sc^{3+}	0	Colourless
Titanium	0.145	4 3 2	Ti^{3+}	1	Purple
Vanadium	0.132	5 4 3 2	V^{3+}	2	Green
Chromium	0.137	6 3 2	Cr^{3+}	3	Violet
Manganese	0.137	7 6 4 3 2	Mn^{3+} Mn^{2+}	4 5	Violet Pink
Iron	0.124	6 3 2	Fe^{3+} Fe^{2+}	5 4	Yellow Green
Cobalt	0.125	4 3 2	Co^{2+}	3	Pink
Nickel	0.125	4 2	Ni^{2+}	2	Green
Copper	0.128	2 1	Cu^{2+}	1	Blue
Zinc	0.133	2	Zn^{2+}	0	Colourless

TABLE 9 The group IV elements

Element	Structure	Chloride	Bonding	Oxide	Nature	Hydride	Bonding	Oxidation states
Carbon	Diamond (giant) Graphite (layer)	CCl_4	Covalent	CO_2 CO	Acidic Neutral	CH_4	Covalent	+4,
Silicon	Giant lattice	$SiCl_4$	Covalent	SiO_2	Acidic	SiH_4	Covalent	+4,
Germanium	Metallic	$GeCl_4$ $GeCl_2$	Covalent Ionic	GeO_2	Acidic	GeH_4	Covalent	+2, +4
Tin	Metallic	$SnCl_4$ $SnCl_2$	Covalent Covalent	SnO_2 SnO	Amphoteric Amphoteric	SnH_4	Covalent	+2, +4
Lead	Metallic	$PbCl_4$ $PbCl_2$	Covalent Ionic	PbO PbO_2 Pb_3O_4	Basic Amphoteric Mixed	PbH_4	Covalent	+2, +4

TABLE 10 The group V elements

Element	Structure	Chloride	Bonding	Oxide	Nature	Hydride	Bonding	Oxidation states
Nitrogen	Simple molecular	NCl_3	Covalent	NO_2	Acidic	NH_3	Covalent	−3 (except in oxides)
Phosphorus	Macro-molecular	PCl_3 PCl_5	Covalent Covalent	P_4O_6 P_4O_{10}	Acidic Acidic	PH_3 P_2H_4	Covalent Covalent	−3, +3, +5
Arsenic	Metallic	$AsCl_3$	Covalent	As_4O_6 As_2O_5	Acidic	AsH_3	Covalent	+3, +5
Antimony	Metallic	$SbCl_3$	Covalent	Sb_4O_6 Sb_2O_5	Amphoteric	SbH_3	Covalent	+3, +5
Bismuth	Metallic	$BiCl_3$	Covalent	Bi_2O_3	Basic	BiH_3	Covalent	+3, +5

Note. The other oxides of nitrogen are covered in *Problem 6*.

in *Table 9* and are also dealt with in *Problem 9*. It can be seen from *Problem 9* that there is a **gradual change in properties on descending the group**.

10 The change in character of group IV elements is quite different to the trends in properties for the groups of elements at the extremities of the periodic table, that is, in groups I and II and in groups VII and O.

11 (i) The elements in group V of the periodic table are **nitrogen, phosphorus, arsenic, antimony and bismuth**. These elements can be compared in the same way as those of group IV, as shown in *Table 10*.

(ii) In this group, the **change in properties is less marked** and only **bismuth** shows a **considerable metallic** character.

12 The properties of the elements in groups IV and V **typify the diversity of the reactions of the p-block elements**, when compared with those of the s- and d-blocks.

B. WORKED PROBLEMS IN INORGANIC CHEMISTRY

Problem 1 What are the metallic characteristics of an element in terms of both physical properties and chemical properties.

The elements can be classified broadly as being metals or non-metals by using a set of physical properties. These are **conductivity, density, malleability, ductility** and a **shiny lustrous appearance**. Of these, the property of conductivity is the most distinguishing property. However, for comparison purposes, **chemical metallic character** may also be considered.

The metallic chemical character of an element can be considered from the following properties:
(a) **the bonding in the elements;**
(b) **the bonding in the chlorides of the elements;**
(c) **the basic nature of the oxides of the elements, and**
(d) **the bonding in the hydrides of the elements.**

(a) The bonding in metals is called **metallic bonding**, in which the atoms are held together in a **close packed arrangement**, but in which there are no bonds formed between the atoms. The structures of the metals are regarded as **giant structures**. The non-metals form a variety of structures, **giant, layer, molecular crystals** and **simple molecules**, in which the atoms are held in position by covalent bonds between the atoms. **X-ray crystallographic data** is most useful in assigning the structure of solid elements.

(b) If the bonding shown by the chloride of the element is predominantly **ionic**, the element is considered to be **metallic**. The degree of ionic bonding can be considered as a **measure of how metallic** an element might be. The non-metals form covalent chlorides with the property of being **hydrolysed by water**, a reaction **not shown by ionic chlorides**. The equations of the reactions are:

Ionic chloride $\quad MCl_n(s) + H_2O = M^{n+}(aq) + nCl^-(aq)$
Covalent chloride $\quad ACl_n + nH_2O = A(OH)_n(aq) + nHCl(aq)$

where M is any metal and A any non-metal.

(c) If the oxide of the element forms **an alkaline solution** when it dissolves in water, the element is considered to be metallic. Some elements form oxides which are only **sparingly soluble** in water, but which will react with both acids and alkalis, these oxides are called **amphoteric** and show that the element can be considered to have only **partial metallic** character. The elements, whose oxides are soluble in water to give **acidic solutions**, are called **acidic oxides** and the elements are considered to be non-metallic. Examples of these oxides are:

(i) $Na_2O(s) + H_2O(l) = 2NaOH(aq)$ *basic*

(ii)   (a) $Al_2O_3(s) + 3H_2SO_4(aq) = Al_2(SO_4)_3(aq) + 3H_2O(l)$ *basic amphoteric*

      (b) $Al_2O_3(s) + 2NaOH + 3H_2O = 2NaAl(OH)_4(aq)$ *acidic*

(iii) $SO_3(g) + H_2O(l) = H_2SO_4(aq)$ *acidic*

(d) The hydrides of the elements can themselves be classified as (i) **ionic hydrides**, (ii) **covalent hydrides** and (iii) **interstitial hydrides**. Ionic hydrides are formed by the elements of group I and II and the elements are classified as metallic. Covalent hydrides are formed by non-metals and interstitial hydrides by the transition metal elements. The **interstitial hydrides are not true compounds** but are best regarded as **inclusion compounds**. For some hydrides which are inclusion compounds the application of a vacuum to the compound will degrade it, leaving the pure metal after the removal of hydrogen.

Consideration of the properties in (a) and (b) allows the metallic character of an element to be identified.

Problem 2 How can the properties of the *s*-block elements be explained in terms of their physical properties.

The *s*-block elements occupy groups I and II of the periodic table. They occupy these positions as a result of their **electronic configurations** which are shown in *Table 2*. The elements of group I have **one electron** in the final *s*-orbital, for example, Li is $1s^2 2s^1$, Na is $1s^2 2s^2 2p^6 3s^1$ and K is $1s^2 2s^2 2p^6 3s^2 3p^6 4s^1$, whereas the elements in group II have two electrons in its final *s*-orbital, for example Be is $1s^2 2s^2$, Mg is $1s^2 2s^2 2p^6 3s^2$ and Ca is $1s^2 2s^2 2p^6 3s^2 3p^6 4s^2$. The elements in **group I** all have a **valency of +1** and group II elements, a **valency of +2**. This can be explained by the values of the **ionisation energies** shown in *Table 4*. The group I elements have a relatively **low 1st** ionisation energy (I.E.) but a **high 2nd** I.E., this results in the formation of the **stable M^+ cation** when forming compounds. The group II elements have relatively **low 1st and 2nd** I.E. values but a **high 3rd** I.E. resulting in the formation of the **stable M^{2+} cation** when forming compounds. **One exception is beryllium**, which has a **small atomic radius** and whose compounds are more stable as covalent compounds.

The formation of ionic chlorides can be explained by the **ease of electron exchange** between *s*-block elements and chlorine, due to the **low I.E. values** of the metals and the **low electron affinity** of chlorine. The **lattice energies** of the group I chlorides are most stable for the MCl structure, and for the group II chlorides they are most stable for the MCl_2 formula.

The basic nature of the oxides can be shown by their reaction with water to produce solutions containing hydroxide ions as shown by the equations

$$M_2O + H_2O = 2MOH = 2M^+ + 2OH^- \quad \text{(group I)}$$

and $$MO + H_2O = M(OH)_2 = M^{2+} + 2OH^- \quad \text{(group II)}$$

The group I oxides are more basic than those of group II, and in each group, **the basic strength increases** on descending the group.

Problem 3 How can the properties of the *p*-block elements be explained in terms of their physical properties?

By comparison with the *s*-block elements the *p*-block elements are more diverse in their properties. The major differences are the tendency of the elements to form covalent bonds in their compounds and the ability of the elements to show variable oxidation states. The formation of positive ions can only be achieved if **sufficient electrons can be removed to produce a stable noble gas electronic configuration.**

When the size of the atom is small this becomes particularly difficult from an energy point of view. Consequently, beryllium (an *s*-block element) and boron form **only covalent** compounds. As any *p*-block group is descended, the size of the atom increases, and for groups III, IV and V the lower elements are able to form positive ions.

The elements in groups V, VI and VII are able to accept electrons and form negative ions. The ability of an element to form negative ions is greatest for the first element in each group and can be considered to reflect the attractive force the element shows towards electrons. The values of electronegativities of the elements is a good measure of this attraction, **being highest for fluorine.**

The ability of *p*-block elements to show **variable oxidation states** is usually due to the use of **available vacant orbitals** of the elements. However, the *p*-block element, nitrogen also shows variable oxidation states by the formation of a mixture of covalent and dative bonding.

The electronic configuration of the elements places the elements in their respective *p*-block groups. Those elements which have electrons in energy levels greater than 2*p* will have vacant orbitals available for the so-called **expansion of the octet**. This together with group comparisons are discussed in *Problems 6 to 10*.

Problem 4 How may the properties of the *d*-block elements be explained in terms of the physical properties of the elements?

(i) These elements occupy their position in the periodic table as a result of their electronic configurations. The 4*s* orbital is filled before the 3*d* orbital due to the lower energy of the 4*s* orbital. Since the 4*s* orbital is completely filled, the size of the atomic radii of the ten elements which constitute the *d*-block elements, are much more closely in agreement than the six *p*-block elements which follow them.

(ii) **The variable oxidation states** of these metallic elements is a **result of the small difference in energy levels of the 3*d* orbitals,** and the 4*s* and 4*p* orbitals. The formation of positive ions rarely exceeds the removal of three electrons. The **high oxidation states** of the *d*-block elements are due to the **formation of covalent or dative bonds in complex ions** with non-metals, (see *Table 8*).

(iii) The ability of *d*-block elements to exhibit paramagnetism is considered to be due to the number of unpaired electrons shown by the element in its compounds. The ions with the greatest number of unpaired electrons, Mn^{2+} and Fe^{3+}, compounds show the greatest magnetic moment, as shown in *Table 8*.

(iv) The **five 3*d*-orbitals are not all of equal energy.** Two of the orbitals are considered to be of slightly higher energy than the other three. Any electron in any of the five orbitals can move from the lower energy level to the higher level if it is supplied with **energy of the correct wavelength**. For many **electronic transitions**, the wavelength of energy required is within the **visible spectrum**.

Thus the absorption of parts of the visible spectrum and the consequent reflection of other parts, enables the compounds to become **coloured**.

(v) With the exception of Sc, Cu and Zn, the remaining *d*-block elements all form **interstitial compounds**. The size of the atoms is such that small elements like hydrogen, carbon and nitrogen can be enclosed within the metal crystal lattice when the molten metals solidify. **The properties of the metals change considerably when other elements are enclosed within their structures.**

(vi) The formation of complex ions is dependent on the **central metal ion** (or atom in the case of carbonyls) having **vacant orbitals** which can form **dative bonds** with surrounding **ligands**. The number of ligands which surround a central ion is either six or four, the six ligands form an **octahedral** shape and the four ligands form either **square planar** or **tetrahedral** shapes.

The elements at the extremities of the *d*-block group are not true transition elements but are included in the *d*-block on the basis of the electronic configuration of the elements.

The properties which are considered to be characteristic of the transition metals are a result of the partially filled 3d orbitals.

Problem 5 Discuss the stereochemistry of the complex ions (a) dichlorotetrammine chromium (*III*) and (b) *tris*(ethylenediamino) chromium (*III*).

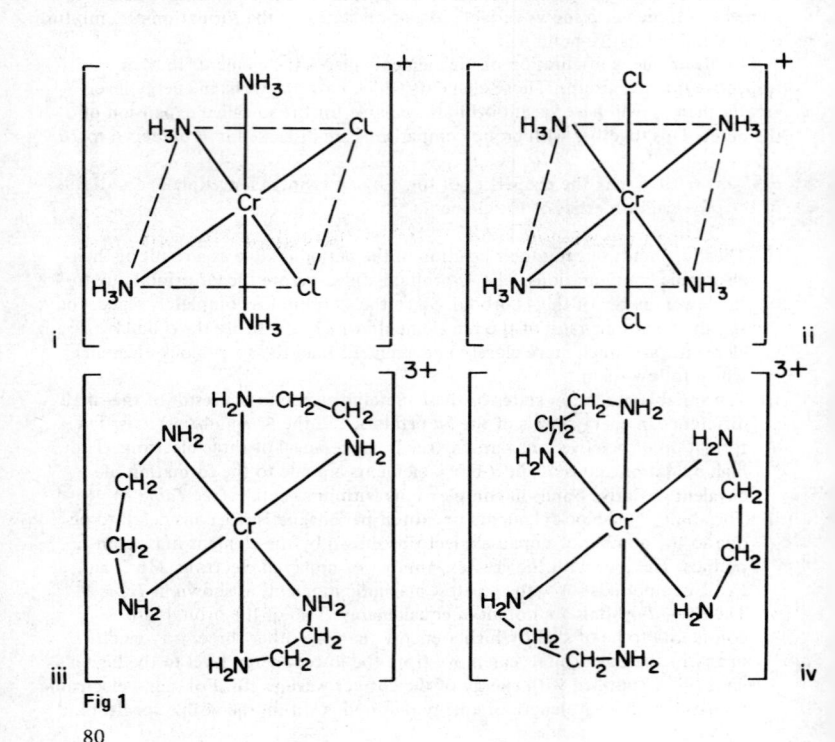

Fig 1

The structures of dichlorotetrammine chromium (*III*) are shown in *Fig 1*. It is quite clear that there are two distinct non-superimposable structures (*i*) and (*ii*). These structures are of the same molecular composition. In order to differentiate between the two structures the prefixes *cis* and *trans* are used to denote either similar groups on the same side of the structure, i.e. *cis* as shown in *Fig 1(i)* or similar groups on opposite sides of the structure, i.e. *trans* as shown in *Fig 1(ii)*. Although the structures are different and called **geometrical isomers**, they both possess **a plane of symmetry** and are therefore not **optically active**.

The structures of *tris*(ethylenediamino) chromium are similarly shown in *Fig 1(iii and iv)*. In this case the structures are a **pair of non-superimposable mirror images**, neither of which has any element of symmetry. As a result these isomers are **optically active**, that is, they are capable of rotating the plane of plane-polarised light if it is passed through a solution of the isomer.

Thus, depending on the constitution of the complex ion, geometrical or optical isomers can be formed.

Problem 6 Discuss the bonding in the oxides of nitrogen using the dot and cross notion.

There are six oxides of nitrogen, **dinitrogen oxide** N_2O, **nitrogen oxide** NO, **dinitrogen trioxide** N_2O_3, **nitrogen dioxide** NO_2, **dinitrogen tetroxide** N_2O_4 and **dinitrogen pentoxide** N_2O_5.

Nitrogen has seven electrons, five of which are bonding electrons and oxygen has eight electrons, six of which are bonding electrons, the distribution of the electrons are shown in *Fig 2(a)*.

(i) The distribution of the electrons in **dinitrogen oxide** is shown in *Fig 2(b)*. There are two possible ways in which the electrons can be distributed shown as (*i*) and (*ii*). The lower diagrams in each case show the bonds formed and the electrons not used in bonding. Either structure shows that by forming covalent bonds and a dative bond, each atom in the molecule is associated with eight electrons.

(ii) **Nitrogen oxide** shown in *Fig 2(c)* can also exist in two possible electronic arrangements. In arrangement (*i*) the oxygen atom is associated with eight electrons, but the nitrogen atom is only associated with seven electrons, one short of the ideal number. In arrangement (*ii*) the reverse can be observed. This results in a molecule containing **an unpaired electron**, and nitrogen oxide is **paramagnetic**, a property which is associated with such a structure.

(iii) **Dinitrogen trioxide** is shown in *Fig 2(d)*, and structures (*i*) and (*ii*) show that each atom is associated with eight electrons.

(iv) **Nitrogen dioxide** is shown in *Fig 2(e)*. Both structures (*i*) and (*ii*) show that the nitrogen atom is associated with seven electrons, similar to the structure of nitrogen oxide. This molecule is also **paramagnetic** due to the **unpaired electron** on nitrogen.

(v) **Dinitrogen tetroxide** is found in the pure state only as a solid, having a melting point of 263.6 K. At all temperatures above this an equilibrium is formed with nitrogen dioxide according to the equation

$$N_2O_4(g) \rightleftharpoons 2NO_2(g)$$

The structures shown in *Fig 2(f)*, (*i*) and (*ii*) show that each atom is associated with eight electrons.

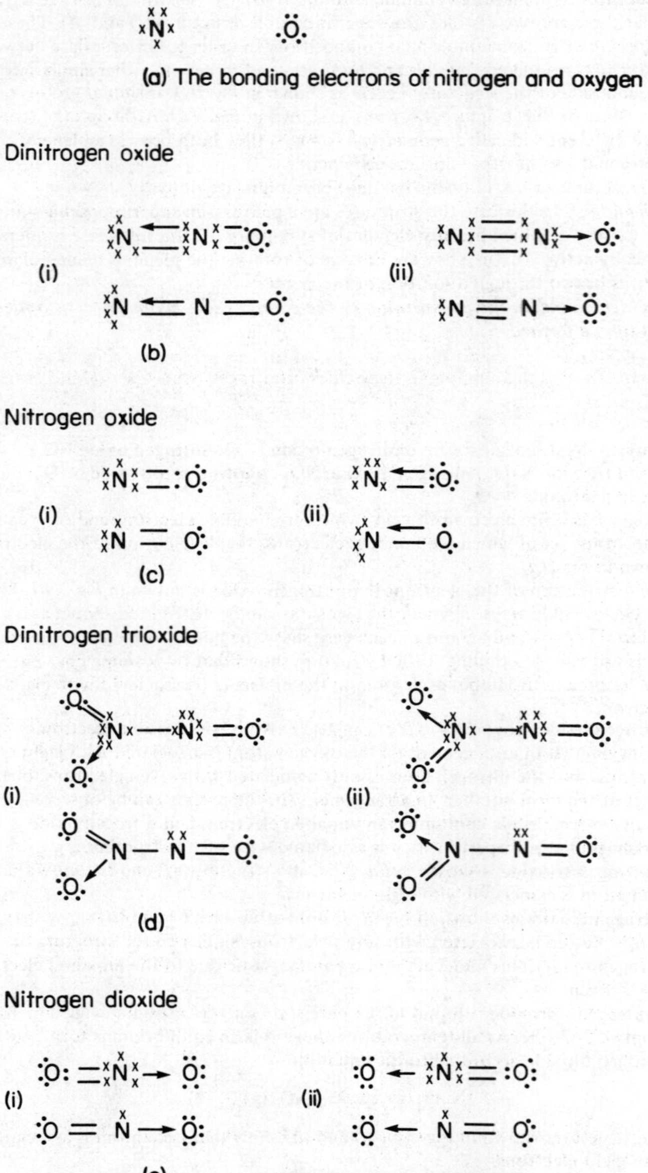

(a) The bonding electrons of nitrogen and oxygen

Dinitrogen oxide

(i)
(ii)

(b)

Nitrogen oxide

(i)
(ii)

(c)

Dinitrogen trioxide

(i)
(ii)

(d)

Nitrogen dioxide

(i)
(ii)

(e)

Fig 2 The oxides of nitrogen

Dinitrogen tetroxide

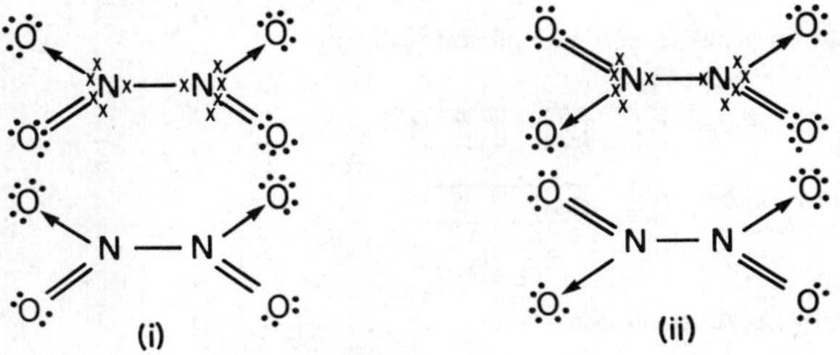

(f)

Dinitrogen pentoxide

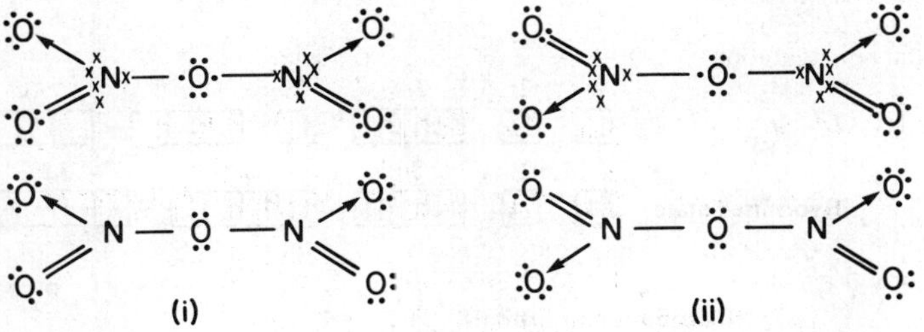

(g)

Fig 2 (continued)

(vi) **Dinitrogen pentoxide** is shown in *Fig 2(g)*. All of the atoms involved in the molecule have the ideal number of eight electrons associated with them.

It is important to note that in all of these structures nitrogen forms only three covalent bonds even though it is able to form a dative bond in addition to these three covalent bonds.

Problem 7 Explain why nitrogen forms only one chloride, nitrogen trichloride NCl_3, whereas phosphorus can form two chlorides, phosphorus trichloride PCl_3 and phosphorus pentachloride PCl_5.

Nitrogen has the electronic configuration $1s^2 2s^2 2p^3$, and since its electrons are occupying the K and L shells of electrons, it has **no available set of vacant d-orbitals**. Hence nitrogen has a **maximum covalency of three**. The formation of nitrogen trichloride is shown in *Fig 3* together with the hybridisation of the s and p orbitals.

Phosphorus has the electronic configuration $1s^2 2s^2 2p^6 3s^2 3p^3$, and since its electrons are occupying the K, L and M shells of electrons, it has the **set of vacant $3d$ orbitals available for increasing its covalency**. The formation of phosphorus trichloride is shown in *Fig 3* and it can readily be seen that the bond formation is very similar to that in NCl_3.

However in phosphorus pentachloride, five covalent bonds are formed by

Nitrogen trichloride

Orbital representation of nitrogen in ground state

N $1s^2$ $2s^2$ $2p^3$

1s	2s	2p
↑↓	↑↓	↑ ↑ ↑

Hybridised state

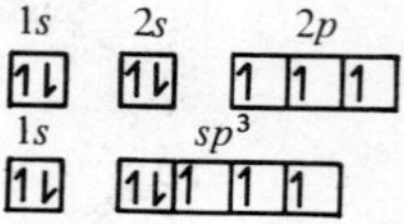

1s	sp³
↑↓	↑↓ ↑ ↑ ↑

Distribution of orbitals (diagrammatic)

Structure of NCl_3 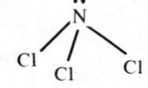   pyramidal

Phosphorus trichloride

Orbital representation

P s $1s^2$ $2s^2$ $2p^6$ $3s^2$ $3p^3$

1s	2s	2p	3s	3p	3d
↑↓	↑↓	↑↓ ↑↓ ↑↓	↑↓	↑ ↑ ↑	

Hybridised state

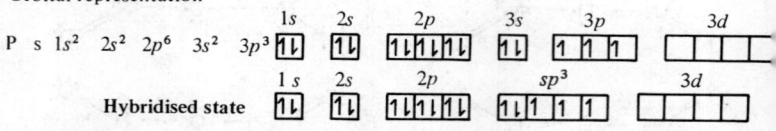

1s	2s	2p	sp³	3d
↑↓	↑↓	↑↓ ↑↓ ↑↓	↑↓ ↑ ↑ ↑	

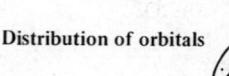

Distribution of orbitals

Structure of PCl_3 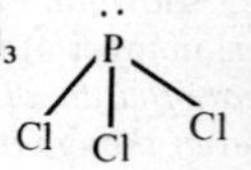   pyramidal

Phosphorus pentachloride

Orbital representation as above

Hybridised state

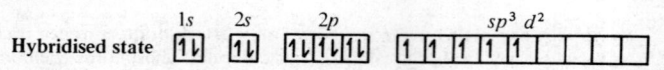

1s	2s	2p	sp³d²
↑↓	↑↓	↑↓ ↑↓ ↑↓	↑ ↑ ↑ ↑ ↑ ↑

Distribution of orbitals (diagrammatic)

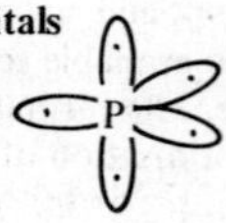

Structure of PCl_5

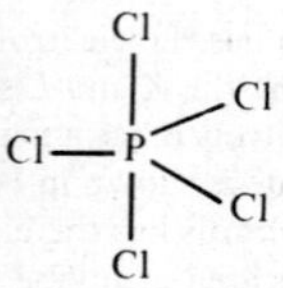

trigonal bipyramidal

Fig 3 The chlorides of nitrogen and phosphorus

phosphorus. This is achieved by the **promotion of one electron** into the vacant 3d orbitals. The distribution of the five hybridised orbitals around phosphorus are arranged to the apices of a triangular bipyramid, as shown in *Fig 3*, to **achieve the minimum electronic bonding-pair repulsions.**

Thus phosphorus can form two chlorides because it has an available set of d orbitals into which electrons can be promoted. **This is a property which can be exhibited by any element (usually a non-metal) with an atomic number greater than ten.**

Problem 8 Explain why the elements of the third short period show the oxidation states shown in *Table 11*.

TABLE 11

Element	Electronic configuration	Oxidation states
Sodium	$1s^2 2s^2 2p^6 3s^1$	+1
Magnesium	$1s^2 2s^2 2p^6 3s^2$	+2
Aluminium	$1s^2 2s^2 2p^6 3s^2 3p^1$	+3
Silicon	$1s^2 2s^2 2p^6 3s^2 3p^2$	+4, −4
Phosphorus	$1s^2 2s^2 2p^6 3s^2 3p^3$	−3, +3, +5
Sulphur	$1s^2 2s^2 2p^6 3s^2 3p^4$	−2, +1, +2, +4, +6
Chlorine	$1s^2 2s^2 2p^6 3s^2 3p^5$	−1, +1, +3, +5
Argon	$1s^2 2s^2 2p^6 3s^2 3p^6$	0

(a) Sodium has an invariable oxidation state of +1 because the ionisation energy of the $2p^6$ electrons are very high compared to that of the $3s$, and because the difference in electronegativity between sodium and any non-metal is large, ensuring only ionic bonds are formed.

(b) Magnesium has an invariable oxidation number of +2 whether it is in an ionic or covalent compound. Although magnesium is a group II metal, **Fajan's rules** indicate that it is likely to form covalent compounds, of which the **Grignard reagents**, R—Mg—Br, are synthetically very important.

(c) Aluminium has an invariable oxidation state of +3, most of the compounds of aluminium show considerable covalent character as might be expected from **Fajan's rules.**

(d) Silicon shows an oxidation state of +4 or −4 depending upon the compound it is forming. For example in $SiCl_4$ it is +4 but in SiH_4 it is −4. The compounds formed are predominantly covalent due to the high energy change required for the formation of Si^{4+} or Si^{4-}. Ions of such high charges are rarely found due to the instability of such ions.

(e) Phosphorus can accept 3 electrons to complete the $3p$ orbitals and hence forms the P^{3-} anion, to form **phosphides with certain metals**. The element can also share 3 electrons to form covalent compounds which are sp^3 hybridised and pyramidal in shape. Phosphorus is able to form a variety of compounds in which its oxidation state is +5, for example PCl_5. This means that phosphorus is forming five covalent bonds and showing sp^3d hybridisation in the form of a trigonal bipyramid which has been discussed in *Problem 7*.

(f) Sulphur can accept two electrons to complete the $3p$ orbitals forming the S^{2-} anion found in the form of the **sulphides of the metals.** The other oxidation

S_2Cl_2

S Ground state: 1s [↑↓] 2s [↑↓] 2p [↑↓][↑↓][↑↓] 3s [↑↓] 3p [↑↓][↑][↑] 3d [ ][ ][ ][ ][ ]

Hybridised state: 1s [↑↓] 2s [↑↓] 2p [↑↓][↑↓][↑↓] sp³ [↑↓][↑↓][↑][↑] 3d [ ][ ][ ][ ][ ]

Cl Ground state: 1s [↑↓] 2s [↑↓] 2p [↑↓][↑↓][↑↓] 3s [↑↓] 3p [↑↓][↑↓][↑] 3d [ ][ ][ ][ ][ ]

Hybridised state: 1s [↑↓] 2s [↑↓] 2p [↑↓][↑↓][↑↓] sp³ [↑↓][↑↓][↑↓][↑] 3d [ ][ ][ ][ ][ ]

Orbital shapes (diag)

Molecular shape

bi planar angular

SCl_a Hybridised states as shown above.

Molecular shape

planar angular

SF_4

S Hybridised state: 1s [↑↓] 2s [↑↓] 2p [↑↓][↑↓][↑↓] sp³d [↑↓][↑][↑][↑][↑][ ][ ][ ]

F Hybridised state: 1s [↑↓] sp³ [↑↓][↑↓][↑↓][↑]

Orbital shapes (diag)

Molecular shape

distorted tetrahedral

SF_6

S Hybridised state: 1s [↑↓] 2s [↑↓] 2p [↑↓][↑↓][↑↓] sp³d² [↑][↑][↑][↑][↑][↑][ ][ ][ ]

Orbital shapes (diag)

Molecular shape

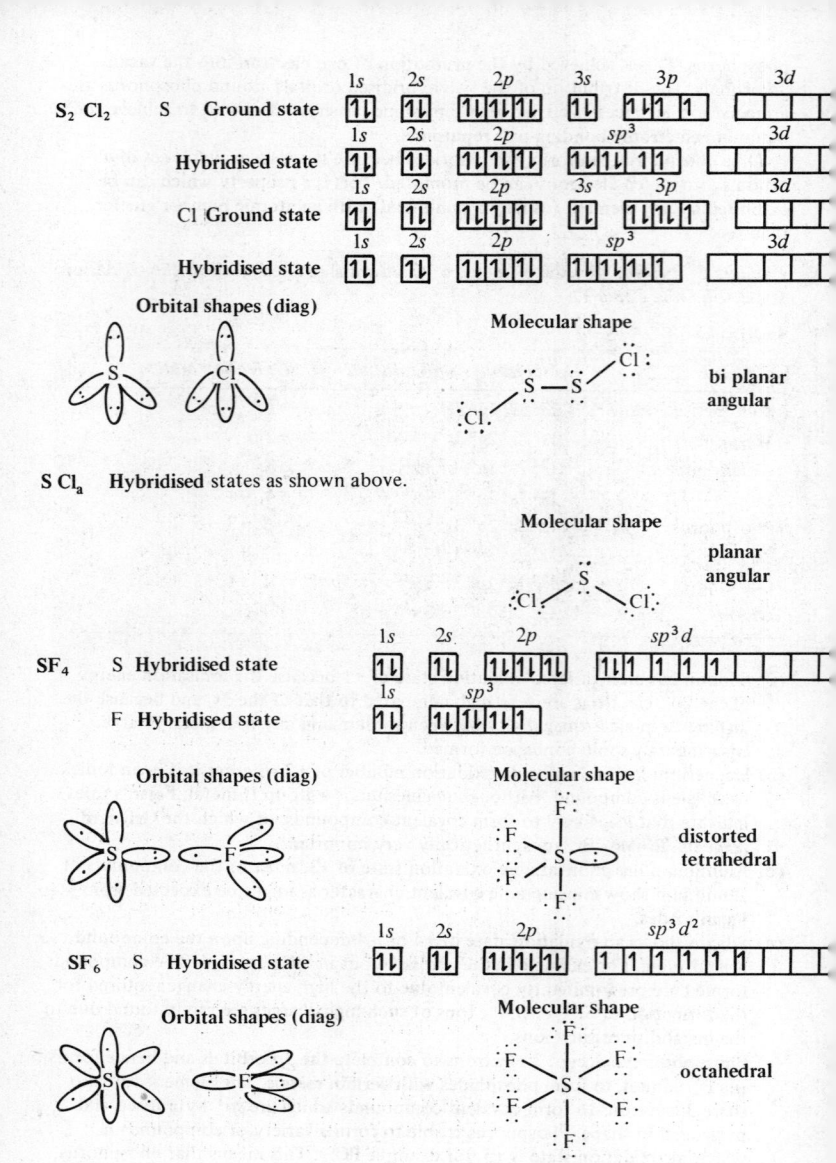

octahedral

Fig 4 The oxidation states of sulphur

states are a result of sharing electrons to form covalent bonds. The halides of sulphur, S_2Cl_2, SCl_2, SF_4 and SF_6 can be used as examples of these oxidation states. S_2Cl_2 and SCl_2 are formed by sharing the 3p electrons, but the SF_4 and SF_6 structures make use of **the available 3d orbitals** to reach these oxidation numbers, a process often referred to **as expanding the octet**. The diagrams in *Fig 4* show in a convenient way how these orbitals are utilised and the types of hybridisation and molecular shapes of the compounds.

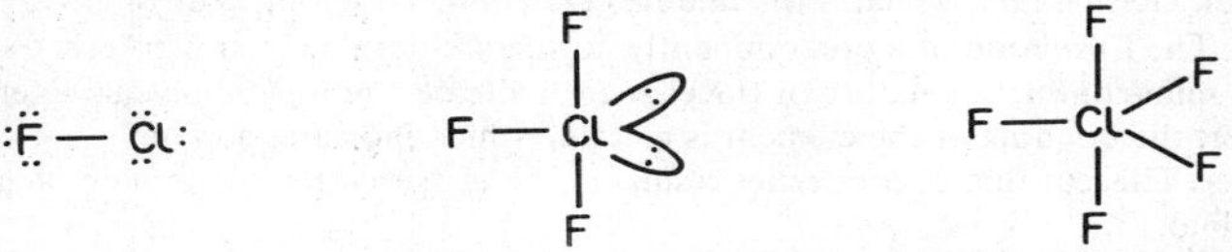

Linear   **'T' shape**   **Trigonal bi pyramid**

Fig 5

(g) Chlorine can accept one electron to form Cl^-, the **chloride ion**. The oxidation state of +1 can be achieved by sharing the unpaired 3p electron. The oxidation states of +3 and +5 can only be achieved by using the **available 3d orbitals**. The shapes of ClF, ClF_3 and ClF_5 are shown in *Fig 5*.

(h) The element argon shows no oxidation states because it has a stable electronic configuration even in the presence of fluorine.

These changes in oxidation states within a period show the change in metallic character in crossing a period from group I to group 0.

Problem 9 Describe how the properties of group IV elements show that they are p-block elements.

(i) The elements of group IV are carbon, silicon, germanium, tin and lead. The characteristics of the group can be determined by considering the structure of the element, the bonding of the chloride, the bonding of the hydride and the basic or acidic nature of the oxide.

(ii) The structures of the elements are given in *Table 9* showing that only the last two elements are true metals and **germanium is a metalloid**. The existence of **allotropes** for tin shows that it has certain elements of non-metallic character.

(iii) The chlorides of the elements which have the formulae CCl_4, $SiCl_4$, $GeCl_4$, $SnCl_4$ and $PbCl_4$ are all **predominantly covalent chlorides** which with the exception of CCl_4 are hydrolysed by water. The dichlorides $GeCl_2$, $SnCl_2$ and $PbCl_2$ are solids, unlike the tetrahalides which are liquids. $GeCl_2$ and $PbCl_2$ are **predominantly ionic** in structure but $SnCl_2$ is predominantly covalent. The existence of covalent chlorides shows the elements to have some non-metallic character. However an ionic chloride for lead shows the metallic character of that element.

(iv) The hydrides of the elements, CH_4, SiH_4, GeH_4, SnH_4 and PbH_4 are all covalent but the stability of these hydrides decrease down the group, PbH_4 being particularly unstable. The existence of covalent hydrides is also a sign of non-metallic character.

(v) The oxides of the elements are (a) CO and CO_2, of which CO is neutral and CO_2 is **acidic**, (b) SiO_2 which is **acidic**, (c) GeO_2 which is **weakly acidic**, (d) SnO and SnO_2, of which SnO is **amphoteric** and SnO_2 is also **amphoteric** but **more acidic** than SnO, and (e) the oxides of lead are Pb_3O_4, PbO_2 and

PbO. PbO_2 is **amphoteric** and PbO is **predominantly basic**, the other oxide of lead, Pb_3O_4, is a **mixed oxide** containing PbO and PbO_2 in a ratio of 1:2.

(vi) This change in properties from an acidic to a basic character for the oxides, exhibits the change in properties from non-metallic to metallic character.

This change in properties on descending the group shows that the elements become more metallic with increasing atomic number, and although they are not considered here, the lower elements in group III, also show increasing metallic character. Germanium, which is the middle element of the group is difficult to classify. The formation of a predominantly covalent chloride, an amphoteric oxide, and the semi-conducting nature of the element indicate a non-metallic character. However, the bonding of the element is metallic which indicates a metallic character. This conflict of properties results in the classification of germanium as a metalloid.

Problem 10 Discuss the group V elements to show that the characteristics of the group change from non-metallic to metallic as the atomic number of the elements increase.

(i) The elements of group five are nitrogen, phosphorus, arsenic, antimony and bismuth. Nitrogen, a gas, is a diatomic molecule, and phosphorus is a solid structure at room temperature, composed of P_4 molecules. Phosphorus can exist as three allotropes, there being white, red and black phosphorus, of which red phosphorus is the most stable. Arsenic and antimony also exhibit allotropy, each element forms an unstable allotrope similar to white phosphorus as shown in *Fig 6*. The unstable forms are converted into the more dense metallic form similar to black phosphorus also shown in *Fig 6*. Bismuth does not form allotropes and is metallic in its structure.

Nitrogen and phosphorus are clearly non-metallic and although the stable forms of arsenic, antimony and bismuth are metallic in appearance, their electrical conductivities are higher in the liquid state than in the solid state, a property unusual in metals. This shows a lack of metallic character for these three elements.

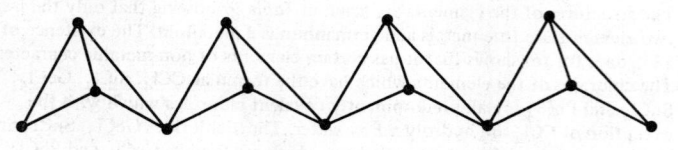

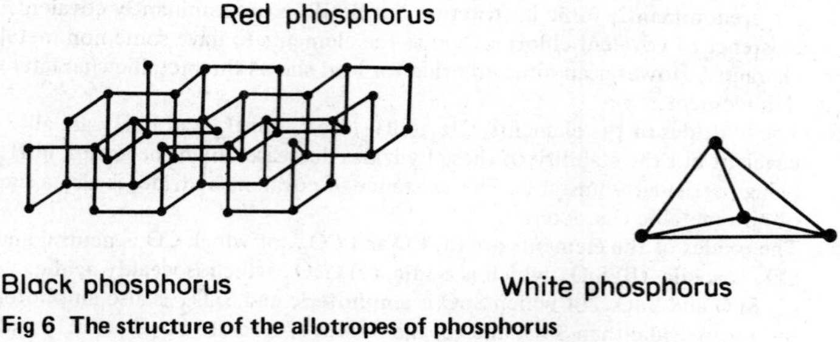

Red phosphorus

Black phosphorus

White phosphorus

Fig 6 The structure of the allotropes of phosphorus

(ii) The trichlorides of the elements, NCl_3, PCl_3, $AsCl_3$, $SbCl_3$ and $BiCl_3$ are covalently bonded and react with water in slightly different ways, as shown by the equations

$$NCl_3(l) + 3H_2O(l) = NH_3(aq) + 3HClO(aq)$$

$$PCl_3(l) + 3H_2O(l) = H_3PO_3(aq) + 3HCl(aq)$$

$$4AsCl_3(l) + 6H_2O(l) = As_4O_6(aq) + 12HCl(aq)$$

$$SbCl_3(s) + H_2O(l) = SbOCl(s) + 2HCl(aq)$$

$$BiCl_3(s) + H_2O(l) = BiOCl(s) + 2HCl(aq)$$

The formation of insoluble oxychlorides of Sb and Bi shows the increase in metallic character. Pentachlorides are formed by phosphorus and antimony. PCl_5 exists in the ionic stable state when solid, containing PCl_4^+ and PCl_6^- ions, but is covalent in the vapour state. The bonding in $SbCl_5$ is covalent and the molecule readily decomposes to $SbCl_3$ and Cl_2.

(iii) The hydrides of the elements are NH_3, PH_3, AsH_3, SbH_3 and BiH_3 which become increasingly unstable in this order, BiH_3 is particularly unstable. The instability of the lower hydrides shows the increase in metallic character of As, Sb and Bi compared to N and P, even though all of the elements are covalently bonded to hydrogen.

(iv) The oxides of the elements are (a) N_2O, NO, N_2O_3, NO_2, N_2O_4 and N_2O_5 for nitrogen, (b) P_4O_6 and P_4O_{10} for phosphorus, (c) As_4O_6 and As_2O_5 for arsenic, (d) Sb_4O_6 and Sb_2O_5 for antimony and (e) Bi_2O_3 for bismuth. The oxides of nitrogen are discussed at length in *Problem 6* and are typical non-metallic oxides either neutral or acidic in character. The oxides of phosphorus are covalently bonded and show acidic properties, as do the oxides of arsenic and antimony. The oxide of bismuth is ionic and basic, a characteristic of metallic elements.

(v) This comparison shows that the elements change from non-metallic character to metallic character as the group is descended. The transition in this group occurs at antimony rather than arsenic, since there is no evidence to show that arsenic forms As^{3+}. The change in character occurring lower in this group than group IV is consistent with its position nearer to group VII in the periodic table.

C. FURTHER PROBLEMS IN INORGANIC CHEMISTRY

(a) SHORT ANSWER PROBLEMS

Fill in the missing words

1 The *s*-block elements can be identified as the elements which show an .... oxidation state.

2 The *p*-block elements are distinguished from the *s*-block elements by the .... of their reactions.

3 The formation of coloured compounds is a characteristic property of the .... elements.

4 The polarisation of bonds in a compound is due to the difference between the .... of the atoms forming the bonds in the compound.

5 The *p*-block elements show a change from .... character to .... character as a group is ....

6 The chlorides of group II are .... bonded. This shows the elements have a .... character.

7 The high oxidation state chlorides of the *d*-block elements show they are predominantly .... bonded.

8 The oxides of phosphorus are .... bonded giving acidic solutions with water, this indicates the element is .... in character.

9 An oxide which reacts with acids and bases is called an .... oxide and illustrates the .... metallic character of the element.

10 The *p*-block elements in the third short period can show variable valencies by use of ....

11 The degree of paramagnetism shown by the *d*-block elements and their compounds is dependent on the number of .... in their structures.

12 In a period of the periodic table, the elements change from metallic to non-metallic character with .... atomic number.

13 In group IV of the periodic table, carbon is classified as .... , germanium as a .... , and lead as .... in character.

14 The chemical evidence for showing that tin has a degree of non-metallic character is that (i) its two chlorides .... and .... are predominantly .... , and that (ii) its two oxides .... and .... behave as .... oxides.

15 In group V of the periodic table the only element to show predominant metallic character is ....

16 The hydrides of arsenic and antimony are .... bonded, an indication of ....

17 The formation of complex ions by the *d*-block elements is due to the availability of .... *d*-orbitals which form .... bonds with the surrounding ....

18 The factors which are used to detect trends in the periodic table are the structure of the .... , and the bonding in the .... and ....

19 The absorption of some of the wavelengths of visible light by *d*-block element compounds is considered to be due to the .... in .... of the 3*d* orbitals.

20 The formation of several oxidation states by nitrogen is not achieved by using .... *d*-orbitals but by the formation of a combination of .... and .... bonds.

(b) MULTI-CHOICE PROBLEMS (answers on page 181)

Select the correct answer from those given

1 The elements are assigned to their positions in the periodic table by a consideration of the
   (a) atomic masses of the elements;
   (b) electronic configurations of the elements;

 (c) electronegativity differences of the elements;
 (d) density of the elements.

2 If the structure of an element shows metallic bonding it is most likely to have
 (a) a covalent hydride;   (b) a covalent chloride;
 (c) an acidic oxide;   (d) a basic oxide.

3 An element may be considered to show only partial metallic character if it has
 (a) an acidic oxide;   (b) an amphoteric oxide;
 (c) a basic oxide;   (d) a mixed oxide.

4 The most non-metallic element of those mentioned below is
 (a) carbon; (b) nitrogen; (c) oxygen; (d) fluorine.

5 The most metallic of the elements mentioned below is
 (a) magnesium; (b) beryllium; (c) caesium; (d) calcium.

6 In group IV, the element classified as a metalloid is
 (a) silicon; (b) germanium; (c) tin; (d) lead.

7 A property not displayed by the *d*-block elements Titanium to Copper is
 (a) invariable valency;   (b) paramagnetism;
 (c) coloured compounds;   (d) complex ion formation.

8 The oxidation number of manganese in the manganate (*VI*) complex ion, MnO_4^{2-} is
 (a) +7; (b) +6; (c) +5; (d) +4.

9 The number of dative bonds formed in the complex ion $[Cr^{III}(NH_3)_4Cl_2]^+$ is
 (a) 6; (b) 4; (c) 2; (d) 0.

10 The invariable valency states of the *s*-block elements is due to
 (a) the relative sizes of the atoms of the elements;
 (b) the type of bonding in the elements;
 (c) the ionisation energies of the cations formed;
 (d) the formation of ionic chlorides.

(c) CONVENTIONAL PROBLEMS

1 Explain why sodium does not form compounds of the formulae $NaCl_2$ and Na_2O_3.

2 Explain why calcium does not form compounds containing the complex ions $[Ca(NH_3)_4]^{2+}$ and $[Ca(CN)_6]^{4-}$.

3 Explain why the compounds of the *s*-block elements do not have paramagnetic properties.

4 Which physical properties of the elements can be used to distinguish between metals and non-metals?

5 Which chemical properties of the elements can be used to distinguish between metals and non-metals?

6 Discuss the trends shown by the group I elements and explain them in terms of their physical properties.

7 Why are beryllium and magnesium in group II of the periodic table able to form compounds which are predominantly covalent?

8 Explain why nitrogen and phosphorus show several oxidation states with oxygen whereas nitrogen shows only one oxidation state with chlorine.

9. The elements in group I are metallic in character whereas those in group VII are non-metallic. Select a group of elements midway between these to show that they contain a combination of metallic and non-metallic elements.

10. Explain why the **third element of group IV** germanium, is of intermediate metallic character whereas **the fourth element of group V**, antimony, shows the same change

11. Select a group of *p*-block elements which justify this statement 'the properties of *p*-block elements are diverse'. Give suitable examples to explain your selection.

12. What properties of lead show it to be more metallic than tin?

13. Explain why tetrachloromethane, CCl_4, is not hydrolysed by water whereas silicon tetrachloride, $SiCl_4$, reacts readily.

14. Show with the aid of diagrams how sulphur and chlorine make use of the available 3*d* orbitals to form compounds with high oxidation states.

15. Explain why Fe^{2+} ions in solution are green in colour whereas Fe^{3+} ions in solution are yellow.

16. Why are compounds containing Mn^{2+} ions more paramagnetic than compounds containing V^{3+} ions?

17. Select one *d*-block element and use it to illustrate the characteristic properties of *d*-block elements.

18. Why are the properties of the elements vanadium to nickel in the *d*-block elements of such a similar nature?

19. Discuss the formation of complex ions by the *d*-block elements.

20. Name and discuss the stereochemistry of the following complex ions.
    (a) $[Co(HO-CH_2-CH_2-OH)_3]^{3+}$
    (b) $[Fe(NH_3)_4Cl_2]^+$
    (c) $[Cr(H_2N-CH_2-CH_2-NH_2)_2Cl_2]^+$
    (d) $[Mn(H_2O)_3Cl_3]^-$

7 Reaction kinetics

A. MAIN POINTS CONCERNING REACTION KINETICS

1. The **rate of a chemical reaction** can be obtained by either measuring the amount of **products formed** or by measuring the amount of **reagents used up** in a given time.
2. Chemical reactions can be considered as a rearrangement of elements, or groups of elements, into new patterns. Each particular chemical reaction takes place at an **individual rate** which can be very slow or very rapid. Because of this large variation in reaction rates, it is apparent that under a set of conditions one reaction might not take place whilst another does take place with ease.
3. Since reactions depend upon the **breaking** and **forming** of **chemical bonds**, energy must be of prime importance in considering rates of reaction. However since reactions can take place in many different ways **no single theory of reactions** has been established.
4. Chemical reactions do not all take place in the same way. Some chemical reactions take place by a **one step mechanism** whilst others take place as a result of a number of steps each equivalent to the formation of an **intermediate** product before further reaction occurs. When a **multi-stage** reaction occurs, the **rate** of the reaction is taken to be that of the **slowest step** in the reaction mechanism.
5. The rate of a reaction has been found experimentally to depend upon certain factors. These are
   (i) **temperature** (all reactions);
   (ii) **concentration** (non-gaseous systems);
   (iii) **pressure** (gaseous systems);
   (iv) **catalysts** (all reactions);
   (v) **particle size** (solids).
   For **homogeneous** reactions, the **kinetic theory of matter** can be used to justify the variation in reaction rates for reactions which take place as a result of **bi-molecular collisions**, (see *Problem 1*). The **collision theory** makes use of the **frequency** of collisions with sufficient energy to react together, to explain the effect of these factors (see *Problem 2*).
6. (i) It can be shown that for a particular number of molecules in a given volume and at a constant temperature, the number of collisions which occur **does not reflect** the rate at which reaction takes place.
   (ii) It was suggested by Arrhenius that reaction only takes place between **activated molecules** which have an **activation energy** in excess of a particular value.

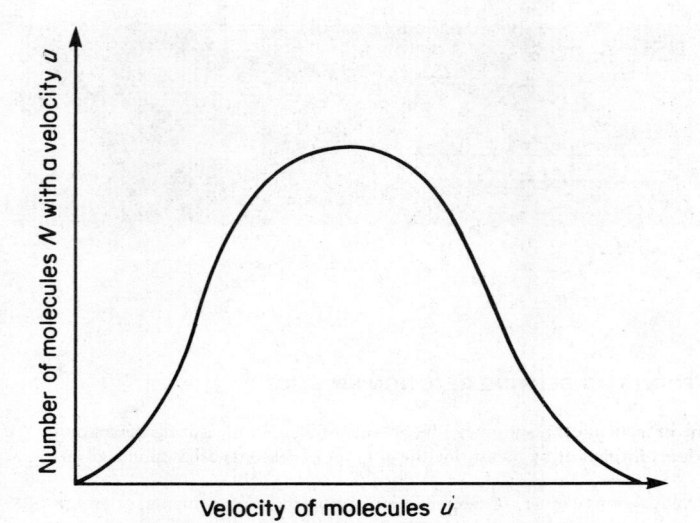

![Graph showing a bell-shaped normal distribution curve with "Number of molecules N with a velocity u" on the y-axis and "Velocity of molecules u" on the x-axis]

Fig 1 The distribution of the velocities of N_0 gas molecules

(iii) The energy associated with a molecule is dependent on the **velocity** of the molecule. The **distribution of velocities** and thus the **energies** of the molecules has been shown by **Maxwell** and **Boltzmann** to be a **normal distribution**, which can be expressed in a simplified equation as

$$N = N_0 e^{-E/RT} \qquad \text{(as shown in Fig 1)}$$

where N_0 is the total number of molecules, N is the number of molecules with energy greater than the energy of activation E, T is the absolute temperature and R is the gas constant. (see *Problem 3*).

(iv) For an activation energy E, the number of molecules of sufficient energy to react will be N, and hence the **rate of reaction** and the **rate constant** for a fixed concentration N_0 at a temperature T K is proportional to N, and can be represented as

Rate of reaction $\propto k \propto e^{-E/RT} \propto \dfrac{N}{N_0}$

This can be written as

$k = Ae^{-E/RT}$, where A is a constant

Taking logarithms to the base e

$$\log_e k = \text{a constant} \times \frac{-E}{RT}$$

or $\qquad 2.303 \log_{10} k = \text{a constant} \times \dfrac{-E}{RT}$

(v) This equation can be used to derive a relationship between the rate constants k_1 and k_2 and the temperature T_1 and T_2 such that

$$\log k_2 - \log k_1 = \frac{E}{2.303R} \left(\frac{T_2 - T_1}{T_2 T_1}\right)$$

This equation gives a fairly good correlation for homogeneous reactions.

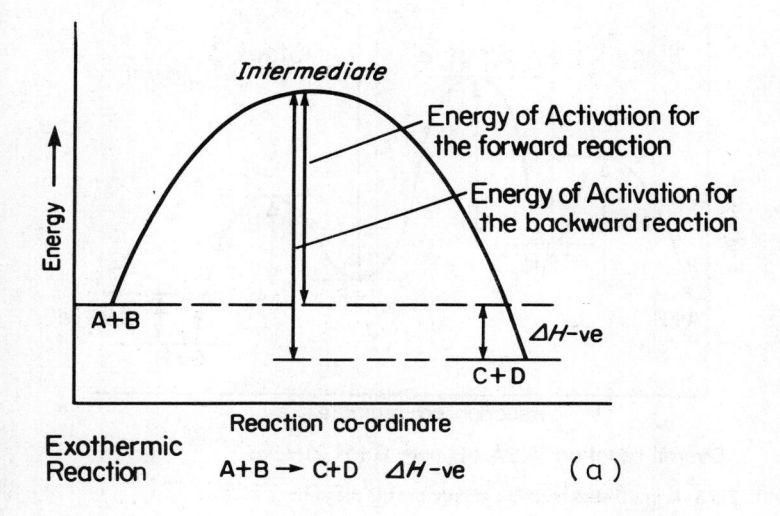

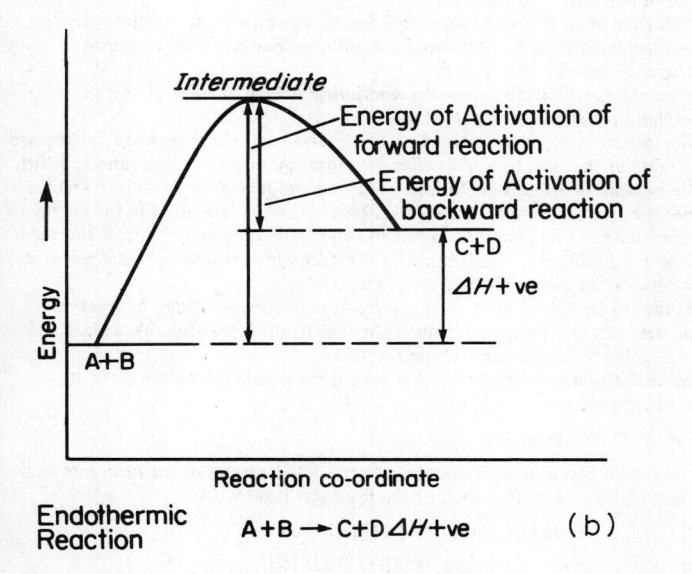

Fig 2(*a*) Reaction profiles of exothermic and endothermic reactions and (*b*) a catalyst which decreases the rate of an endothermic reaction

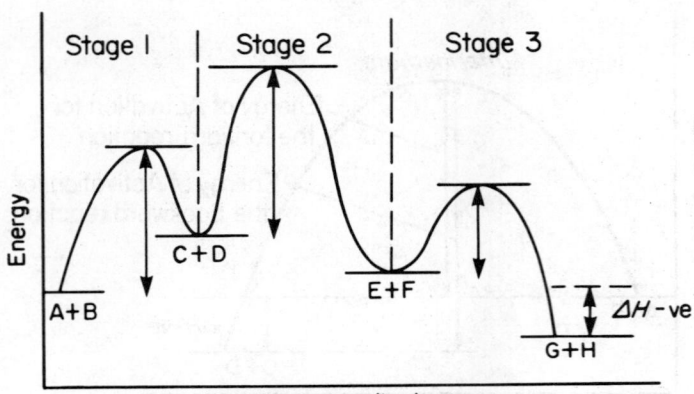

Fig 3 A multi-step reaction energy profile diagram

Overall reaction $A + B \longrightarrow G + H$ ΔH-ve

7. Since the distribution of the energy of molecules is a normal one, the **effect of increasing the temperature** by **small** amounts can have a **large effect** on the **rate of reaction** (*Problem 4*).

8. The existence of an **energy of activation barrier** can be used to construct **energy profile** diagrams for both **exothermic** and **endothermic** reactions as shown in *Fig 2*, and discussed in *Problem 5*.

9. (i) In reactions which are **multi-step reactions** there can be several energies of activation as shown in *Fig 3*.
   (ii) The introduction of a **catalyst** into the reaction can either **increase** or **decrease** the rate of that reaction. This change in reaction rate must be connected with the **number of effective collisions** occurring and hence for a catalyst which **increases** the reaction rate there is an accompanying **reduction** in the energy of activation for that reaction. This is shown diagrammatically in *Fig 4* and discussed in *Problem 5*, together with the effect which would be observed for a catalyst which **decreases** the rate of reaction.

10. In addition to indicating how quickly a reaction occurs, the study of **reaction kinetic data** can give information about how a chemical reaction takes place, which is called the **mechanism of the reaction.**

11. **Experimental** evidence has shown that for a general reaction taking place at constant temperature

$A + B + C \longrightarrow$ **Products**

(i) The **rate of reaction** is proportional to the **active masses** of the reactants and
(ii) The order of reaction of each of the reactants is such that

$$\text{Rate of reaction} \propto [A]^x[B]^y[C]^z$$
or
$$\text{Rate of reaction} = k[A]^x[B]^y[C]^z$$

where k is the **velocity constant** or **rate constant**, $[A], [B]$ and $[C]$ are the active masses of A, B and C which are **assumed to be equal to the concentration**

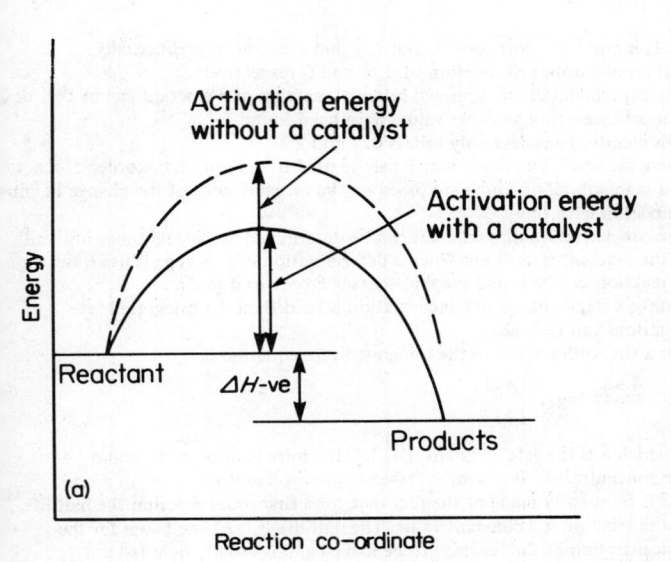

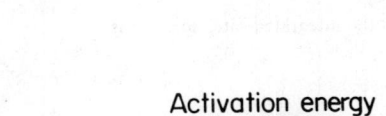

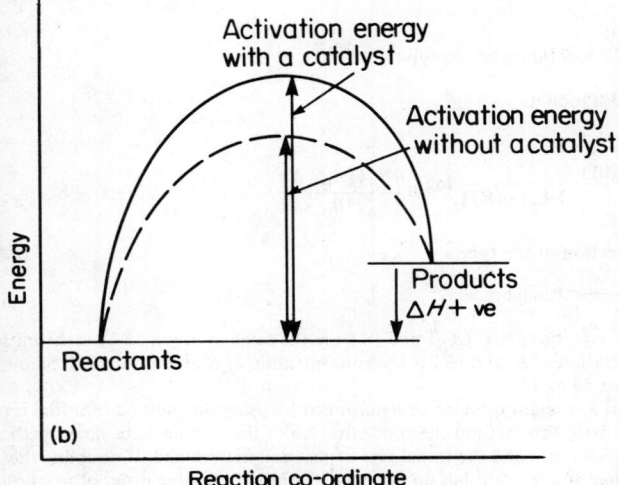

Fig 4 The effect of a catalyst which increases the rate of an exothermic reaction

of A, B and C in moles dm^{-3}, and x, y and z are the **experimentally determined orders of reaction** of A, B and C respectively.

12 (i) The experimentally determined order of reaction of a reactant can be 0, 1 or 2 in most cases, though other values have been found. **This chapter considers only orders 0, 1 and 2.**

(ii) There are several methods which can be used to determine the order of reaction of a reactant, all of which are based on the **measurement of the change in concentration with time.**

(iii) The concentration of a reactant can be determined at varying times until all of the reactant is used up. When a determination of this type is used, the order of reaction can be found graphically (see *Problems 6 to 8*).

(iv) If only a small change in concentration is used then the **integrated** rate equations can be used.

(v) For a first order reaction the integrated rate equation is

$$k = \frac{2.303}{t} \log_{10} \frac{[A_0]}{[A]}$$

in which k is the rate constant, $[A_0]$ is the initial concentration and $[A]$ is the concentration at any time t, (see *Problems 9 and 10*).

(vi) Use is frequently made of the fact that for a **first order reaction** the **half-life** of the reaction is a **constant** value. The half-life is the **time taken for the concentration of the reactant to be halved** and is usually denoted as $t_{1/2}$, (see *Problems 11, 12 and 13*).

(vii) For a second order reaction the integrated rate equation is

$$k = \frac{1}{t} \left(\frac{1}{[A]} - \frac{1}{[A_0]} \right)$$

when the reaction is of the type

$$2A \longrightarrow \text{Products}$$

and

$$k = \frac{2.303}{t} \frac{1}{[A_0]-[B_0]} \log_{10} \frac{[B_0][A_0-X]}{[A_0][B_0-X]}$$

for a reaction of the type

$$A + B \longrightarrow \text{Products.}$$

In these equations k, t, $[A_0]$ and $[A]$ are the same as in (v), $[B_0]$ is the initial concentration of B, and $[B]$ is the concentration of B at any time t, (see *Problems 14 to 16*).

13 The order of a reactant can also be determined by using the method of **initial rate of reaction**. With this method the concentration of the reactants are varied with respect to each other and the initial rate of reaction determined. If **doubling the concentration** of a reactant has **no effect** on the initial rate, the order of reaction of that reactant is **zero**. If the reaction rate is **doubled when the initial concentration is doubled**, the order of reaction is **one**, and if for **doubling the concentration the rate is increased fourfold** then the order of reaction is **two**, (see *Problems 17 and 18*).

4 One use of the order of reaction data is to suggest a reaction mechanism for the reaction. An understanding of reaction mechanisms is very useful in the planning of synthetic routes for the preparation of chemical compounds. Some examples of the deduction of reaction mechanisms are given in *Problem 19*.

3. WORKED PROBLEMS ON REACTION KINETICS

Problem 1 What are the main points of the kinetic theory of matter.

The kinetic theory of matter is a collection of statements made as a result of the work of several scientists, three of whom were **Clausius, Maxwell** and **Boltzmann**. It is a theory based on the nature of particles and can be used to explain the properties of matter within certain limitations. The theory is based on the following main points:
 (i) **Matter** is composed of **particles**, which may be groups of atoms or single atoms.
 (ii) In the gaseous state, the particles are **moving in a continuous state of random motion in straight line directions**. As a result of this random motion, **continual collisions** are occurring between the particles themselves and the walls of the container.
 (iii) In the gaseous state, the particles are **separated** from each other by **distances** which are **large compared to the size of the particles.**
 (iv) The particles are considered to be **perfectly elastic** so that any **collisions** between the particles and the walls are also **perfectly elastic** such that **no loss in the total kinetic energy** takes place.
 (v) An **increase** in **absolute temperature** produces an increase in the motion of the particles which consequently **increases** the **average kinetic energy of the particles** in the gaseous state.

The application of this theory to the properties of matter explains their existence. For example, **the pressure** of a gas in a fixed volume **increases** if the temperature is **increased**. This is explained by the **increased motion** of the particles resulting in an **increased average kinetic energy** and a greater number of collisions on the walls of the vessel.

Problem 2 What is meant by the collision theory of bimolecular reactions, and how is it used to explain why the increases in temperature, concentration, pressure, and particle size can increase rates of reaction.

For bimolecular reactions of the type:

$$A + B \longrightarrow \text{Products}$$

for a reaction to occur, **existing chemical bonds** must be **broken**, and **new bonds** must be **formed**. In order to explain qualitatively why reaction rates can be increased by changing various factors, the collision theory has been formulated. It has been suggested that the reacting molecules must collide together, which is a statement of the kinetic theory of matter. Thus, the rate of a reaction is dependent on collisions occurring between molecules. In the gas phase many reactions do not occur until the **temperature of the reactants is high enough**. The collision theory suggests that since the increase in temperature increases the motion of the molecules, more collisions will occur between molecules of A and B, and hence the reaction rate increases.

If a reaction is at a high enough temperature to occur, an **increase** in the **pressure of the gas** mixture also **increases** the rate of the reaction. This can be achieved either by reducing the volume available to the mixture or by increasing the number of molecules. Whichever process is used, the number of collisions must be increased. For reactions in the liquid phase or in solution, reaction rates can be increased by increasing the temperature or the concentration of the reactants, both these factors will increase the number of collisions which take place in the reaction.

For a reaction in which a solid is involved, the rate of reaction can be increased by **increasing the state of division** of the solid. This **increases the surface area** at which collisions can occur and hence the collision theory qualitatively explains this by an increased number of collisions.

(*Note. The effect of catalysts on reaction rate is discussed later.*)

Problem 3 Why is the rate of a reaction in the gas phase dependent on the number of effective collisions occurring rather than the total number of collisions occurring?

When a mixture of gases is placed into a container, in many cases no reaction takes place between the molecules. However, for any gas contained in a vessel, the kinetic theory of matter suggests that the molecules are constantly colliding. Consequently for any mixture of gases, collisions will occur between them. An increase in the temperature of the gas mixture can bring about a reaction and further increase will cause further increases in reaction rate. It is apparent that **collisions between different molecules are not the controlling factor in causing a reaction to occur.**

From the kinetic theory, an increase in temperature causes an increase in the **average kinetic energy** of the molecules, and hence this increase in energy must be a controlling factor in whether or not a reaction takes place. The average kinetic energy of a gas has been defined as $\frac{1}{2}mu^2$, where m is the mass of the gas molecule and u is the **root mean square velocity** of the particles which is obtained from the expression:

$$u = \sqrt{\frac{u_1^2 + u_2^2 + u_3^2 + u_4^2 \ldots \ldots un^2}{n}},$$

for n molecules of gas having individual velocities u_1, u_2 etc. **Maxwell** and **Boltzmann** showed that the individual velocities are related by a normal distribution which can be expressed by the simplified equation

$$N/N_0 = e^{-E/RT}$$

where N_0 is the total number of molecules, N is the number of molecules which are in excess of kinetic energy E, T is the absolute temperature and R is the gas constant.

It can be seen from the curve of T_1 in *Fig 5*, that for any constant number of molecules, a percentage of them, N, are of **higher energy** than the rest. An increase in temperature from T_1 to T_2 flattens the normal distribution curve and increases the number of molecules of higher energy as shown in *Fig 5*.

Arrhenius suggested that a reaction could occur between activated molecules of sufficient energy content to break the bonds necessary for the reaction to take place. This amount of energy was called the **activation energy** and the collisions resulting in reaction can be termed the **effective collisions**.

The rate of a reaction is proportional to the rate constant of the reaction and **Arrhenius** derived an expression relating the rate constant k, and the activation

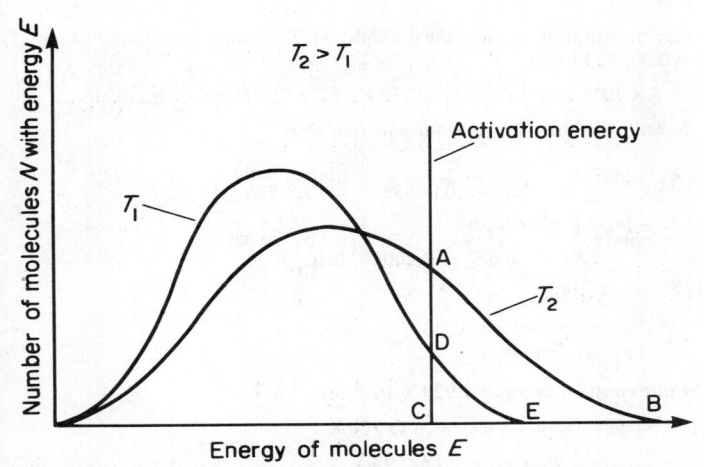

Fig 5 The normal distribution curves for the energies of the molecules of a gas at different temperatures

energy, E, by stating that the rate was proportional to the number of molecules N with an energy greater than E the activation energy. Mathematically this can be expressed as:

Rate of reaction, $\propto k \propto N \propto e^{-E/RT}$

or $k \propto e^{-E/RT}$, which by introducing a constant becomes

$k = Ae^{-E/RT}$ where A is called the Arrhenius constant.

Taking logarithms to the base e for this equation gives

$\log_e k = \log_e A + \log_e e^{-E/RT}$

or $\log_e k = \text{a constant} - \dfrac{E}{RT}$

Hence the rate of a reaction is dependent upon the number of molecules with an energy greater than the activation energy for the reaction, which are those molecules undergoing effective collisions.

Problem 4 At 730 K, the rate constant for the reaction

$2HI(g) \longrightarrow H_2(g) + I_2(g)$

is 5×10^{-1} mol^{-1} s^{-1}.

If the energy of activation is 105 kJ mol^{-1}, calculate the rate constant for the reaction when the temperature is increased by (a) 20 K and (b) 50 K.

The equation relating rate constants, energy of activation and temperature is

$$\log k_2 - \log k_1 = \dfrac{E}{2.303R}\left(\dfrac{T_2 - T_1}{T_2 T_1}\right)$$

where k_2 and k_1 are the rate constants at temperatures T_2 and T_1, E is the energy of activation and R is the gas constant. The values are $E = 105$ kJ mol^{-1}, $R = 0.00832$ kJ mol^{-1} K^{-1}.

$k_1 = 5 \times 10^{-1}$ mol^{-1} s^{-1}, $T_1 = 730$ K, $T_2 = 750$ K and k_2 is unknown.

Substituting the values into the equation gives

$$\log k_2 - \log 0.5 = \frac{105}{2.303 \times 0.00832} \left(\frac{750 - 730}{750 \times 730}\right)$$

$\log k_2 - \log 0.5 = 0.2001$.

$\log k_2 = 0.2001 + \log 0.5 = 0.2001 - 0.3010$

$\log k_2 = -0.1008$

Thus $k_2 =$ antilog (-0.1008)

$k_2 = 0.7929$

The rate constant becomes 7.929×10^{-1} mol^{-1} s^{-1}

When the temperature is increased to 780 K

$$\log k_3 - \log k_1 = \frac{E}{2.303R} \left(\frac{T_3 - T_1}{T_3 T_1}\right)$$

$T_3 = 780$ K, k_3 is unknown,

$$\log k_3 - \log 0.5 = \frac{105}{2.303 \times 0.00832} \left(\frac{780 - 730}{730 \times 780}\right)$$

$\log k_3 - \log 0.5 = 0.4812$

$\log k_3 = 0.4812 + \log 0.5$

$= 0.4812 - 0.3010$

$= 0.1802$

$k_3 =$ antilog (0.1802)

$k_3 = 1.514$.

The rate constant at 780 K is 1.514 mol^{-1} s^{-1}.
Hence for an increase of 50 K the rate constant is increased threefold.

Problem 5 Explain the shape of the energy profile diagram shown in *Fig 6*.

An **energy profile diagram** is used to compare the relative amounts of energy for the different parts of a reaction. The horizontal line associated with A + B is the **energy level of the reactants**. The curve ascending to intermediate 1 represents the ability of the reactants to overcome the activation energy E_1 and produce the products C + D. ΔH_1 + ve shows that this is an **endothermic reaction**. The curve ascending from C + D to intermediate 2 represents the ability of the reactants C and D to overcome the energy of activation E_2 and produce the final products F + G. ΔH_2 – ve shows that this part of the reaction is an **exothermic reaction**.

Since the reaction from A + B to F + G is a two stage reaction, the activation energy for this would be E_3 and ΔH_3 – ve shows that the **overall reaction** is an **exothermic reaction**.

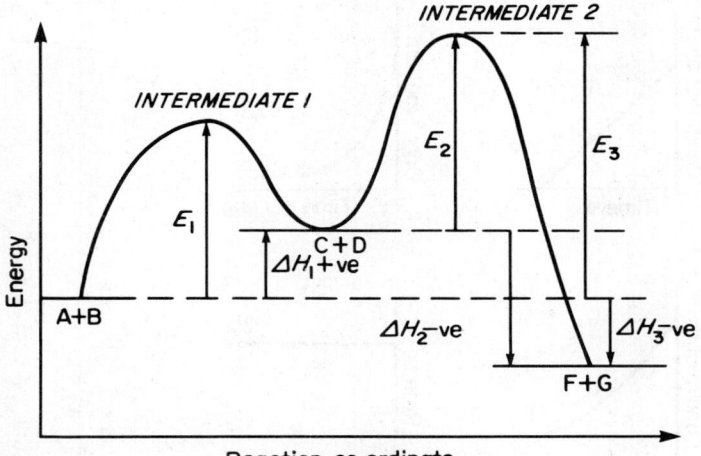

Fig 6

> *Problem 6* (i) Sketch the graphs you would expect to see for the variation in the concentration of a reactant with time for:
> (a) a zero order reaction;
> (b) a first order reaction; and
> (c) a reaction which is neither zero order nor first order.
> (ii) What would be the form of the graphs for the variation in rate of reaction with concentration for a second order reaction.

The concentration of any reactant in a chemical reaction decreases with time. If this variation in concentration is plotted against time to form a graph, the shape of the graph gives an indication of the order of the reaction with respect to the reactant investigated.

The graph (1) in *Fig 7* is a **straight line**, which means that the rate of the decrease is constant and this corresponds to a **zero order** reaction. Graph (2) in *Fig 7* is a **curve** for which the **half-life is a constant**. This type of variation corresponds to a **first order** reaction. Graph (3) in *Fig 7* does not have a constant half-life. A curve of this type can correspond to a second order of reaction, but equally it could show a different order but **never zero or first order**.

(ii) The rate of reaction will also be a decreasing value because the rate of reaction is proportional to the concentration of a reactant hence as the concentration decreases, the rate decreases. The rate of change of a curve is found by finding the value of the **tangent to the curve** at a particular point. Graph (4) in *Fig 7* is obtained by measuring the rate of reaction at different concentrations and plotting the graph of the rate of reaction against concentration. This **straight line parallel to the concentration axis** shows the order of reaction is **zero**. Graph (5) in *Fig 7* shows a **straight line of constant gradient** and shows that the rate of reaction is directly proportional to the concentration of the reactant. This shape of graph corresponds to a **first order** reaction. Graph (6) in *Fig 7* shows that a **curve** is obtained for a graph of rate of reaction against concentration. **No certain conclusion can be**

Fig 7

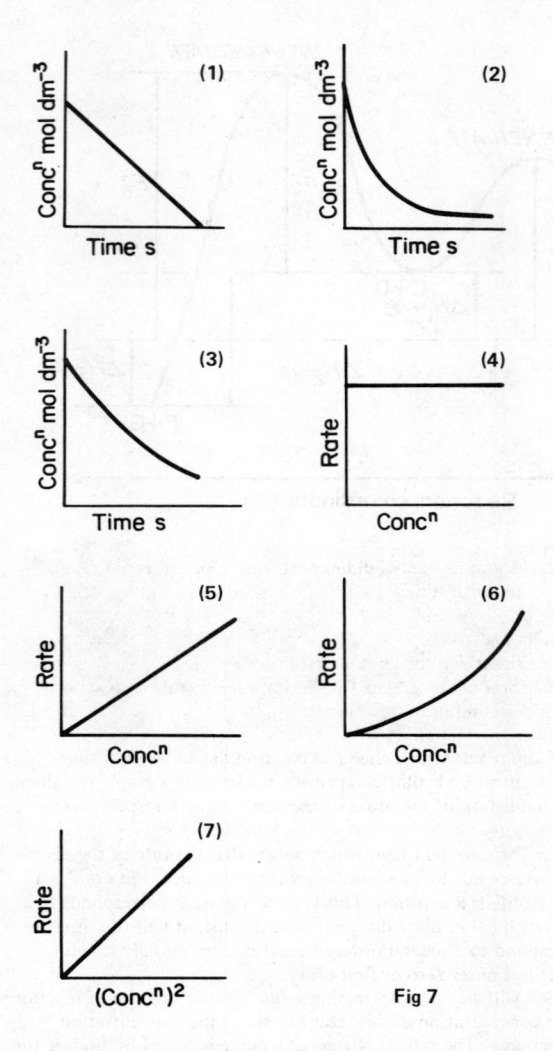

- (1) Conc^n mol dm^{-3} vs Time s
- (2) Conc^n mol dm^{-3} vs Time s
- (3) Conc^n mol dm^{-3} vs Time s
- (4) Rate vs Conc^n
- (5) Rate vs Conc^n
- (6) Rate vs Conc^n
- (7) Rate vs (Conc^n)^2

drawn from this curve. However graph (7) in *Fig 7* shows that **a straight line** is obtained by plotting the rate of reaction against the square of the concentration. This shows that the rate of reaction is directly proportional to the value of (concentration)^2. This corresponds to a **second order** reaction. If sufficient data is available to plot a graph on which the initial concentration has been reduced to less than a quarter of its original value, it is a relatively straight forward method for finding the order of reaction of a reactant. However if such data is not available other methods must be used.

Problem 7 When 25 cm³ of a hydrogen peroxide solution were titrated against 0.02 M $KMnO_4$ solution, the titre value was 50 cm³. A sample of hydrogen peroxide was catalytically decomposed and at various times 25 cm³ of the solution was removed and rapidly titrated with 0.02 M $KMnO_4$. The results are shown below. Use these results to show graphically that the reaction is first order.

Time (min).	0	5	10	20	30	40	50
Volume of $KMnO_4$ (cm³)	50	39.4	32.5	21.2	13.8	9.0	5.8

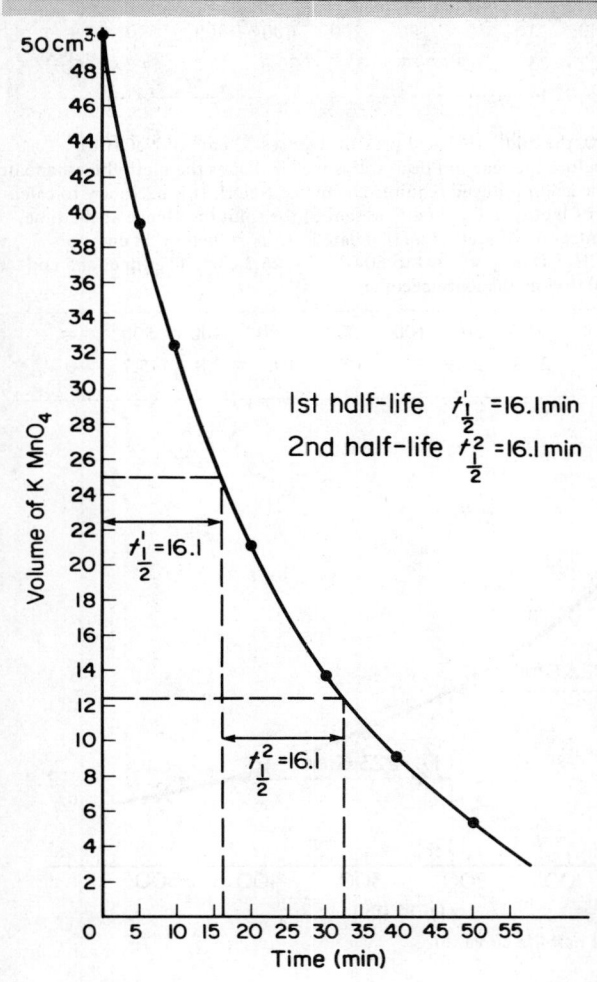

1st half-life $t_{\frac{1}{2}}^1$ = 16.1 min
2nd half-life $t_{\frac{1}{2}}^2$ = 16.1 min

Fig 8 A constant half-life curve

The potassium manganate (VII) reacts directly with the amount of hydrogen peroxide present and consequently the volume of $KMnO_4$ is directly proportional to the concentration of H_2O_2. A graph of the volume of $KMnO_4$ against the time in minutes is plotted, as shown in *Fig 8*. The determination of consecutive half-lives which are constant shows the reaction to be first order.

Problem 8 Use the following results to plot a graph to find the order of reaction of the hydrolysis of methyl methanoate using dilute hydrochloric acid. The titre values were obtained by adding standard sodium hydroxide to 25 cm³ aliquots of the reaction mixture.

Time (min)	0	20	50	100	200	300	400	500	∞
Volume of NaOH cm³	22	23.7	26.1	29.7	35.2	39.3	42.2	44.3	50

At the time $t = 0$, the dilute HCl acid present requires 22 cm³ of NaOH for neutralisation, before the reaction begins, this means that as the methyl methanoate is hydrolysed, the acid produced requires 28 cm³ of NaOH. It is necessary to calculate the amount of methyl methanoate present in the solution. Hence at the time, $t = 0$, the concentration of methyl methanoate is proportional to 28 cm³ for $t = 20$. $[HCOOCH_3]$ is proportional to $50 - 23.7 = 26.3$ cm³. The times and concentrations of methyl methanoate become

Time (min)	0	20	50	100	200	300	400	500	∞
$HCOOCH_3$ cm³	28	26.3	23.9	20.3	14.8	10.7	7.8	5.7	0

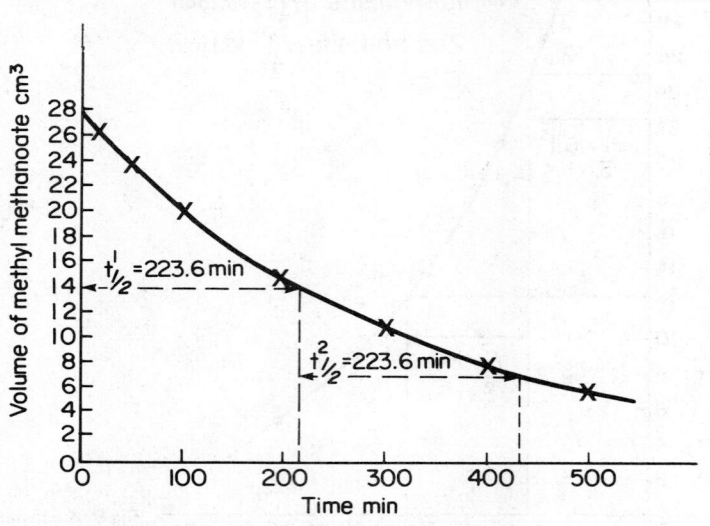

Fig 9 A constant half-life curve

Plot a graph of volume of $HCOOCH_3$ against time as shown in *Fig 9*.
The **half-life** for the change in concentration from 28 cm³ to 14 cm³ is 223.6 min, and the **half-life** for the change in concentration from 14 cm³ to 7 cm³ is also 233.6 min.
Hence since these half-life values are constant the reaction is a first order reaction.

Problem 9 Derive an equation for a first order reaction such as the reaction

$A \longrightarrow$ Products

By the **law of mass action**, the rate of reaction is proportional to the concentration of the reactant. Mathematically this can be written as

Rate $= k[A]$

where k is the velocity constant of the reaction and $[A]$ is the active mass of the reactant. For a first order reaction, the rate of change of reaction is proportional to the concentration,

i.e. $\dfrac{d[A]}{dt} \propto A$

and since the rate is continually decreasing, $\dfrac{d[A]}{dt}$ is negative.

Hence, $-\dfrac{d[A]}{dt} = k[A]$

Collecting the similar terms gives

$-\dfrac{1}{[A]} d[A] = k_1 dt$

Integrating both sides of the equation

$-\int \dfrac{1}{[A]} d[A] = \int k \, dt$

since $\int \dfrac{1}{[A]} d[A]$ is a standard integral and equal to $\log_e [A]$

then $-\log_e [A] = kt +$ a constant

To find the value of the constant let $[A]$ be $[A_0]$, the initial concentration when $t = 0$.
Substituting these values into the equation gives

$-\log [A_0] = 0 +$ a constant

Substituting the value for the constant into equation, gives

$-\log_e [A] = kt - \log_e [A_0]$

or $kt = \log_e [A_0] - \log_e [A] = \log_e \dfrac{[A_0]}{[A]}$

Since $\log_e \dfrac{[A_0]}{[A]} = \log_{10} \dfrac{[A_0]}{[A]} \times 2.303$

Then $kt = 2.303 \log_{10} \dfrac{[A_0]}{[A]}$

This is the rate equation for a first order reaction.

Problem 10 Show why the time for the concentration of a reactant to be halved is independent of the initial concentration of the reactant for a first order reaction.

The derived rate expression for a first order reaction is

$$kt = 2.303 \log_{10} \frac{[A_0]}{[A]}$$

Let the time taken to halve the concentration be $t_{1/2}$, at this time $[A_0]$ the initial concentration will have become $\frac{[A_0]}{2}$. Substituting these values into the equation

$$t_{1/2} = \frac{2.303}{k} \log_{10} \frac{[A_0]}{\frac{[A_0]}{2}} = \frac{2.303}{k} \log_{10} 2$$

Hence, $t_{1/2} = \frac{0.301 \times 2.303}{k}$ or $t_{1/2} = \frac{0.693}{k}$

Since k is a constant, the half-life of the reaction must be a constant, i.e. independent of the initial concentration of the reactant.

Problem 11 The velocity constant for the decomposition of propanedioic acid is 2.16×10^{-4} s^{-1}. Assuming this is a first order reaction, calculate the half-life of the reaction.

For a first order reaction

$$kt = 2.303 \log_{10} \frac{[CH_2(COOH)_2] \text{ initially}}{[CH_2(COOH)_2] \text{ at time } t}$$

Let the initial concentration be X moles dm^{-3} and $\frac{X}{2}$ mol dm^{-3} at time $t_{1/2}$.

Using $k = 2.16 \times 10^{-4}$ s^{-1} and substituting the values into equation

$$t_{1/2} \times (2.16 \times 10^{-4}) = 2.303 \log_{10} \frac{X}{X/2} = 2.303 \log_{10} 2$$

hence $t_{1/2} = \frac{2.303 \times 0.3010}{2.16 \times 10^{-4}} = 3209.27$ s

The half-life of the reaction is 3209.27 s.

Problem 12 When hydrogen peroxide is decomposed, the rate of reaction can be followed by titrating aliquots of the reacting solution with potassium manganate (*VII*). Show that the following results are in accord with first order kinetics and find the half-life of the reaction.

Time (min)	0	10	20	25
Titre (cm^3)	25	15	9	6.97

The integrated rate equation for a first order reaction is

$$kt = 2.303 \log_{10} \frac{[A_0]}{[A]} \qquad (1)$$

Selecting the values of $[A_0] = 25$ cm^3, $t = 10$ mins and $[A] = 15$ cm^3 and substituting them in equation (1), gives

$$k_1 = \frac{2.303}{10} \log_{10} \frac{25}{15} = 0.2303 \log_{10} 1.666$$

then $k_1 = 0.2303 \times 0.2217 = 0.051$ min^{-1}.

Hence, if the reaction is first order, the velocity constant of the reaction (k_1) is 0.051 min^{-1}.

Selecting the values $[A_0] = 25$ cm^3, $t = 20$ min and $[A] = 9$, and substituting them into the equation (1) gives

$$k_2 = \frac{2.303}{20} \log_{10} \frac{25}{9} = 0.1151 \times \log_{10} 2.777$$

$$k_2 = 0.1151 \times 0.4437 = 0.051 \text{ min}^{-1}.$$

Since $k_1 = k_2 = 0.051$ min^{-1}, the reaction is first order with respect to hydrogen peroxide.

To find the half-life, let $[A_0] = 25$ cm^3, $[A] = 12.5$ cm^3 (i.e. half the concentration). $t = t_{1/2}$ and $k = 0.051$ and substituting these values into equation (1), gives

$$0.051 \times t_{1/2} = 2.303 \log_{10} \frac{25}{12.5} = 2.303 \times \log 2$$

Hence $t_{1/2} = \dfrac{2.303 \times 0.3010}{0.051} = 13.59$ min.

The half-life of the reaction is 13.59 min

Problem 13 Derive the integrated rate equation for the second order reaction
$2A \longrightarrow$ Products.

Applying the law of mass action

Rate of reaction $= k [A]^2$

Mathematically the rate of reaction can be expressed as $\dfrac{-d[A]}{dt}$, negative because the concentration is decreasing. The rate equation becomes

$$\frac{-d[A]}{dt} = k[A]^2.$$

Collecting similar terms gives

$$-\frac{1}{[A]^2} d[A] = k \, dt$$

Since $\dfrac{1}{[A]^2} d[A] = -\dfrac{1}{[A]}$, is a standard integral,

then the equation becomes

$$\frac{1}{[A]} = kt + \text{a constant} \tag{1}$$

To find the value of the constant, use $[A] = [A_0]$ when $t = 0$.

Then $\dfrac{1}{[A_0]} = $ a constant.

Substituting this value into equation (1) gives

$$\frac{1}{[A]} = kt + \frac{1}{[A_0]}$$

or $kt = \dfrac{1}{[A_0]} - \dfrac{1}{[A]}$, **the integrated equation for second order kinetics.**

Problem 14 Derive the integrated rate expression for the second order reaction
$A + B \longrightarrow$ Products.

Let the initial concentrations of A and B be $[A_0]$ and $[B_0]$ respectively, and after a time t, let X moles of A and X moles of B be used up. At any time t,

Rate of reaction $= k[A_0-X][B_0-X]$

Since the concentration X is increasing, the rate of reaction can be expressed as $\dfrac{dX}{dt}$. Substituting this into the equation gives

$$\frac{dX}{dt} = k[A_0-X][B_0-X]$$

Collecting similar terms and integrating this equation gives

$$\frac{dX}{[A_0-X][B_0-X]} = k\,dt$$

Since $\dfrac{dX}{[A_0-X][B_0-X]} = \dfrac{1}{[A_0-B_0]} \log_e \dfrac{B_0[A_0-X]}{A_0[B_0-X]}$

Then $\dfrac{1}{A_0-B_0} \log_e \dfrac{B_0}{A_0} - \dfrac{[A_0-X]}{[B_0-X]} = kt +$ a constant

To find the value of the constant, let $X = 0$ when $t = 0$

Hence $\dfrac{1}{[A_0-B_0]} \log_e \dfrac{B_0 A_0}{A_0 B_0} = 0 +$ a constant

i.e. $\dfrac{1}{[A_0-B_0]} \log_e 1 =$ a constant

Since $\log_e 1 = 0$, then the constant $= 0$.
Hence the integrated rate equation for a second order reaction is

$$k = \frac{2.303}{t} \frac{1}{[A_0-B_0]} \log_{10} \frac{B_0}{A_0} \frac{[A_0-X]}{[B_0-X]}$$

Problem 15 When equal volumes of 0.2 M bromoethane and sodium hydroxide were reacted together, 20 cm³ aliquots of the mixture were titrated with 0.1 M hydrochloric acid with the following results

Time (min)	0	10	20	30	40	50
Volume of acid (cm³)	20	17.1	14.9	13.2	11.9	10.75

Show that the reaction is a second order reaction.

Since sodium hydroxide reacts with hydrochloric acid in a 1:1 ratio, the volume of acid is proportional to the concentration of sodium hydroxide at any time during the reaction. Since the equation for the reaction is

$$C_2H_5Br + NaOH \longrightarrow C_2H_5OH + NaBr$$

the volume of acid is also proportional to the concentration of bromoethane. For equal quantities of reactants, the integrated rate expression is

$$kt = \frac{1}{[A]} - \frac{1}{[A_0]} \qquad (1)$$

where k = the velocity or rate constant, $[A_0]$ = the initial concentration of NaOH and C_2H_5Br and $[A]$ = the concentration of NaOH and C_2H_5Br at a time t.
At $t = 10$ min $[A_0] = 20$ cm³ and $[A] = 17.1$ cm³. Substituting these values into equation (1)

$$10k_1 = \frac{1}{17.1} - \frac{1}{20} \quad \text{or} \quad k_1 = \frac{1}{10}(0.0585 - 0.05)$$

Hence, $k_1 = \frac{0.0086}{10} = 0.00086$ min⁻¹.

For a second case at $t = 30$ min $[A_0] = 20$ cm³ and $[A] = 13.2$ cm³. Substituting into equation (1)

$$30k_2 = \frac{1}{13.2} - \frac{1}{20} \quad \text{or} \quad k_2 = \frac{1}{30}(0.0757 - 0.05)$$

$$k_2 = \frac{0.0257}{30} = 0.00085 \text{ min}^{-1}$$

For a third case at $t = 50$ min $[A_0] = 20$ cm³ and $[A] = 10.75$ cm³

Substituting these values into equation (1)

$$50k_3 = \frac{1}{10.75} - \frac{1}{20} \quad \text{or} \quad k_3 = \frac{1}{50}(0.093 - 0.05)$$

Hence, $k_3 = \frac{0.043}{50} = 0.00086$ min⁻¹

Since $k_1 = k_2 = k_3$ this is a second order reaction.

Problem 16 The relative initial rates of reaction for the iodination of propanone using different concentrations of reactants are given in *Table 1*. The equation for the reaction is

$$CH_3-\underset{\underset{O}{\|}}{C}-CH_3 + I_2 \xrightarrow{H^+} CH_2I-\underset{\underset{O}{\|}}{C}-CH_3 + HI$$

What is the order of reaction (a) with respect to propanone, (b) with respect to iodine and (c) with respect to the acid? Write down an expression for the rate equation.

TABLE 1 The iodination of propanone

Reaction	Concentrations (moles)			Relative rate
	CH_3COCH_3	I_2	H_3^+O	
A	0.01	0.01	0.01	1
B	0.02	0.01	0.01	2
C	0.02	0.01	0.02	4
D	0.01	0.02	0.01	1

Since this reaction involves propanone, iodine and an acid, the rate equation can be written as

$$R = k\,[CH_3COCH_3]^x [I_2]^y [H^+]^z$$

where R is the relative rate of reaction and x, y and z are the orders of reaction with respect to propanone, iodine and hydrogen ion concentration. By considering reactions A and B and substituting the values into the rate equation gives

For A $\quad 1 = k\,(0.01)^x (0.01)^y (0.01)^z$ \hfill (1)

For B $\quad 2 = k\,(0.02)^x (0.01)^y (0.01)^z$ \hfill (2)

Dividing equation (1) by (2) gives

$$\frac{1}{2} = \frac{k\,(0.01)^x \cancel{(0.01)^y} \cancel{(0.01)^z}}{k\,(0.02)^x \cancel{(0.01)^y} \cancel{(0.01)^z}}$$

by cancelling similar terms as shown the expression reduces to

$$\frac{1}{2} = \frac{(0.01)^x}{(0.02)^x} = \left(\frac{1}{2}\right)^x \qquad \text{Hence, } x \text{ must } = 1$$

Thus for propanone the order of reaction is one.

Similarly, considering reactions B and C

For B $\quad 2 = k\,(0.02)^1 (0.01)^y (0.01)^z$

For C $\quad 4 = k\,(0.02)^1 (0.01)^y (0.02)^z$

By dividing and cancelling similar terms the expression which can be derived is

$$\frac{2}{4} = \frac{(0.01)^z}{(0.02)^z} = \left(\frac{1}{2}\right)^z \qquad \text{Hence, } z \text{ must } = 1$$

Thus for hydrogen ions the order of reaction is one.

Similarly considering reactions A and D

For A $\quad 1 = k\,(0.01)^1 (0.01)^y (0.01)^1$

For D $\quad 1 = k\,(0.01)^1 (0.02)^y (0.01)^1$

By dividing and cancelling the derived expression is

$$\frac{1}{1} = \frac{(0.01)^y}{(0.02)^y} = \left(\frac{1}{2}\right)^y \qquad \text{Hence, } y \text{ must } = 0$$

Hence the order of reaction for iodine is zero.

The rate equation becomes

Rate $= k\,[CH_3COCH_3]^1 [I_2]^0 [H^+]^1$

where k is the rate constant.

TABLE 2 Equation $A + B + 2C \longrightarrow D + 2E$
(the solutions of A, B, and C are molar solutions)

Reaction	Volume of A	Volume of B	Volume of C	Volume of H_2O	Initial rate of D (Ms^{-1})
1	200	200	200	400	3×10^{-5}
2	400	800	400	400	12×10^{-5}
3	400	200	200	200	6×10^{-5}
4	200	200	400	200	3×10^{-5}

Problem 17 For a certain chemical reaction the effects of the differing reactions on the initial rate are shown in *Table 2*. Find the order of reaction with respect to A, B and C and hence write down a rate expression for the reaction.

In this problem the concentrations are given as volumes and to avoid confusion, they should be converted to the number of moles before any comparison is made.

In reaction (1) 200 cm³ of molar A is contained in 1000 cm³ of solution hence its concentration is 0.2 moles dm^{-3}, as are the concentrations of B and C.

In reaction (2) 400 cm³ of molar A is contained in 2000 cm³ of solution and hence its concentration is 0.2 moles dm^{-3}, whilst B and C are 0.4 and 0.2 moles dm^{-3} respectively. The effect of doubling the relative concentrations of B increases the initial rate four times, this means that the reaction is second order with respect to B.

A comparison of reactions (1) and (3) shows that doubling the concentration of A doubles the initial rate of reaction and hence it shows **first order kinetics for this reaction**.

A comparison of reactions (1) and (4) shows that doubling the concentration of C has no effect on the initial rate of reaction.
Hence, the **order of reaction with respect to C is zero**.
The rate equation can be expressed as

Rate $= k [A]^1 [B]^2 [C]^0$

where k is the rate constant.

Problem 18 The hydrolysis of 1-bromobutane has been shown to be a second order reaction, whereas the hydrolysis of 2-methylpropan-2-ol is a first order reaction. What can be deduced about the mechanisms of both reactions from this data.

The equation of reaction for the hydrolysis of 1-bromobutane is

$CH_3CH_2CH_2CH_2Br(l) + NaOH(aq) \longrightarrow CH_3CH_2CH_2CH_2OH(aq) + NaBr(aq)$.

Since this is a second order reaction the rate equation can be written

Rate of reaction $= k_1 [CH_3CH_2CH_2CH_2Br]^1 [NaOH]^1$

This means that both bromobutane and sodium hydroxide are involved in the **rate determining step**. This implies the formation of a **transition complex** involving both compounds, and can be shown as the breaking of the C–Br bond concurrent with the formation of the C–OH bond as shown in *Fig 10*. The nucleophilic substitution is due to the polarisation of the C–Br covalent bond.

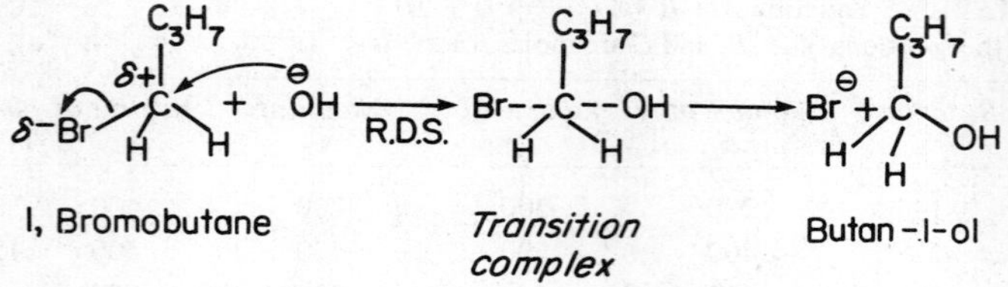

(a) Bimolecular nucleophilic reaction

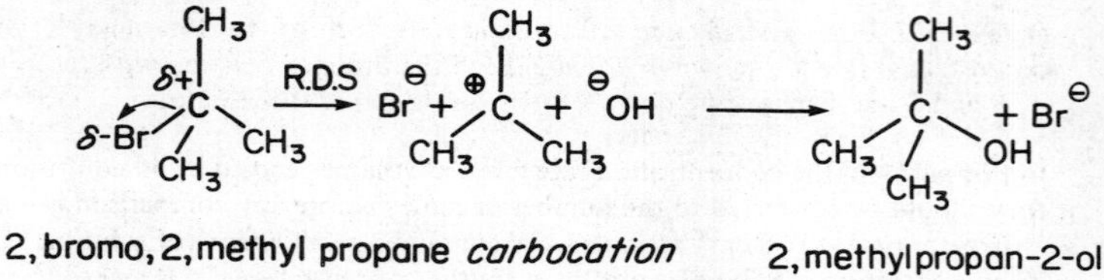

(b) Uni molecular nucleophilic reaction

Fig 10

The equation of reaction for the hydrolysis of 2,methylpropan-2-ol, is

$$CH_3COH(CH_3)CH_3 + NaOH = CH_3COH(CH_3)CH_3 + NaBr.$$

Since this is a first order reaction the rate equation can be expressed as

$$\text{Rate of reaction} = k_2\,[CH_3COH(CH_3)CH_3]^1$$

This means that only 2, methylpropan-2-ol is involved in the **rate determining step**. This implies the existence of a **molecular modification** of the molecule due to the degree of polarisation of the C–Br bond in this molecule. The rate determining step is the ionisation of the 2,methylpropan-2-ol molecule as shown in *Fig 9*.

This application of reaction kinetic data to mechanisms of reaction shows that although both reactions are hydrolysis reactions, they take place in different ways, dependent upon the polarisation of the molecule.

C. FURTHER PROBLEMS ON REACTION KINETICS

(a) SHORT ANSWER PROBLEMS

Fill in the missing words

1. The kinetic theory of matter states that in the gas state, the particles are in a state of ...., and that collisions between the particles are perfectly ....

2. The expression .... relates the number of particles to the average .... of the particles.

3. Arrhenius suggested that not all of the collisions which occur between reacting molecules are .... because they must have an energy greater than the .... before reaction will occur.

4. An increase in the temperature of a gas can be considered to increase the .... of the particles.

5. The average kinetic energy of a gas is equal to $\tfrac{1}{2}mu^2$ where u is the .... velocity of the particles.

6. The rate of a chemical reaction is dependent upon the ...., the .... and the presence of a .... in the reaction mixture.

7. For a reaction which takes place in the gas phase the reaction rate is dependent on the .... of the reacting gases rather than their concentrations.

8. The law of mass action states that the rate of a chemical reaction is proportional to the .... of the reactants.

9. The rate of any chemical reaction is dependent on rate of the slowest stage in that reaction. This stage is called the ....

10. For the equation

    Rate $= k[A]^1[B]^0$

    k is called the ...., and for $[A]^1$ the suffix 1 indicates that the rate of reaction is .... order with respect to reactant A.

11. For the rate equation

    Rate $= k[A]^2[B]^1[C]^0$

    the overall order of the reaction is ....

12. The half-life of a chemical reaction is the time taken for the .... concentration of a reactant to be ....

13. When the rate of reaction for a reactant is constant the order of reaction of that reactant is ....

14. When the half-life of the concentration of a reactant is constant, the reaction is .... order with respect to that reactant.

15. The determination of the order of reaction for each reactant in a reaction is an aid for the investigation of the .... of that reaction.

(b) MULTI-CHOICE PROBLEMS (answers on page 181)

Select the correct answer from those given

1. Which of the following statements on the kinetic theory of matter is incorrect?
   (a) The velocity of the particles is proportional to the pressure of the particles.
   (b) The collisions between the particles are elastic.
   (c) The velocity of the particles is proportional to the temperature of the particles.
   (d) The collisions between the particles and the walls of the vessel are elastic.

2. The equation relating the ratio of particles with a particular energy is

   (a) $\dfrac{N_0}{N} = e^{\frac{-ER}{T}}$; (b) $\dfrac{N}{N_0} = e^{\frac{ER}{T}}$; (c) $\dfrac{N}{N_0} = e^{\frac{-ER}{T}}$; (d) $\dfrac{N}{N_0} = e^{\frac{-ER}{T}}$;

3. The velocity of the particles of a gas which is used to calculate the average kinetic energy of the gas is
   (a) the average velocity;
   (b) the mean velocity;
   (c) the medial velocity;
   (d) the root mean square velocity.

4. The equation relating together the rate constant of a reaction k, with the energy of activation of the reaction is
   (a) $\log_e k \propto e^{\frac{-E}{RT}}$;
   (b) $\log_{10} k \propto e^{\frac{-E}{RT}}$;
   (c) $\log_{10} k = e^{\frac{-E}{RT}}$;
   (d) $\log_e k = e^{\frac{-E}{RT}}$;

5. When the rate constant of a reaction k_1 is known for a temperature $T_1 K$, the value of a different rate constant k_2 at an increased temperature $T_2 K$ is given by the expression

   (a) $\log_e k_2 = \frac{E}{R}\left(\frac{1}{T_1} - \frac{1}{T_2}\right) - \log_e k_1$

   (b) $\log_e k_2 = \frac{E}{R}\left(\frac{1}{T_1} + \frac{1}{T_2}\right) + \log_e k_1$

   (c) $\log_e k_2 = \frac{E}{R}\left(\frac{1}{T_2} - \frac{1}{T_1}\right) + \log_e k_1$

   (d) $\log_e k_2 = \frac{E}{R}\left(\frac{1}{T_1} - \frac{1}{T_2}\right) + \log_e k_1$

Problems 6 to 8 refer to Fig 11.

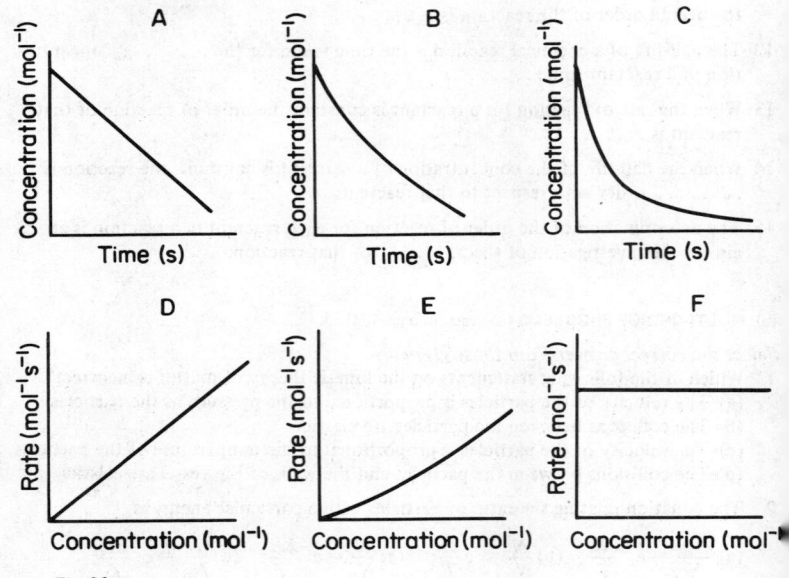

Fig 11

6. Which of the graphs would correspond to the data obtained for the first order kinetics of a reactant.
   (a) A and D; (b) B and E; (c) C and D; (d) A and F.

7. Which of the graphs would correspond to the data obtained for the zero order kinetics of a reactant.
   (a) B and E; (b) A and F; (c) C and D; (d) C and F.

8. For the rate equation

   Rate = $k[X]^0[Y]^1[Z]^2$

   the most likely graph representing the variation in Z is
   (a) A; (b) B; (c) C; (d) D.

9. For the equation in *Problem 8* the overall rate order of reaction is
   (a) 0; (b) 1; (c) 2; (d) 3.

10. The derived integrated rate equation for a first order reaction where k = the velocity constant, $[A_0]$ = the initial concentration and $[A]$ = the concentration at any time t is

    (a) $k = \dfrac{2.303}{t} \log \dfrac{[A_0]}{[A]}$;

    (b) $k = 2.303t \log \dfrac{[A_0]}{[A]}$;

    (c) $t = \dfrac{2.303}{k} \log \dfrac{[A]}{[A_0]}$;

    (d) $t = 2.303k \log \dfrac{[A]}{[A_0]}$.

11. In a first order reaction, $k = 6.93 \times 10^{-5}$ s^{-1}, the half-life of the reaction is
    (a) 2.77 hr; (b) 1.36 hr; (c) 4.66 hr; (d) 10 hr.

12. The integrated rate equation for a second order reaction can be expressed as

    $$kt = \dfrac{1}{[A]} - \dfrac{1}{[A_0]}$$

    where k is the rate constant, $[A_0]$ is the initial concentration and $[A]$ is the concentration at any time t. If the half-life for a reaction which has an initial concentration of 1 mol, is 10^3 s, the rate constant has a value of
    (a) 10 mol^{-1} s^{-1}; (b) 100 mol^{-1} s^{-1}; (c) 0.01 mol^{-1} s^{-1}; (d) 0.001 mol^{-1} s^{-1}.

Problems 13 to 15 refer to the data given in Table 3.

13. The order of reaction with respect to $[A][B]$ is
    (a) 0; (b) 1; (c) 2; (d) 3.

TABLE 3 Reaction $A + 2B + C \longrightarrow 2D + E$

Concentration in moles	A	B	C	Initial rate of formation of E, moles sec^{-1}
Reaction 1	0.1	0.1	0.1	2×10^{-4}
Reaction 2	0.1	0.2	0.1	2×10^{-4}
Reaction 3	0.2	0.2	0.1	8×10^{-4}
Reaction 4	0.1	0.2	0.4	8×10^{-4}

14 The order of reaction with respect to $[B][C]$ is
(a) 0; (b) 1; (c) 2; (d) 3.

15 The order of reaction with respect to $[A][B][C]$ is
(a) 0; (b) 1; (c) 2; (d) 3.

(c) CONVENTIONAL PROBLEMS

1 What factors affect the rate of chemical reactions?

2 How can the effects of the factors which affect chemical reactions be explained qualitatively?

3 Comment on the contributions made by Maxwell, Boltzmann and Arrhenius to the understanding of the relationship between reaction rates and the energy of the interacting molecules.

4 Show with suitable diagrams how an increase in temperature changes the rate of reactions.

5 Draw energy profile diagrams to show the following reactions.
 (a) $A + B \longrightarrow C \; \Delta H + ve$
 (b) $D + E \longrightarrow F \; \Delta H - ve$
 (c) $G + I \xrightarrow{\Delta H + ve} J + K \xrightarrow{\Delta H - ve} L$, and
 (d) $M + N \longrightarrow P \; \Delta H - ve$, (i), without a catalyst and (ii), with a catalyst which increases the reaction rate.

6 For the reaction $2N_2O_5(g) \longrightarrow 2N_2O_4(g) + O_2(g)$ the rate constant at 400 K is 7.253×10^{-1} s^{-1} and 2.341×10^4 s^{-1} at 600 K.
Calculate the energy of activation for the reaction. (Take $R = 8.314 \times 10^{-3}$ kJ mol^{-1} K^{-1}). [103.6 kJ mol^{-1}]

7 The energy of activation of the reaction

$$CH_3CHO(g) \longrightarrow CH_4(g) + CO(g)$$

is 190 kJ mol^{-1}. If the rate constant at 650 K is 6.6×10 dm^3 mol^{-1} s^{-1}, what is the value of the rate constant at 850 K? (Take $R = 8.314 \times 10^{-3}$ kJ mol^{-1} K^{-1})
[2.5 dm^3 mol^{-1} s^{-1}]

8 For the reaction in *Problem 7*, calculate the value of the Arrhenius constant at 650 K. (Note, use $k = Ae^{-E/RT}$.) [1.219×10^{12} s^{-1}]

9 Show that the rate of decay of a radioactive sample of an isotope of sodium is a first order reaction and determine the half-life of this isotope from the data given

Activity (c.p.m.)	2500	2385.5	2276.9	2173.9
Time (min)	0	60	120	180

[$t_{1/2}$ = 888.8 hr]

10 Show that the following reaction is a second order reaction from the data given

$$CH_3CHO(g) \longrightarrow CH_4(g) + CO(g)$$

Concentration of CH_3CHO mol dm^{-3}	0.01	0.075	0.09	0.093
Time, s	0	100	300	500

11. When the decomposition of hydrogen peroxide, H_2O_2, is followed using a titration technique with potassium manganate (*VII*) the following results were obtained

Time (s)	0	600	831	1200	1662
$KMnO_4$ (cm^3)	22.8	13.8	11.4	8.25	5.7

Find the order of reaction by plotting a graph of the volume of $KMnO_4$ against time. [1st order]

12. The rate of reaction for the hydrolysis of bromoethane with potassium hydroxide can be measured by taking equal volumes of the reaction mixture at different times and titrating them against standard acid. The following results were obtained.

Time, 10^2 s	0	12.5	25	50	75	100	150	200
Vol of acid cm^3	40	24	19	12	9	7.4	5	4

Plot a graph of the titre against time. What conclusions can you draw from the curve. [The order of reaction is not zero or first order]

13. The reaction of dinitrogen pentoxide, N_2O_5, to nitrogen dioxide, NO_2 and oxygen O_2 is according to the equation

$$2N_2O_5 \longrightarrow 4NO_2 + O_2$$

The rate of decrease with time is determined and the results are as follows

Concentration mol dm^{-3}	2	1.5	1	0.5	0.1	0.001
Rate of reaction as a decrease 10^{-4} mol dm^{-3} s^{-1}	21.4	16.0	10.7	5.35	1.07	0.011

(i) Find the order of reaction with respect to N_2O_5 and
(ii) Find the rate constant. [1st Order]

14. The decomposition of hydrogen iodide to hydrogen and iodine in the gas phase at 720 K takes place according to the equation

$$2HI(g) = H_2(g) + I_2(g)$$

The rates of decrease with time are as follows

Concentration mol dm^{-3}	0.1	0.25	0.4	0.7	0.9	1.2
Rate of reaction as a decrease 10^{-3} mol dm^{-3} s^{-1}	5	31.3	80	245	405	720

(i) Find the order of reaction with respect to hydrogen iodide,
(ii) Write down an expression for the rate equation,
(iii) Find the value of the rate constant.
  [2nd $R = k\,[HI]^2$. $k = 5 \times 10^{-1}$ mol^{-1} s^{-1}]

119

15 Derive an expression relating the initial concentration $[A_0]$ the rate constant and the concentration $[A]$ at any time t for a first order reaction of the type

Rate of reaction = $k[A]$

16 For the reaction

$H_2O_2(aq) + 2I^-(aq) + 2H_3^+O(aq) = I_2(aq) + 2H_2O(l)$

The concentration of a sample of hydrogen peroxide is determined at varying times as follows

Rate of reaction (s) 10^{-3}	5	31.3	80	245	720
Concentration (mol dm^{-3})	0.1	0.25	0.4	0.7	1.2

(i) Find the order of reaction, and (ii) the rate constant for the reaction
[2nd, 5×10^{-1} mol^{-1} dm^3 s^{-1}]

17 The following data has been derived experimentally for the reaction

$H_2O_2(aq) + 2I^-(aq) + 2H^+(aq) \longrightarrow I_2 + 2H_2O$

	Molarities		*Rate of formation*
H_2O_2 mol.	I^- mol.	H^+ mol.	I_2 (mol. s^{-1})
0.001	0.001	0.002	1.7 × 10^{-7}
0.002	0.001	0.002	6.8 × 10^{-7}
0.001	0.003	0.002	5.1 × 10^{-7}
0.001	0.003	0.001	2.5 × 10^{-7}

(i) Express the order of reaction with respect to (a) H_2O_2; (b) I^- and (c) H^+.
(ii) Express the rate law for the formation of I_2.
[(i)(a) 2nd; (b) 1st; (c) 1st. Rate = $k[H_2O_2]^2[I^-]^1[H^+]^1$]

18 The following data is determined experimentally for the reaction

$A + B \longrightarrow C$

Volume of 1 M. A	Volume of 1 M. B	Volume of H_2O	Rate of formation of C (mol s^{-1})
100	300	600	2.5 × 10^{-3}
200	300	500	1 × 10^{-2}
100	900	0	7.5 × 10^{-3}

(i) Express the rate equation for the reaction.
(ii) Calculate the value of the rate constant.
[Rate = $k[A]^2[B]^0$, $k = 2.5 \times 10^{-1}$ mol^{-1} dm^3 s^{-1}]

19 For the gas phase reaction

$$2NO + 2H_2 \longrightarrow N_2 + 2H_2O$$

reaction kinetics show that the order of reaction of NO is second order and of H_2 first order. When the concentration of nitrogen oxide is 0.04 mol dm^{-3} and that of hydrogen 0.02 mol dm^{-3}, the rate of reaction is 2.66 mol s^{-1}.
Calculate the value of the rate constant and the initial rate of reaction if NO = 0.5 mol dm^{-3} and H_2 = 0.1 mol dm^{-3}.

[$k = 8.3 \times 10^4$ mol^{-2} dm^6 s^{-1}. Rate = 2.075×10^3 mol s^{-1}]

20. For the gas phase reaction

$$Cl_2 + 2NO \longrightarrow 2NOCl$$

The rate equation is found to be

$$\text{Rate} = k\,[Cl_2]^1[NO]^2 \text{ and } k = 1.3 \times 10^{-3} \text{ mol}^2 \text{ s}^{-1}.$$

If the initial rate of reaction is 1.56×10^{-6} mol s^{-1} when the concentration of chlorine is 0.3 moles, calculate (a) the concentration of nitrogen oxide and (b) the rate of reaction, if the initial concentrations of chlorine and nitrogen oxide are 0.01 and 0.1 moles respectively.

[[NO] = 0.2 moles. Rate = 1.3×10^{-7} mol s^{-1}]

21. For the reaction

$$2A + 5B + C \longrightarrow D + 3E$$

the following data is derived

Concentrations			Rate of formation
A	B	C	D
0.001	0.001	0.001	3.6×10^{-5}
0.001	0.002	0.001	1.44×10^{-4}
0.003	0.002	0.001	4.32×10^{-4}
0.002	0.002	0.002	5.76×10^{-4}

(a) Calculate the order of reaction with respect to A, B and C.
(b) Write down the rate equation for the reaction.

[Rate = $k\,[A]^1[B]^2[C]^1$]

8 Organic reaction mechanisms

A. MAIN POINTS CONCERNING ORGANIC REACTION MECHANISMS

1. A **reaction mechanism** can be considered as an explanation of how a reaction takes place and through what **intermediate stages** a reaction passes before being converted into products.
2. At this level only an **elementary treatment** is possible and is based mainly on **polarisation effects** within the molecules.
3. For any organic reaction to occur bonds must be broken and new bonds formed. By considering the polarisation effects present in the reactants it is possible to formulate what can be considered as **the driving force of the reaction**.
4. The reactions of organic compounds can be broadly classified into four categories:
   - (i) **addition** reactions;
   - (ii) **substitution** reactions;
   - (iii) **elimination** reactions;
   - (iv) **rearrangement** reactions.
   - (i) **Addition reactions** take place in **unsaturated** molecules and result in the formation of a **single** product. Examples of this are shown in *Fig 1*.
   - (ii) **Substitution reactions** involve the **replacement** of one atom or group of atoms in a molecule by a **different** atom or group of atoms. A general equation can be written for this type of reaction,

   $$R-X + Y \longrightarrow R-Y + X$$

   some examples are given in *Fig 1*.
   - (iii) **Elimination reactions** are those reactions involving the **loss** of atoms or groups of atoms from a molecule which are subsequently **not replaced**. This introduces a **multiple bond** into the molecule formed as the reaction product. (See *Fig 1* for examples.)
   - (iv) **Rearrangement reactions** involve the **migration** of an atom or group of atoms from one part of a molecule to another. Most examples of rearrangement reactions at this level constitute part of a reaction mechanism, as can be seen from *Fig 1*.
5. The **polarisation** of organic molecules can be assigned in an elementary way by a consideration of the **electronegativity values** of the atoms within the molecule. These values are given in *Table 1*. The larger the difference between the electronegativities of constituent atoms, the greater the polarisation of the bond. The diagrammatic representation of the extremes of polarisation are shown in *Fig 2* and discussed in *Problem 1*. The use of the **arrow notation** in polarisation is given in *Problem 2*.

Reactants	Products	Classification
$\underset{H}{\overset{R}{>}}C=C\underset{H}{\overset{H}{<}} + H_2$ alkene	$\underset{H}{\overset{R}{H-C}}-\underset{H}{\overset{H}{C-H}}$ alkane	Addition
$\underset{H}{\overset{R}{>}}C=O + HCN$ aldehyde	$R-\underset{CN}{\overset{H}{C}}-OH$ cyanohydrin	Addition
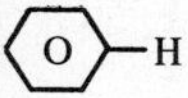 ⌬—H + NO_2^+ benzene	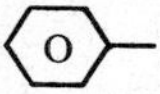 ⌬—NO_2 + H^+ nitrobenzene	Substitution
$R-CH_2-BR + \overline{O}H$ bromoalkane	$R-CH_2-OH + B\overline{r}$	Substitution
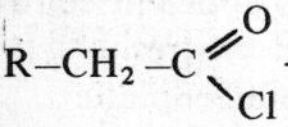 $R-CH_2-C\underset{Cl}{\overset{O}{<}} + NH_3$ acid chloride	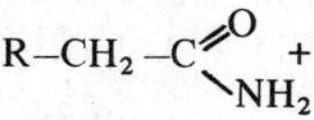 $R-CH_2-C\underset{NH_2}{\overset{O}{<}} + HCl$ acid amide	Substitution
$R-CH_2-CH_2-OH + P_2O_5$ alcohol	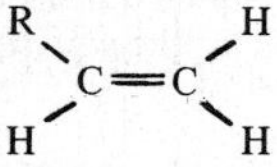 $\underset{H}{\overset{R}{>}}C=C\underset{H}{\overset{H}{<}} + H_2O$ alkene	Elimination
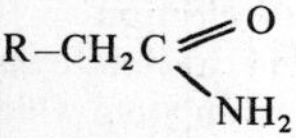 $R-CH_2C\underset{NH_2}{\overset{O}{<}} + P_2O_5$ acid amide	$R-CH_2-C\equiv N + H_2O$ acid nitrile	Elimination
$R-CH_2-\underset{+NH_3}{\overset{H}{\underset{|}{C}}}-O^-$ aldehyde ammonia intermediate	$R-CH_2-\underset{NH_2}{\overset{H}{\underset{|}{C}}}-OH$ aldehyde ammonia product	Rearrangement

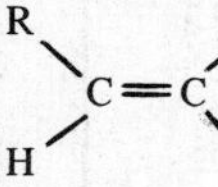

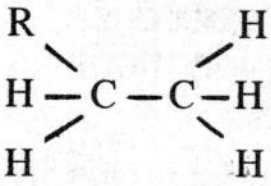

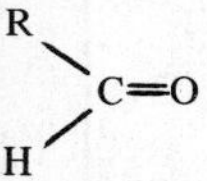

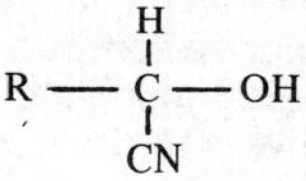

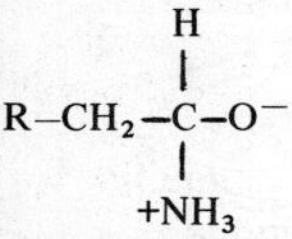

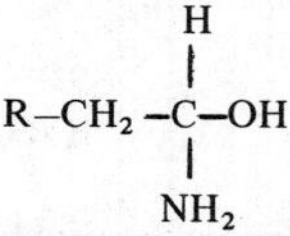

Fig 1 The classification of some organic reactions

Structure	Extent of polarisation	Examples
A× ×A	No polarisation because the atoms are identical	H—H, Cl—Cl,
A× ·B	Partial polarisation due to atom B being more electronegative than A	CH₃—Br CH₃—NH₃
$\overset{+}{A}$ ×B⁻	Complete polarisation due to atom B being much more electronegative than A	NaCl KBr

Fig 2

TABLE 1 The electronegativities of some elements

Element	F	O	N	Cl	Br	S	C	I	P	H
Electronegativity	4.0	3.5	3.0	3.0	2.8	2.5	2.5	2.5	2.1	2.1

6 The partial polarisations of organic molecules result in an **electron deficient** centre (positive, δ+) and an **electron rich** centre (negative, δ−). It is these centres which can undergo reactions. (i) An electron deficient centre is called a **nucleophilic** centre because electron rich reagents are attracted towards it. Such electron rich reagents are called **nucleophiles** (Greek: nucleus loving) and are either **negatively charged** or **possess at least one non-bonded pair** of electrons, (see *Problem 3*). This type of reaction can be represented by the equation

$$A \overset{\delta+}{\underset{}{\frown}} \overset{\delta-}{B} + X^- \quad\quad ^-X \cdots \overset{\delta+}{A} \cdots \overset{\delta-}{B}$$

(ii) An electron rich centre is called an **electrophilic** centre because electron deficient reagents or **electrophiles** (Greek: electron loving) are attracted towards it. Reagents of this type are either **positively charged** or **possess an atom which is electron deficient** as a result of polarisation effects (see *Problem 4*). This type of reaction can be represented by the equation

$$A \overset{\delta+}{\underset{}{\frown}} \overset{\delta-}{B} + Y^+ \quad\quad \overset{\delta+}{A} \cdots \overset{\delta-}{B} \cdots Y^+$$

(iii) Some examples of electrophiles and nucleophiles are given in *Table 2*.

7 The classification of reagents as electrophiles and nucleophiles leads to a subdivision of the reaction categories given in para 4.
  (i) Addition reactions can be sub-divided into **electrophilic addition** reactions and **nucleophilic addition** reactions. These reactions rarely take place in isolation but occur consecutively, for example the first stage in the addition

TABLE 2 Some examples of electrophiles and nucleophiles

Electrophiles	H^+	Br^+	NO_2^+	Cl^+	$R_3-\overset{+}{C}$	SO_3	R^+	
Nucleophiles	HO^-	^-CN	Br^-	RO^-	H_2O	NH_3	ROH	RNH_2

to an alkene is electrophilic addition, followed by nucleophilic addition as shown by

(ii) **Substitution reactions** can also be sub-divided into **electrophilic substitution** and **nucleophilic substitution**. Unlike addition reactions, these two reaction types are not interdependent. Electrophilic substitution at this level involves mainly the reactions of benzene and are followed by nucleophilic addition. For example, the nitration of benzene is brought about by the electrophile NO_2^+ which is the **nitronium ion** formed from concentrated sulphuric and nitric acid. The equation of reaction can be written

followed by

$$H^+ + HSO_4^- \rightleftharpoons H_2SO_4$$

where the nucleophiles come from the reaction

$$2H_2SO_4 + HNO_3 \rightleftharpoons 2HSO_4^- + H_3O^+ + NO_2^+$$

An example of **nucleophilic substitution** is the reaction between ethanal and hydroxylamine

Other examples are given in *Problem 8*.

8   A further type of substitution reaction which occurs in the chemistry of the hydrocarbons is free radical substitution. The reaction of methane and chlorine in the presence of ultraviolet radiation is well established. The products of reaction are a mixture of compounds which are reasonably explained by a **free radical** mechanism. The reaction in stages can be represented by the equations

$$CH_4 + Cl_2 \longrightarrow CH_3Cl + HCl$$
$$CH_3Cl + Cl_2 \longrightarrow CH_2Cl_2 + HCl$$
$$CH_2Cl_2 + Cl_2 \longrightarrow CHCl_3 + HCl$$
$$CHCl_3 + Cl_2 \longrightarrow CCl_4 + HCl$$

The formation of **free radicals** is a result of the **homolytic fission** of a covalent bond. The mechanism of this reaction is found in *Problem 6* and other examples of this reaction type are given in chapter 10, on polymerisation.

9 An **elimination reaction** is one in which a multiple bond is introduced into a molecule by the loss of an atom or group of atoms from adjacent atoms, with no subsequent replacement of the atoms or groups removed. For example

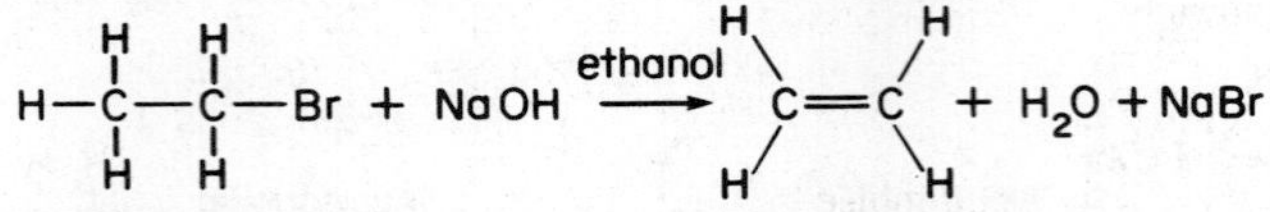

$$H-\underset{H}{\overset{H}{C}}-\underset{H}{\overset{H}{C}}-Br + NaOH \xrightarrow{ethanol} \underset{H}{\overset{H}{C}}=\underset{H}{\overset{H}{C}} + H_2O + NaBr$$

The mechanism of this reaction can be considered as a stepwise wise reaction,

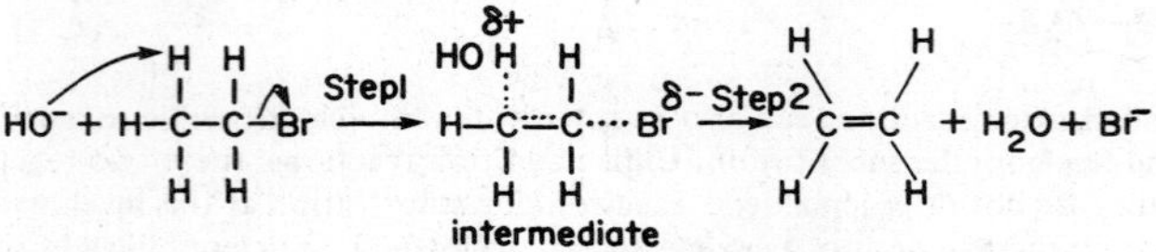

$$HO^- + H-\underset{H}{\overset{H}{C}}-\underset{H}{\overset{H}{C}}-Br \xrightarrow{Step1} H-\overset{HO}{\overset{\delta+}{\underset{H}{C}}}\cdots\overset{H}{\underset{H}{C}}\cdots Br \xrightarrow{\delta-\ Step 2} \underset{H}{\overset{H}{C}}=\underset{H}{\overset{H}{C}} + H_2O + Br^-$$

intermediate

Other examples are shown in *Table 1* and *Problem 7*.

10 The **rearrangement** of atoms within a reaction intermediate often takes place to **stabilise the molecule**. For example, the reaction intermediate formed between an aldehyde and hydroxylamine has a **positive** and **negative** centre within its structure. These are removed by the **redistribution of electrons** within the intermediate by **transferring a proton** from the nitrogen atom to the oxygen atom.

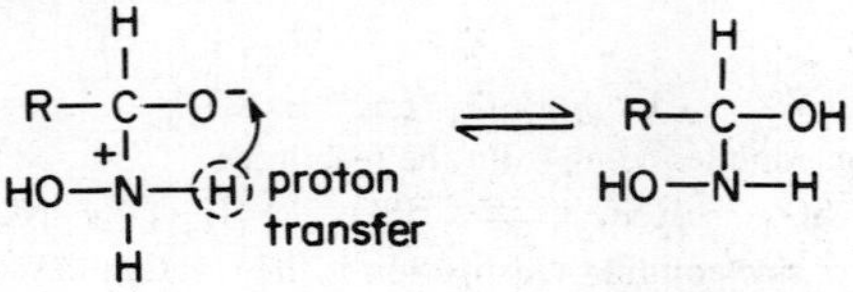

$$\begin{array}{c} H \\ | \\ R-C-O^- \\ | \\ HO-\overset{+}{N}-(H) \\ | \\ H \end{array} \text{ proton transfer} \rightleftharpoons \begin{array}{c} H \\ | \\ R-C-OH \\ | \\ HO-N-H \end{array}$$

The intermediate formed by this proton transfer then undergoes an elimination reaction, caused by the transfer of another proton to the oxygen attached to carbon as shown in *Problem 3*.

B. WORKED PROBLEMS ON ORGANIC REACTION MECHANISMS

Problem 1 Discuss the polarisation of carbon to non-metal bonds caused by (a) **inductive** effects, and (b) **mesomeric** effects.

(a) In organic molecules, carbon is bonded to a variety of non-metals which comprise part of, or constitute completely, the functional group of the molecule. The sharing of the bonding electron pair in these bonds is not equal, the electrons being attracted more towards the more electronegative element. Since carbon has a low relative electronegativity value, most other non-metals attract electrons away from it resulting in the polarisation shown below

$$C \longrightarrow X \quad \text{or} \quad \overset{\delta_+}{C}-\overset{\delta_-}{X}$$

This effect can be transmitted through one carbon atom to another carbon atom, though the effect weakens as the distance from the non-metal atom increases. For example, in the structure $-C_2-C_1-X$, carbon C_2 loses its equal share in the electrons between C_2 and C_1 when X is more electronegative than carbon. When a carbon atom is attached to three alkyl groups and one hydrogen, it is found that the alkyl groups contribute a share of their bonding electron pair to that carbon atom, for example

$$CH_3 \rightarrow \underset{\underset{CH_3}{\uparrow}}{\overset{\overset{CH_3}{\downarrow}}{C}}\overset{\delta+}{-}H^{\delta-}$$

These **inductive** effects are **permanent** polarisations within the molecule.

(b) The **mesomeric** electronic effects are found in molecules which contain a double bond involving carbon and a heteroatom, for example, the carbonyl group >C=O. This contains a **sigma bond** and a **pi bond**, the sigma bond giving rise to an **inductive** effect, but the pi bond giving rise to a **mesomeric** effect. This is evident by the **greater** polarisation of the C=O bond than can be explained by the inductive effect. The effect of the redistribution of electrons is to cause the oxygen of the bond to be more electron dense than the carbon atom. The polarisations can be represented by the structures

$$\diagdown\!\!\!\!\diagup C{=}O \longleftrightarrow \diagdown\!\!\!\!\diagup C^+{-}O^-$$

neither of which is accurate. The structure

$$\left[\diagdown\!\!\!\!\diagup \overset{\delta+}{C} {=\!=\!=\!=} \overset{\delta-}{O} \right]$$

represents the **average** of the two extremes, which are called **the canonical structures** of the carbonyl group, and is called the **resonance hybrid**.

Problem 2 Explain what is represented by the following mechanistic symbols

(a) $R-\overset{\delta+}{CH_2}-X^{\delta-}$

(b) $\underset{R}{\overset{R}{\diagdown}}\overset{\delta+}{C}{=}\overset{\delta-}{O}$

(c) $R-\underset{R}{\overset{R}{\underset{|}{C}}}-\overset{+}{\underset{②}{O}}\diagdown\!\!\!\!\diagup\overset{H}{\underset{H}{}}$ ① $:\!\underline{N}-X$

(d) $R-\underset{H}{\overset{H}{\underset{|}{C}}}-\overset{+}{\underset{R}{\underset{|}{C}}}\diagdown\!\!\!\!\diagup\overset{H}{\underset{}{}}$

(a) The symbol δ_+ represents a **reduction** in the electron density at the carbon atom and δ_- represents an **increase** in the electron density at the X atom, at the extremities of a covalent bond. This is caused by the difference in electronegativity between C and X. The arrow represents the drift of electrons within

127

the covalent bond from carbon towards X. If other molecules enhance this drift of electrons, the result can be represented by the equation below showing that the bond breaks

$$R-CH_2-X \rightleftharpoons R-\overset{+}{C}H_2 + X^-$$

(b) The $\delta+$ and $\delta-$ symbols represent the electron densities as in (a). The arrow represents the drift of electrons which can result in the formation of the species shown in the equation

$$\underset{R}{\overset{R}{>}}C\overset{\delta+}{=}\overset{\delta-}{O} \rightleftharpoons \underset{R}{\overset{R}{>}}\overset{+}{C}-O^-$$

(c) The arrows in this structure represent the drift of electrons not only in one covalent bond in the structure, but also, in two covalent bonds. The arrow labelled (1) shows the drift of electrons from the negatively charged nitrogen to the bond position between the carbon and nitrogen atoms. The complete transfer of an electron to this position is shown by the formation of another bond between carbon and nitrogen as shown by

$$R-\overset{*}{\underset{\underset{N-X}{\overset{\|\,②}{C}}}{\overset{R}{|}}}-\overset{+}{O}\overset{H}{\underset{H}{\diagdown}}$$

If all the bonds remain intact the covalency of the carbon atom is five. The arrow labelled (2) shows the drift of electrons from the covalent bond towards the positive oxygen. The result of this drift of electrons is that the carbon to oxygen bond breaks and the water molecule is formed. This can be represented by the equation

$$R-\underset{\underset{N-X}{\overset{\|}{C}}}{\overset{R}{|}}-\overset{+}{O}\overset{H}{\underset{H}{\diagdown}} \rightleftharpoons \underset{R}{\overset{R}{>}}C=N-X + H_2O$$

(d) In this structure the arrow represents the drift of electrons from the carbon to hydrogen bond to the bond position between the carbon atoms, one of which is electron deficient and has a positive charge. This drift of electrons results in the C–H bond breaking, forming H^+, and the formation of a new carbon to carbon bond, as shown in the equation

$$R-\underset{H}{\overset{R}{\underset{|}{C}}}-\overset{+}{\underset{R}{\overset{H}{C}}} \rightleftharpoons \underset{R}{\overset{R}{>}}C=C\underset{R}{\overset{H}{<}} + H^+$$

The use of these symbols in organic mechanism reactions is helpful in establishing the changes taking place within the reaction.

Problem 3 Explain what is meant by the term nucleophilic addition in carbonyl compounds.

Nucleophiles are reagents which are electron rich at one position of their structures. Aldehydes and ketones are examples of molecules containing carbonyl groups which are not affected by other functional groups attached to the carbon atom. The electronic effects in these carbonyl groups result in a polarisation of the C=O bond. The mechanism of the reaction can be represented by the general equation

$$\underset{R'}{\overset{R}{}}C{=}O^{\delta-}_{\delta+} + Y^- \longrightarrow R'-\underset{Y}{\overset{R}{\underset{|}{C}}}-O^-$$

intermediate

Depending on the nature of Y^-, the next step in the reaction to produce the product can either be an electrophilic addition to the negative part of the intermediate, or an elimination reaction to stabilise the product. For example, if Y^- is CN^-, then the general equation is:

$$\underset{R'}{\overset{R}{}}C{=}O^{\delta-}_{\delta+} \xrightarrow{\;\;^-CN\;\;} \overset{①}{\longrightarrow} R'-\underset{CN}{\overset{R}{\underset{|}{C}}}-O^- \xrightarrow[H^+]{②} R-\underset{CN}{\overset{R}{\underset{|}{C}}}-OH$$

In this reaction, **part (1)** is a **nucleophilic addition** and **part (2)** is an **electrophilic addition**.

If the nucleophile is NH_2-OH, hydroxyamine, the non-bonded pair of electrons on nitrogen is the reactive part of the molecule. The reaction can be represented by the equation

$$\underset{R'}{\overset{R}{}}C{=}O^{\delta-}_{\delta+} \;\rightleftharpoons\; R'-\underset{\underset{H}{\overset{+|}{HO-N-H}}}{\overset{R}{\underset{|}{C}}}-O^- \;\rightleftharpoons\; \underset{R'}{\overset{R}{}}C{=}N-OH$$

Here, part (1) of the reaction mechanism is the **nucleophilic** addition reaction. Part (2) of the mechanism is the **elimination** reaction involving the loss of water. The mechanism of this part of the reaction involves the transfer of hydrogen atoms from nitrogen to oxygen, according to the equation

$$R'-\underset{\underset{H}{\overset{+|}{HO-N-H}}}{\overset{R}{\underset{|}{C}}}-O^- \underset{\text{transfer}}{\overset{\text{proton}}{\rightleftharpoons}} R'-\underset{\underset{(H)}{\overset{|}{HO-N}}}{\overset{R}{\underset{|}{C}}}-OH \underset{\text{transfer}}{\overset{\text{proton}}{\rightleftharpoons}} R'-\underset{HO-N^-}{\overset{R}{\underset{|}{C}}}-\overset{+H}{O}\!\!\diagdown\!\!H \;\rightleftharpoons\; \underset{R}{\overset{R}{}}C{=}NOH + H_2O$$

Thus, reactions between aldehydes and ketones with nucleophiles can result in the formation of addition reactions or condensation reactions.

Problem 4 What are electrophiles and what type of reactions do they undergo?

Electrophiles are reagents which are electron deficient either as a result of being positively charged, as in H^+, or by virtue of their structure, as in SO_3. Reagents of the SO_3 type are electron deficient as a result of the polarisation in the molecule, as shown in *Fig 3*.

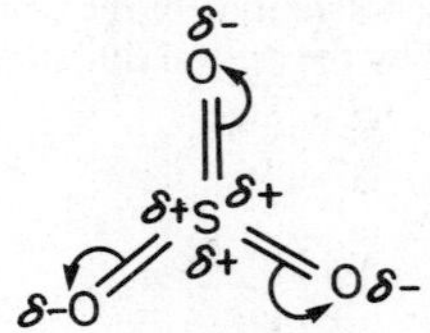

Fig 3 The polarisation of the sulphur trioxide molecule

This deficiency in electron density in electrophiles is relieved by reaction with other molecules which are electron-rich. Molecules of this type are generally those which have a double-bond in their structures or which are negatively charged. The reactions which take place can be addition or substitution reactions. Examples of these reactions are given below:

Electrophilic substitution by the nitronium ion

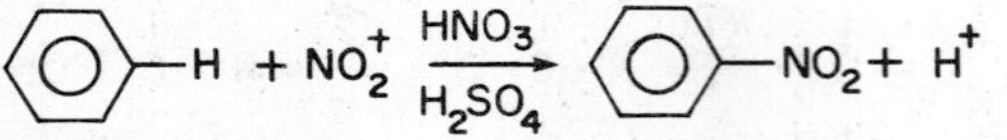

$$C_6H_5-H + NO_2^+ \xrightarrow[H_2SO_4]{HNO_3} C_6H_5-NO_2 + H^+$$

Electrophilic substitution by SO_3

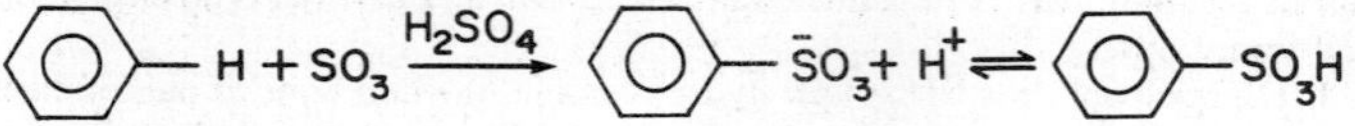

$$C_6H_5-H + SO_3 \xrightarrow{H_2SO_4} C_6H_5-\bar{S}O_3 + H^+ \rightleftharpoons C_6H_5-SO_3H$$

Electrophilic addition

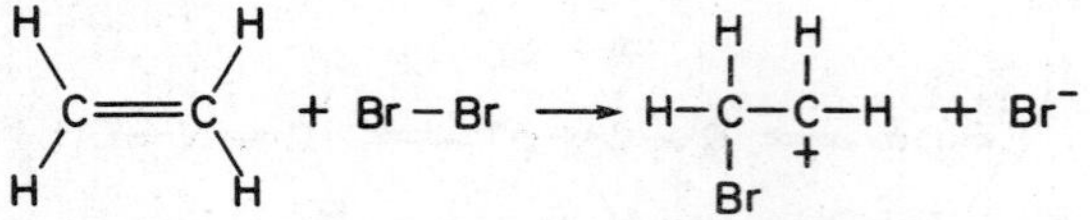

$$H_2C=CH_2 + Br-Br \longrightarrow H-CH_2-\overset{+}{C}H-H + Br^-$$
(with Br on the left carbon)

The addition of electrophiles to other molecules usually results in the formation of a further electrophile prior to the completion of a reaction. For example,

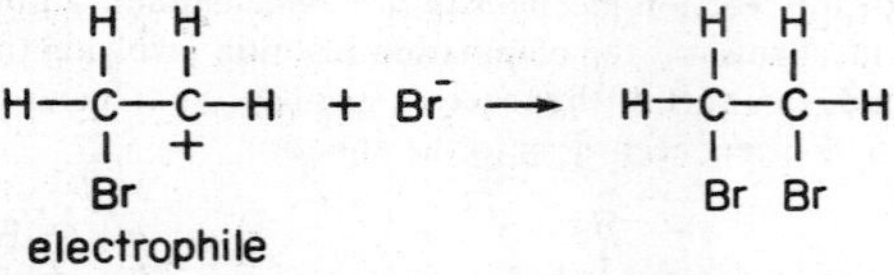

$$H-\underset{Br}{CH}-\overset{+}{C}H-H + Br^- \longrightarrow H-\underset{Br}{CH}-\underset{Br}{CH}-H$$

electrophile

which is a nucleophilic addition reaction to the electrophile formed.

Problem 5 The following reagents are used in organic chemical reactions, assign them as electrophiles or nucleophiles, explaining the reasons for your assignments.

(a) HO^-;
(b) NH_3;
(c) SO_3;
(d) $CH_3-\overset{+}{C}=O$;
(e) $C_2H_5O^-$;
(f) NO_2^+.

(a) The hydroxide ion HO⁻ is classified as a nucleophile because it contains a negative charge. Such a reagent will react with electron deficient positions in other molecules.

(b) The ammonia molecule is classified as a nucleophile because it contains a non-bonded pair of electrons in its structure, i.e. H₃N: This non-bonded pair is a position of high electron density which can react with a position of low electron density in another molecule.

(c) The sulphur trioxide molecule is classified as an electrophile because of the electron deficiency produced at the sulphur atom, shown in *Fig 3*. This polarisation provides sufficient electron deficiency to allow SO_3 to react with electron rich molecules.

(d) The reagent $CH_3-\overset{+}{C}=O$ is an example of an **acylium ion** formed by the reaction between an acid chloride and a suitable **Lewis acid**, such as aluminium trichloride. The formation of this ion with its positive charge (**carbocation**), leads to its classification as an electrophile, which will react with an electron rich part of another molecule.

(e) The **ethoxide ion**, $C_2H_5O^-$, has a negative charge in its structure and consequently is classified as a nucleophile.

(f) The **nitronium ion** NO_2^+ has a positive charge in its structure and consequently is classified as an electrophile.

Problem 6 Describe how the formation of chlorine radicals in ultraviolet light takes place, and hence how a free radical substitution takes place.

In the presence of ultraviolet radiation, the covalent bond joining the two chlorine atoms together receives sufficient energy to undergo homolytic fission. This results in each chlorine atom retaining one electron from the bond. This action can be represented by the equation

$$Cl\dotdiv Cl \xrightarrow{h\nu} Cl\cdot + Cl\cdot$$

The dot (·) convention is used to signify a **radical**, sometimes called a **free radical**. These species are very reactive and can react with methane by the following mechanism

$$CH_4 + Cl\cdot \longrightarrow H_3C\cdot + HCl \quad \cdots \textcircled{1}$$

$$CH_3\cdot + Cl\cdot \longrightarrow CH_3Cl \quad \cdots \textcircled{2}$$

$$\text{or} \quad CH_3\cdot + Cl-Cl \longrightarrow CH_3Cl + Cl\cdot \quad \cdots \textcircled{3}$$

A possible side reaction is

$$CH_3\cdot + CH_3\cdot \longrightarrow CH_3-CH_3 \quad \cdots \textcircled{4}$$

Reaction (1) corresponds to the formation of a methyl radical, which itself is also highly reactive, and can combine with a chlorine radical to form chloromethane, (2). Alternatively, it can react with a chlorine molecule to produce chloromethane and a chlorine radical (3).

The reaction (3) results in the propagation of radicals, and has been called a **chain reaction**.

If two methyl radicals collide as shown in equation (4), the free radicals are used up and the reaction is called **termination**.

Problem 7 When 2-bromobutane reacts with potassium hydroxide, a mixture of products is produced. This mixture contains butan-2-ol, and the alkenes but-1-ene and but-2-ene. Explain this, using reaction mechanism principles.

Potassium hydroxide solution contains the nucleophile, OH$^-$. If nucleophilic substitution takes place, it can be represented by

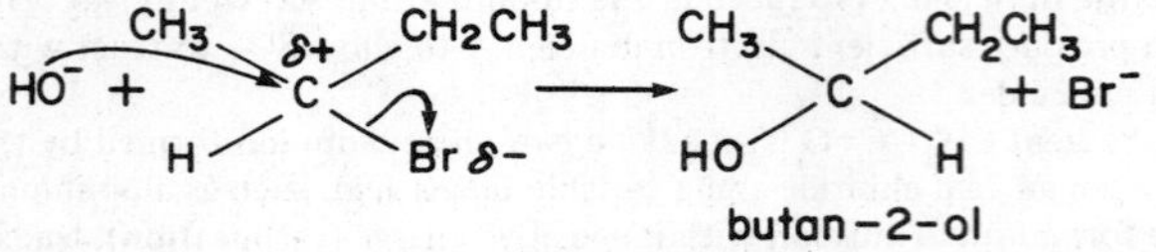

$$HO^- + \underset{H}{\overset{CH_3}{>}}C^{\delta+}\underset{Br\ \delta-}{\overset{CH_2CH_3}{<}} \longrightarrow \underset{HO}{\overset{CH_3}{>}}C\underset{H}{\overset{CH_2CH_3}{<}} + Br^-$$

butan-2-ol

However, the HO$^-$ reagent is also a strong base and has a considerable affinity for hydrogen. Thus, another possible reaction is shown by the reaction mechanism

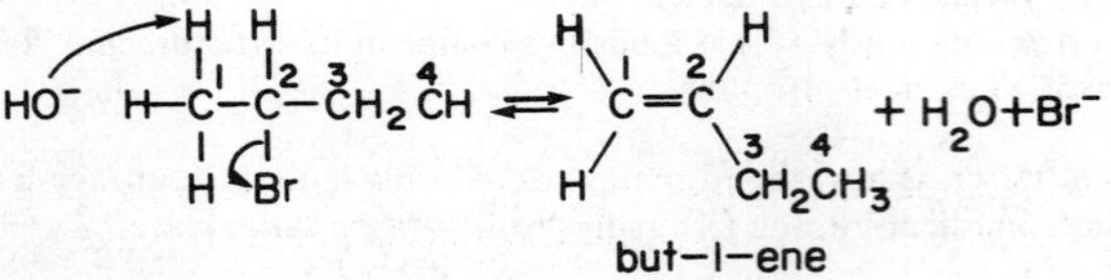

$$HO^- \quad H-\underset{H}{\overset{H}{\underset{|}{C}}}-\underset{Br}{\overset{H}{\underset{|}{C}}}-CH_2\ CH \rightleftharpoons \underset{H}{\overset{H}{>}}C=C\underset{CH_2CH_3}{\overset{H}{<}} + H_2O + Br^-$$

but-1-ene

The elimination of bromine and hydrogen results in the formation of but-1-ene. Alternatively the hydrogen of the 3-carbon atom might be involved, rather than the hydrogen of the 1-carbon atom. This can be shown by the equation

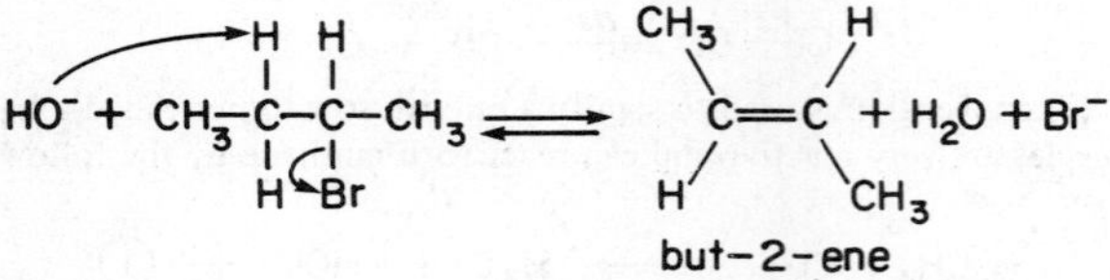

$$HO^- + CH_3-\underset{H\ Br}{\overset{H\ H}{\underset{|\ |}{C-C}}}-CH_3 \rightleftharpoons \underset{H}{\overset{CH_3}{>}}C=C\underset{CH_3}{\overset{H}{<}} + H_2O + Br^-$$

but-2-ene

This type of elimination results in the formation of but-2-ene.

The proportions of these three reaction products can vary, depending upon the conditions under which the reaction is carried out.

Problem 8 How can the following reactions be classified under the headings, electrophilic addition, electrophilic substitution, nucleophilic addition, nucleophilic substitution and elimination

(a) $CH_3CH_2CH_2OH + H_2SO_4 \longrightarrow CH_3CH=CH_2 + H_2O + H_2SO_4$

(b) $CH_3CHO + HCN \longrightarrow CH_3C(OH)HCN$

(c) $CH_3CH_2CH_2Br + KOH \longrightarrow CH_3CH_2CH_2OH + KBr$

(d) $CH_3CH_2CH=CH_2 + HBr \longrightarrow CH_3CH_2CHCH_3$
$|$
Br

(e) $C_6H_6 + Cl_2 \xrightarrow{AlCl_3} C_6H_5Cl + HCl$

(f) $CH_3COCH_3 + NH_2NH_2 \longrightarrow CH_3-C=N-NH_2 + H_2O$
$|$
CH_3

(g) $CH_3CH_2-Cl + NH_3 \longrightarrow CH_3CH_2-\overset{+}{N}H_3Cl^-$

(h) $C_6H_5CHO + NH_2-NH-C_6H_5 \longrightarrow C_6H_5C=N-NH-C_6H_5 + H_2O$

(a) This reaction is the dehydration of an alcohol to produce an alkene. The product is formed by eliminating a molecule of water from the alcohol and consequently the reaction is classified as an **elimination reaction**.

(b) The reaction results in the formation of only one product and is classified as an addition reaction. The reaction takes place in two stages, firstly

$$\underset{H}{\overset{CH_3}{>}}C=O + CN^- \longrightarrow H-\underset{CN}{\overset{CH_3}{\underset{|}{\overset{|}{C}}}}-O^-$$

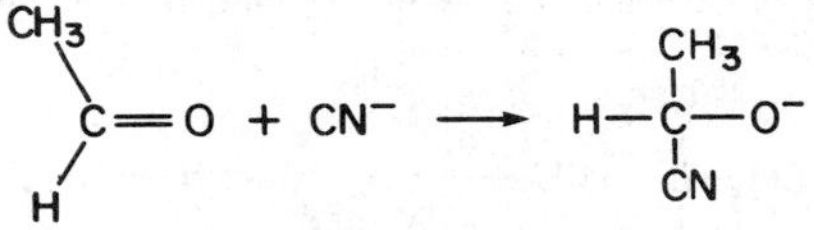

which is an example of **nucleophilic addition**. The second stage of the reaction involves the addition of H^+

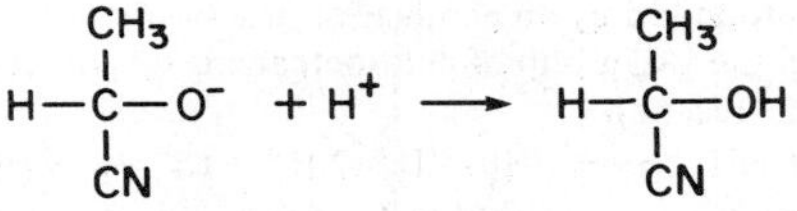

$$H-\underset{CN}{\overset{CH_3}{\underset{|}{\overset{|}{C}}}}-O^- + H^+ \longrightarrow H-\underset{CN}{\overset{CH_3}{\underset{|}{\overset{|}{C}}}}-OH$$

The second stage of the reaction is an example of **electrophilic addition**.

(c) In this reaction there is a substitution of the $-Br$ group by the $-OH$ group according to the equation

$$CH_3CH_2CH_2Br + {}^-OH \longrightarrow CH_3CH_2CH_2-OH + Br^-$$

Since the group is negatively charged it is classified as a **nucleophilic substitution**.

(d) The hydrobromination of an alkene takes place in two stages, firstly

$$CH_3CH_2CH=CH_2 + H-Br \longrightarrow CH_3CH_2\overset{+}{C}H-CH_3 + Br^-$$

133

This is an example of **electrophilic addition**, H^+ from H—Br adding to the 1-carbon atom. The second stage of the reaction can be written

$$CH_3CH_2\overset{+}{C}H-CH_3 + Br^- \longrightarrow CH_3CH_2\underset{\underset{Br}{|}}{C}H-CH_3$$

and is an example of **nucleophilic addition**.

(e) This reaction involves the substitution of a hydrogen atom by a chlorine atom in a benzene molecule. When chlorine reacts with aluminium chloride, the following reaction takes place.

$$Cl-Cl + AlCl_3 \longrightarrow \overset{\delta+}{Cl}-\overset{\delta-}{Cl} \ldots . AlCl_3 \longrightarrow Cl^+ + AlCl_4^-$$

The **chloronium ion** reacts with the benzene molecule

$$C_6H_6 + Cl^+ \longrightarrow C_6H_5Cl + H^+$$

and is an **electrophilic substitution** resulting in the formation of chlorobenzene. The electrophile H^+, which is released, reacts with the complex $AlCl_4^-$ ion, giving

$$H^+ + AlCl_4^- \longrightarrow H-Cl + AlCl_3$$

(f) A water molecule is formed during this reaction, but unlike reaction (a), the water is formed by two molecules rather than one. The first stage in the reaction is the **nucleophilic addition** of NH_2-NH_2 to propanone,

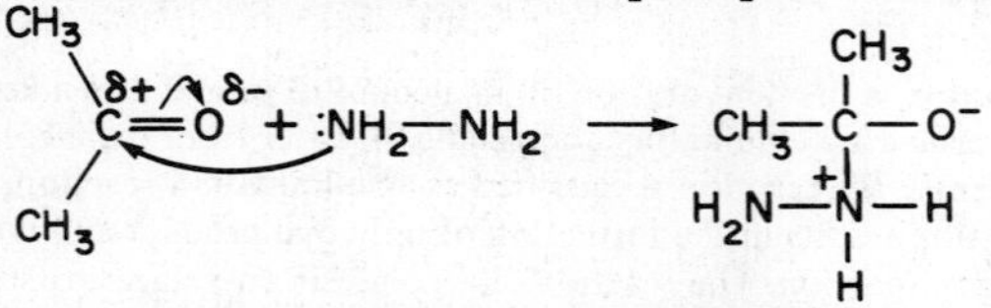

$$\underset{CH_3}{\overset{CH_3}{\diagdown}}\overset{\delta+}{C}{=}\overset{\delta-}{O} + :NH_2-NH_2 \longrightarrow \underset{H_2N-\overset{+}{\underset{|}{N}}-H}{\overset{CH_3}{\underset{|}{C}}}-O^-$$

The next stage of the reaction involves the **elimination of water** from this intermediate product, i.e.,

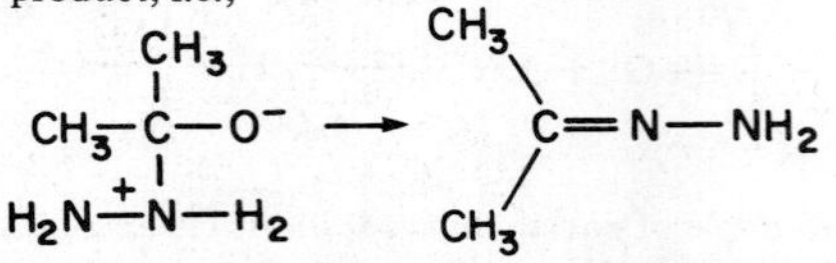

$$\underset{H_2N-\overset{+}{\underset{|}{N}}-H_2}{\overset{CH_3}{\underset{|}{CH_3-C-O^-}}} \longrightarrow \underset{CH_3}{\overset{CH_3}{\diagdown}}C{=}N-NH_2$$

This reaction, which is classified as **a condensation reaction**, involves a nucleophilic addition followed by an elimination reaction.

(g) In this reaction the —Cl group of chloroethane is substituted by ammonia, according to the reaction

$$CH_3CH_2-Cl + NH_3 \longrightarrow CH_3-CH_2-\overset{+}{N}H_3 + Cl^- \longrightarrow CH_3-CH_2-\overset{+}{N}H_3Cl^-$$

The chloride ion then combines with positive ion to form ethylamine hydrochloride. This is a **nucleophilic substitution**, followed by salt formation.

(h) This reaction involves the elimination of a water molecule and mechanistically is identical to reaction (f) and can be represented by the equation

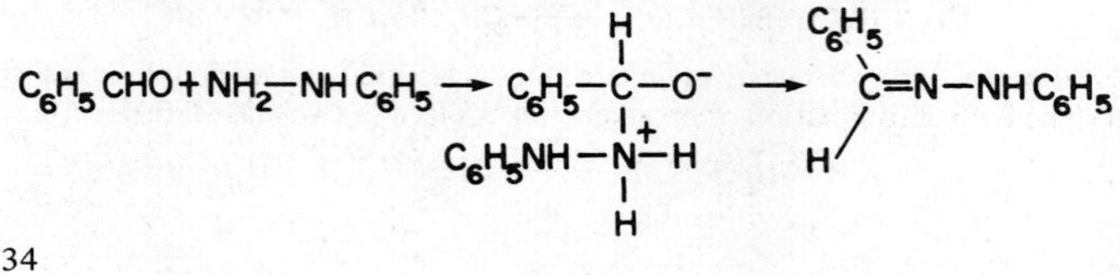

$$C_6H_5CHO + NH_2-NHC_6H_5 \rightarrow \underset{C_6H_5NH-\overset{+}{\underset{|}{N}}-H}{\overset{H}{\underset{|}{C_6H_5-C-O^-}}} \longrightarrow \underset{H}{\overset{C_6H_5}{\diagup}}C{=}N-NHC_6H_5$$

Problem 9 Benzene reacts with chlorine, chloromethane and ethanoyl chloride in the presence of aluminium chloride. What is the role of the aluminium chloride in these reactions?

The type of reaction which benzene undergoes with these reagents are electrophilic substitution reactions. This means that electrophiles must be formed in the course of the reaction. The aluminium chloride acts as an agent for their production. The distribution of electrons in aluminium chloride is such that there is a **vacant orbital** in the structure which can be used to form a **dative bond**. Chlorine has three non-bonded pairs of electrons, one of these non-bonded pairs forms the dative bond, resulting in the polarisation of the chlorine molecule, as shown in *Fig 4(i)*. This results in the formation of the positive chlorine ion which is the reactive electrophile.

(i) With chlorine

$${}^{xx}_{xx}Cl{}^{x}_{x} - Cl{}^{xx}_{xx}{}^{x}_{x} + AlCl_3 \rightleftharpoons \overset{\delta+}{Cl} \cdots \overset{\delta-}{Cl} \rightarrow AlCl_3 \rightleftharpoons Cl^+ + [ClAlCl_3]^-$$
chloronium ion

(ii) With chloromethane

$$H-\underset{\underset{H}{|}}{\overset{\overset{H}{|}}{C}}-Cl{}^{xx}_{xx}{}^{x}_{x} + AlCl_3 \rightleftharpoons H-\underset{\underset{H}{|}}{\overset{\overset{H}{|}}{C}}-\overset{\delta+}{}\cdots\overset{\delta-}{Cl}\rightarrow AlCl_3 \rightleftharpoons H-\underset{\underset{H}{|}}{\overset{\overset{H}{|}}{C}}+ + [ClAlCl_3]^-$$
methyl carbocation

(iii) With ethanoyl chloride

$$CH_3-\underset{\underset{O}{\|}}{C}-Cl{}^{xx}_{xx}{}^{x}_{x} + AlCl_3 \rightleftharpoons CH_3-\underset{\underset{O}{\|}}{\overset{\delta+}{C}}\cdots\overset{\delta-}{Cl}\rightarrow AlCl_3 \rightleftharpoons CH_3-\overset{+}{C}=O + [ClAlCl_3]^-$$
acylium carbocation

(iv) Decomposition of the complex

$$[ClAlCl_3]^- + H^+ \rightleftharpoons AlCl_3 + HCl$$

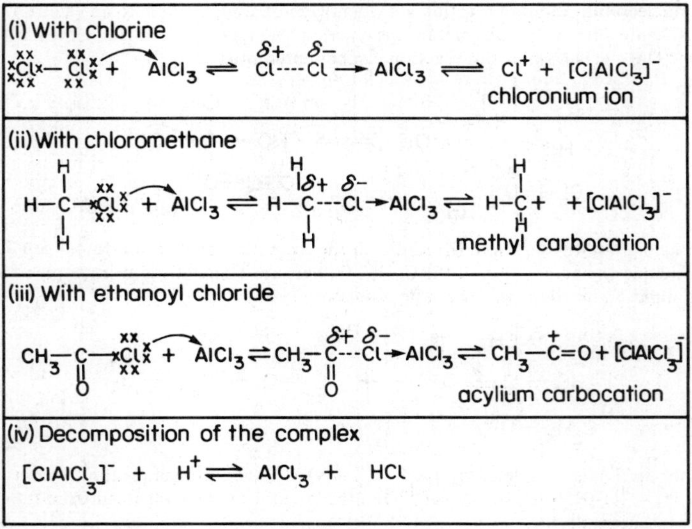

Fig 4 The action of aluminium chloride as a Lewis acid

Both chloromethane and ethanoyl chloride are polarised in the same way as shown in *Fig 4(ii) and (iii)*. The carbocations formed are the reactive electrophiles in these reactions. The aluminium tetrachloride ion is decomposed by the protons released from benzene in the substitution reaction to form aluminium chloride and hydrogen chloride, as shown in *Fig 4(iv)*.

A molecule which can accept an electron pair is called a Lewis acid, thus aluminium chloride is a Lewis acid. As a result of this mode of action, aluminium chloride can be called a **halogen carrier**. Other examples of halogen carriers are iron(III) chloride and iron(III) bromide.

Problem 10 The **hydrolysis** of esters has been investigated using O^{18} **isotopic labelling** and has been shown to proceed by a **nucleophilic addition** followed by an **elimination reaction**. Using ethyl ethanoate, $CH_3COO^{18}C_2H_5$ as an example, explain the terms which are underlined.

A **hydrolysis** reaction is one which involves the reaction of a molecule with water, for example

$$CH_3COOC_2H_5 + H_2O \longrightarrow CH_3COOH + C_2H_5OH$$

These reactions often require acidic or basic catalysts. **Isotopic labelling** is the incorporation of a heavier isotope of an element into a molecule. It is not practicable to introduce the ^{18}O atom completely thus an **enrichment** procedure is used instead. Whereas oxygen is composed mainly of ^{16}O containing 8 protons and 8 neutrons, its isotope ^{18}O contains 8 protons and 10 neutrons. This increase in mass can be detected using a **mass spectrometer** which measures molecular masses. A **nucleophilic addition** reaction is the addition of a nucleophile to an electron deficient centre in a molecule. In this reaction the nucleophile is HO^-, the hydroxide ion. The mechanism of this reaction can be represented as

The polarisations shown in (ii) results in the formation of a carbon to oxygen double bond and the elimination of the $C_2H_5-O^{18}$ group. Thus, this is an example of an elimination reaction, which can be represented as

The reaction is completed by the $C_2H_5-{}^{18}O^-$ ion accepting a proton to form $C_2H_5-{}^{18}O-H$. The presence of ^{18}O in the ethanol can be confirmed from its mass spectrum.

C. FURTHER PROBLEMS ON ORGANIC REACTION MECHANISMS

(a) SHORT ANSWER PROBLEMS

Fill in the missing words

1   The polarisation of a carbon to oxygen bond is due to the difference in .... of the ....

2   An electrophile is a reagent which has, as part of its structure, a .... charge or an atom which is electron ....

3   A nucleophile is a reagent which has as part of its structure a .... charge, or an atom bearing a .... of electrons.

4   The reaction between hydrogen bromide and ethene to produce bromoethane is classified as an .... reaction.

5   The reaction between bromoethane and aqueous potassium hydroxide to produce ethanol is classified as a .... reaction.

6   The reaction between 2,bromobutane and alcoholic potassium hydroxide resulting in the formation of butenes is classified as an .... reaction.

7   When benzene is converted into nitrobenzene in the presence of concentrated sulphuric and nitric acids it is called an .... reaction.

8   When a covalent bond is broken such that one electron is retained by each of the separated atoms, the type of bond breaking is called .... and results in the formation of ....

9   When an aldehyde reacts with hydrazine, a hydrazone and .... are formed. The mechanism of this reaction is considered to take place in two stages, the first of which is a .... mechanism followed by an .... mechanism.

10 The polarisation of a molecule results in one atom becoming electron .... and the other electron .... For such a polarisation the former position can react with .... and the latter ....

(b) MULTI-CHOICE PROBLEMS (answers on page 181)

Select the correct answer from those given
  Problems 1 to 4 refer to *Fig 5*

1   In mechanistic terms, step A is classified as
    (a) an electrophilic substitution;   (b) a nucleophilic substitution;
    (c) a rearrangement;   (d) a nucleophilic addition.

The acid catalysed hydrolysis of propanonitrile

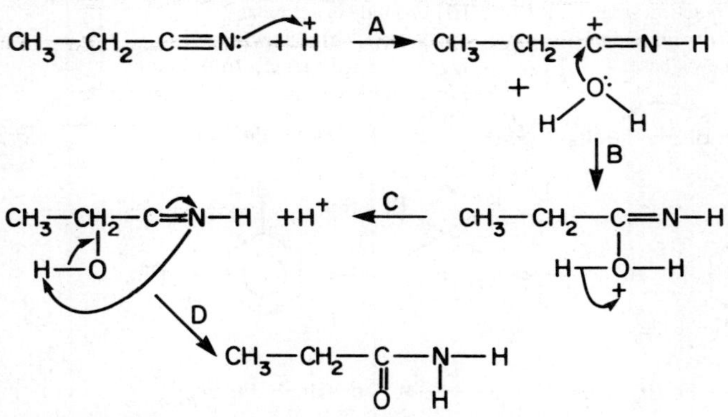

Fig 5 The acid catalysed hydrolysis of propanonitrile

2. In mechanistic terms step B is classified as
   (a) an electrophilic substitution;
   (b) a nucleophilic substitution;
   (c) an electrophilic addition;
   (d) a nucleophilic addition.

3. In mechanistic terms step C is classified as
   (a) an elimination;
   (b) a rearrangement;
   (c) an addition;
   (d) a substitution.

4. In mechanistic terms step D is classified as
   (a) an elimination;
   (b) a rearrangement;
   (c) an addition;
   (d) a substitution.

   Problems 5 to 7 refer to Fig 6

5. The reaction shown in *Fig 6* is classified as
   (a) an elimination reaction;
   (b) an addition reaction;
   (c) a substitution reaction;
   (d) a rearrangement reaction.

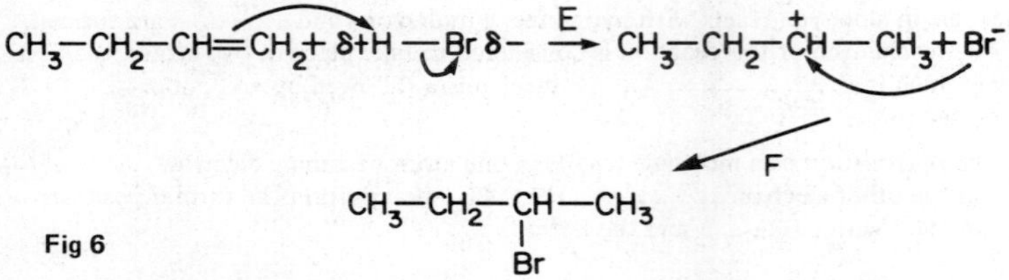

$$CH_3-CH_2-CH=CH_2 + \delta+H-Br\delta- \xrightarrow{E} CH_3-CH_2-\overset{+}{C}H-CH_3 + Br^-$$

$$\xrightarrow{F}$$

$$CH_3-CH_2-CH-CH_3$$
$$\qquad\qquad\;\;|$$
$$\qquad\qquad\;Br$$

Fig 6

6. In mechanistic terms step E is classified as
   (a) an electrophilic addition;
   (b) an electrophilic substitution;
   (c) a nucleophilic addition;
   (d) a nucleophilic substitution.

7. In mechanistic terms step F is classified as
   (a) an electrophilic addition;
   (b) an electrophilic substitution;
   (c) a nucleophilic substitution;
   (d) a nucleophilic addition.

   Problems 8 to 11 refer to Fig 7

8. In the reaction stage G, the iron(III) bromide is acting as
   (a) a reducing agent;
   (b) a Lewis acid;
   (c) a Lewis base;
   (d) an electron donor.

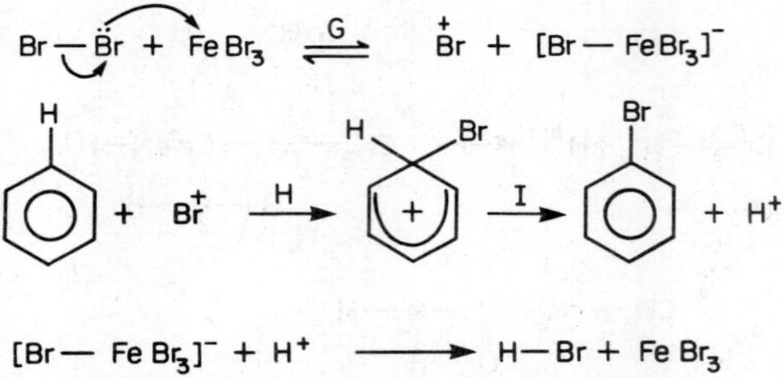

$$Br-\ddot{B}r + FeBr_3 \xrightleftharpoons{G} \overset{+}{B}r + [Br-FeBr_3]^-$$

$$C_6H_6 + Br^+ \xrightarrow{H} [C_6H_6Br]^+ \xrightarrow{I} C_6H_5Br + H^+$$

$$[Br-FeBr_3]^- + H^+ \longrightarrow H-Br + FeBr_3$$

Fig 7

9. The production of bromobenzene in this reaction is a result of
   (a) nucleophilic substitution;
   (b) nucleophilic addition;
   (c) electrophilic substitution;
   (d) electrophilic addition.

10. In mechanistic terms, stage H of the reaction is classified as
    (a) a nucleophilic substitution;
    (b) a nucleophilic addition;
    (c) an electrophilic substitution;
    (d) an electrophilic addition.

11. In mechanistic terms, stage I of the reaction classified as
    (a) an addition reaction;
    (b) an elimination reaction;
    (c) a substitution reaction;
    (d) a rearrangement reaction.

Problems 12 to 14 refer to Fig 8

12. In mechanistic terms, stage J of the reaction is classified as
    (a) a nucleophilic substitution;
    (b) a nucleophilic addition;
    (c) an electrophilic substitution;
    (d) an electrophilic addition.

13. In mechanistic terms stage K of the reaction is classified as
    (a) an elimination;
    (b) a substitution;
    (c) a rearrangement;
    (d) an addition.

Fig 8

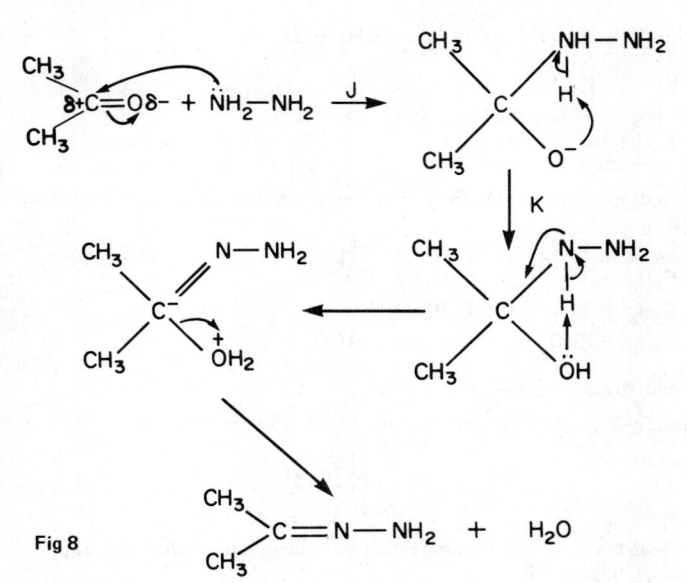

14. In the final stage of the mechanism, stage L, the reaction is classified as
    (a) an elimination;
    (b) a substitution;
    (c) a rearrangement;
    (d) an addition.

15. Which of the following reagents is not a nucleophile?
    (a) NH_3; (b) H_2O; (c) CH_3OH; (d) SO_3.

Problems 16 to 19 refer to Fig 9

16 In the reaction between ethane and bromine in the presence of ultraviolet radiation, the initiation step in the reaction is stage
(a) M; (b) N; (c) O; (d) P.

17 In this same reaction, the propagation stage is represented by
(a) M; (b) N; (c) O; (d) Q.

18 The termination of the reaction can be stage
(a) M; (b) N; (c) O; (d) Q.

$$Br-Br \xrightarrow{\text{u.v. light}}_{M} Br\cdot + Br\cdot$$

$$Br\cdot + CH_3-CH_3 \xrightarrow{N} CH_3-CH_2\cdot + HBr$$

$$CH_3-CH_2\cdot + Br-Br \xrightarrow{O} CH_3-CH_2-Br + Br\cdot$$

$$CH_3-CH_2\cdot + \cdot CH_2-CH_3 \xrightarrow{P} CH_3-CH_2-CH_2-CH_3$$

$$CH_3-CH_2\cdot + \cdot Br \xrightarrow{Q} CH_3-CH_2-Br$$

Fig 9

19 The type of reaction shown in *Fig 9* is classified as
   (a) an elimination reaction;   (b) an addition reaction;
   (c) a substitution reaction;   (d) a rearrangement reaction.

20 Which of the following reactions of benzene do not take place by electrophilic substitution.
   (a) $C_6H_6 + Cl_2 \longrightarrow C_6H_6Cl_6$;
   (b) $C_6H_6 + Br_2 \longrightarrow C_6H_5Br + HBr$;
   (c) $C_6H_6 + SO_3 \longrightarrow C_6H_5SO_3H$;
   (d) $C_6H_6 + HNO_3 \longrightarrow C_6H_5NO_2 + H_2O$.

(c) CONVENTIONAL PROBLEMS

1 Using *Table 2*, assign the electronegativity values to the molecule

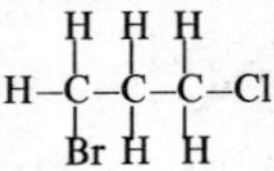

$$\begin{array}{c} \text{H H H} \\ | \; | \; | \\ \text{H}-\text{C}-\text{C}-\text{C}-\text{Cl} \\ | \; | \; | \\ \text{Br H H} \end{array}$$

and from the assignments indicate the carbon atom most likely to undergo nucleophilic addition.

2 Assign the following reagents as electrophiles or nucleophiles explaining your reasons.
   (i) CH_3OH;   (ii) CH_3NH_2;   (iii) SO_3;   (iv) $\overset{+}{Br}$;   (v) Br^-.

3 Halogeno alkanes undergo elimination reactions and nucleophilic substitution reactions with sodium hydroxide. Give an example of each reaction stating the conditions necessary for the reactions. Outline a reaction mechanism for one of these reactions.

4 Which of the following molecules have a dipole moment?
   (i) hydrogen; (ii) bromine; (iii) hydrogen bromide; (iv) ethane;
   (v) tetrachloromethane, and (vi) ethanamide.
   Show the direction of the dipole moment in each molecule.

5 When ethanoic acid reacts with ethanol in which the oxygen atoms are enriched with the ^{18}O isotope, which product of esterification contains the ^{18}O, the ester or the water. Draw a mechanism which explains your answer.

6 Benzene can be brominated with bromine using iron filings as a catalyst. Explain how the Br^+ electrophile can be generated for this reaction.

7 When ethenes react with bromine water containing sodium chloride solution, three products are produced, i.e.

$$Br-CH_2-CH_2OH; \quad Cl-CH_2-CH_2-Br \quad \text{and} \quad Br-CH_2-CH_2-Br$$

Explain how these occur using mechanistic principles.

8 What is the product of (a) the addition of hydrogen bromide to propene in hexane and (b) the addition in the presence of a peroxide. Suggest a mechanism for reaction (a).

9 When propanone reacts with sodium hydrogen sulphite, the product of the reaction is

$$CH_3-\underset{\underset{H}{|}}{\overset{\overset{CH_3}{|}}{C}}-SO_3Na$$

What type of reaction is this and by what mechanism is it formed?

10 When propanal reacts with phenylhydrazine to form propanal phenylhydrazone, the mechanism takes place in three stages. Draw the three stages and explain each intermediate change.

11 When methane reacts with bromine in an inert solvent and under ultraviolet radiation, a chain reaction takes place. Explain what is meant by this term and identify a mechanism by which the reaction can occur.

12 When but-1-ene is hydrated in the presence of sulphuric acid the main product is butan-2-ol, explain why this happens using mechanistic principles.

13 The pK_b values for ammonia, methylamine and dimethylamine are 4.75, 3.4 and 3.2 respectively. What information does this give about the effect of alkyl groups in a molecule.

14 Electronic polarisation effects can be passed from one carbon atom to another. Use the following data to illustrate this principle.

Compound	CH_3COOH	$ClCH_2COOH$	Cl_3CCOOH
pKa	4.8	2.9	0.7

15 Classify the following reaction types
- (i) $RCH=CH_2 + H_2 \longrightarrow RCH_2-CH_3$
- (ii) $R_2C=O + NH_2-OH \longrightarrow R_2C=NOH + H_2O$
- (iii) $C_6H_6 + CH_3-Br \longrightarrow C_6H_5CH_3 + HBr$
- (iv) $RCHO + HCN \longrightarrow RCH(OH)CN$
- (v) $R-H + Br_2 \longrightarrow R-Br + HBr$
- (vi) $R-CH_2-Br + NaOH \longrightarrow R-CH_2-OH + NaBr$

9 Organic chemistry

A. MAIN POINTS CONCERNING ORGANIC CHEMISTRY

(a) The alkyl halides or halogenoalkanes

1. The alkyl halides are organic molecules which contain one of the **halogens**, fluorine, chlorine, bromine or iodine in their structures. In addition, there is another sub-division of the alkyl halides into **primary, secondary** and **tertiary** structures, which are shown in *Fig 1*.
2. For molecules with n equal to and greater than 3 in the general formula $C_nH_{2n+1}X$, (where X can be any halogen), **isomers** exist as shown by C_3H_7Br and C_4H_9I in *Fig 1*.
3. The alkyl halides can be prepared by a variety of reactions, the selection of reagents governing the product formed.

PREPARATION FROM ALCOHOLS

(a) Chloroalkanes

General reactions with thionyl chloride and hydrogen chloride

(i) $R-OH(l) + SO_2Cl_2(l) \xrightarrow{\text{pyridine}} R-Cl(l) + SO_2(g) + HCl(g)$.
              thionyl chloride

An organic base can be added to neutralise the hydrogen chloride, e.g. pyridine, C_5H_5N.

(ii) $R-OH(l) + HCl(g) \xrightarrow[\text{catalyst}]{ZnCl_2} R-Cl(l) + H_2O(l)$

The zinc chloride catalyst must be anhydrous, because dry conditions are essential for good yields in the reaction. Examples of the reaction are

$$CH_3CH_2OH(l) + SOCl_2(l) \xrightarrow{\text{pyridine}} CH_3CH_2Cl(l) + SO_2(g) + HCl(g)$$
                                                chloroethane

and

$$\underset{\underset{OH}{|}}{CH_3-CH-CH_3}(l) + HCl(g) \xrightarrow{ZnCl_2} \underset{\underset{Cl}{|}}{CH_3-CH-CH_3}(l) + H_2O(l)$$
                                                             2-chloropropane

Formula	Name	Structure	Type
CH_3F	Fluoromethane	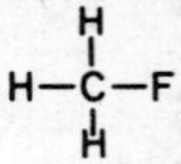 H–CH₂–F	Primary
C_2H_5Cl	Chloroethane	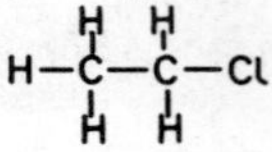 H–CH₂–CH₂–Cl	Primary
C_3H_7Br	1,Bromopropane	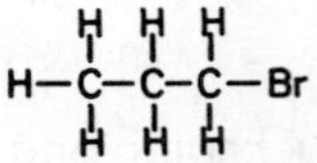 H–CH₂–CH₂–CH₂–Br	Primary
	2,Bromopropane	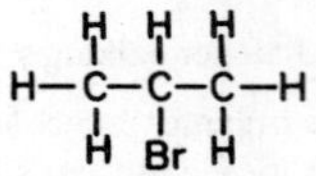 CH₃–CHBr–CH₃	Secondary
C_4H_9I	1,Iodobutane	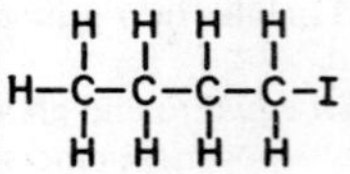 H–CH₂–CH₂–CH₂–CH₂–I	Primary
	2,Iodobutane	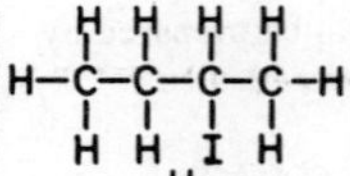 CH₃–CH₂–CHI–CH₃	Secondary
	2,Iodo,2,methyl propane	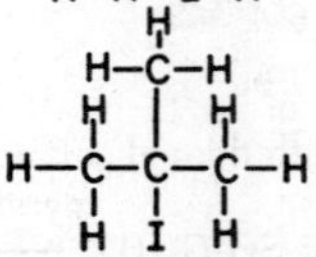 (CH₃)₃C–I	Tertiary

Fig 1 The structure and names of some alkyl halides

(b) Bromoalkanes

General reactions with phosphorous tribromide and hydrogen bromide given by

(i) $3R–OH(l) + PBr_3(l) \longrightarrow 3R–Br(l) + H_3PO_3(l)$

The phosphorus tribromide, PBr_3, can be made *in situ* (during the reaction) from red phosphorus and bromine,

$$P_4(s) + 6Br_2(l) \longrightarrow 4PBr_3(l)$$
$$\text{phosphorus tribromide}$$

(ii) $R–OH(l) + HBr(aq) \longrightarrow R–Br(l) + H_2O(l)$

The hydrogen bromide is conveniently prepared from sodium bromide and concentrated sulphuric acid as an *in situ* reaction, i.e.,

$$2Na–Br(s) + H_2SO_4(l) \longrightarrow Na_2SO_4(aq) + 2HBr(g)$$

(c) **Iodoalkanes**

(i) General reactions with phosphorus triodide and hydrogen iodide

$$3R-OH(l) + PI_3(l) \longrightarrow 3R-I(l) + H_3PO_3(l)$$

The phosphorus triiodide is prepared *in situ* from red phosphorus and iodine in dry ether, giving

$$P_4(s) + 6I_2(s) \longrightarrow 4PI_3(l)$$

(ii) $R-OH(l) + H-I(g) \longrightarrow R-I(l) + H_2O(l)$

The hydrogen iodide is prepared *in situ* from potassium iodide and phosphoric (V) acid, giving

$$3KI(s) + H_3PO_4(l) \longrightarrow 3HI(g) + K_3PO_4(aq)$$

(d) **Fluoroalkanes**

Fluoroalkanes are usually prepared from an alkene and hydrogen fluoride. Only the first four members of the homologous series are stable, the remainder decomposes readily back to the alkene. An example of the method is

$$H_2C=CH_2 + HF \longrightarrow H_3C-CH_2F$$
$$\text{fluoroethane}$$

These compounds are rarely used in synthetic preparations due to their low reactivity compared to the other alkyl halides.

4. REACTIONS OF THE ALKYL HALIDES

(i) **With aqueous alkaline solutions**
General reaction where X = halogen is given by

$$R-X + {}^-OH \longrightarrow R-OH + X^-$$

This is an example of a substitution reaction.
The hydroxide ion, which is a **nucleophile**, is **substituted** into the organic molecule in place of the halogen atom. This is released as an ion, for example

$$CH_3CH_2-Br(l) + NaOH(aq) \longrightarrow CH_3CH_2-OH(l) + NaBr(aq)$$

(ii) **With ethanolic alkaline solution**
General reaction where X = halogen, gives

$$R-CH_2-CH_2-X + NaOH \xrightarrow{\text{ethanol}} R-CH=CH_2 + NaX + H_2O$$
primary

or

$$R-\underset{\underset{X}{|}}{CH}-CH_3 + NaOH \xrightarrow{\text{ethanol}} R-CH=CH_2 + NaX + H_2O$$
secondary

These are examples of **elimination reactions** in which the halogen is displaced from the molecule, followed by the elimination of a hydrogen atom from a carbon atom adjacent to the carbon, which has lost the halogen atom. Some examples are

$$CH_3CH_2CH_2CH_2-Br(l) + NaOH(s) \xrightarrow{\text{ethanol}} CH_3CH_2CH=CH_2(g) + H_2O(l) + NaBr(aq)$$

l, bromobutane   **but—l—ene**

and

$$CH_3-\underset{\underset{Cl}{|}}{CH}-CH_3(l) + NaOH(s) \xrightarrow{\text{ethanol}} CH_3-CH=CH_2(g) + H_2O(l) + NaCl(aq)$$

2, chloropropane   **propene**

It should be noted that these reactions with alkyl halides in ethanolic alkaline solution usually take place to give a mixture of products. The conditions outlined give a predominant amount of the product stated. These reactions are considered mechanistically in para 9, Chapter 8.

(iii) **With ethanolic potassium cyanide**
The general reaction is

$$R-X + KCN \xrightarrow{\text{ethanol}} R-CN + KX$$

This is a **substitution reaction** in which the cyanide ion, ^-CN, displaces the halogen atom as a halide ion. The product is a member of the homologous series called the **acid nitriles**. An example of this reaction is

$$CH_3-CH_2-CH_2-I + KCN \xrightarrow{\text{ethanol}} CH_3-CH_2-CH_2-CN + KI$$
$$\text{butanonitrile}$$

This is a very important reaction because it **introduces a new carbon atom** into the molecule and hence is a method for **ascending the homologous series** (see *Problem 1*)

(iv) **With alcoholic ammonia solution**
General reactions of the four stage synthesis are

(a) $R-CH_2-X + NH_3 \xrightarrow{\text{ethanol}} R-CH_2-NH_2 + HX \longrightarrow RCH_2^+NH_3X^-$,
                              primary amine   amine salt

(b) $R_2-CH_2-X + R-CH_2-NH_2 \xrightarrow{\text{ethanol}} R-CH_2-\underset{\underset{H}{|}}{N}-CH_2-R + HX$,
                                                             secondary amine

(c) $R-CH_2-X + (R-CH_2)NH \xrightarrow{\text{ethanol}} R-CH_2-\underset{\underset{CH_2-R}{|}}{N}-CH_2-R + HX$,   and
                                                             tertiary amine

(d) $R-CH_2-X + (R-CH_2)_3N \xrightarrow{\text{ethanol}} R-CH_2-\underset{\underset{CH_2-R}{|}}{\overset{\overset{CH_2-R}{|}}{N}}-CH_2-R \;\;^+ + X^-$
                                                              quaternary ammonium salt

Iodoalkanes are good materials for this reaction, an example of which is the reaction of iodomethane, given by

$$CH_3-I + NH_3 \xrightarrow{ethanol} \underset{\text{methylamine}}{CH_3-NH_2} + HI \xrightarrow[CH_3-I]{ethanol} \underset{\text{dimethylamine}}{CH_3-N-CH_3} + HI$$

$$\xrightarrow[CH_3-I]{ethanol} \underset{\underset{\text{trimethylamine}}{CH_3}}{\overset{CH_3}{CH_3-N-CH_3}} + HI \xrightarrow[CH_3-I]{ethanol} \underset{\text{tetramethyl ammonium iodide}}{\left[\overset{CH_3}{\underset{CH_3}{CH_3-N-CH_3}}\right]^+ I^-}$$

It is possible to obtain a high percentage of the primary amine by using an excess of ammonia.

(v) **With magnesium metal**

When magnesium turnings react with an alkyl halide in dry ether, **a Grignard reagent** is formed. The reaction can be represented by the general equation

$$R-X + Mg = R-Mg-X$$

The type of alkylhalide used for preference are the iodoalkanes. This is because the iodoalkanes are the most reactive of the halogens in these reactions. An example is

$$CH_3CH_2-I + Mg \xrightarrow[I_2 \text{ catalyst}]{dry \text{ ether}} \underset{\text{ethyl magnesium iodide}}{CH_3CH_2-Mg-I}$$

The reagents **cannot be obtained free from solvent** and consequently are used in **ethereal solution**. They are **versatile reagents** for use in organic synthesis.

5 REACTIONS OF GRIGNARD REAGENTS

(i) **With water**

The general reaction is

$$R-Mg-I + H_2O \longrightarrow R-H + Mg(OH)I$$

An example of this reaction is

$$C_2H_5-Mg-I + H_2O \longrightarrow \underset{\text{ethane}}{C_2H_5-H} + Mg(OH)I$$

This reaction explains why Grignard reagents **must be kept dry** during synthetic reactions, otherwise alkanes will be formed as by-products.

(ii) **With carbon dioxide**

The general reaction is

$$R-CH_2-Mg-I + CO_2 \longrightarrow R-CH_2-\underset{\underset{O}{\parallel}}{C}-O-MgI$$

followed by hydrolysis

$$R-CH_2-\underset{\underset{O}{\parallel}}{C}-O-MgI + H_2O \longrightarrow \underset{\text{carboxyllic acid}}{R-CH_2-\underset{\underset{O}{\parallel}}{C}-OH} + Mg(OH)I$$

147

An example of this reaction is

$$\underset{\text{propyl magnesium iodide}}{(CH_3)_2CH-Mg-I} + CO_2 \rightarrow (CH_3)_2CH-C(CH_3)-O-MgI \xrightarrow{H_2O} \underset{\text{2 methylpropanoic acid}}{(CH_3)_2CH-C(CH_3)-OH} + Mg(OH)I$$

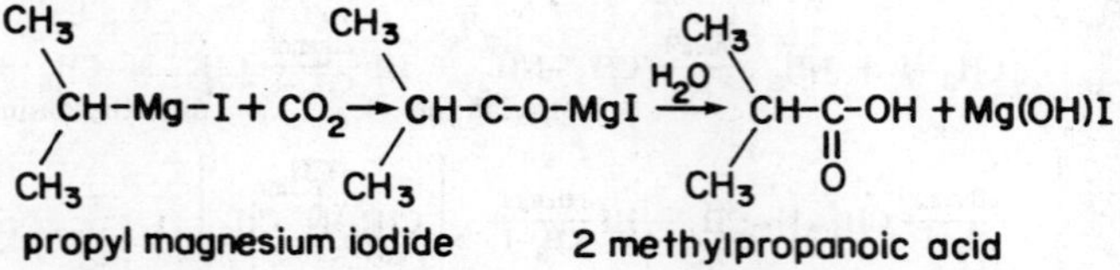

This is an important reaction because it is a method of extending the number of carbon atoms in a molecule and consequently a method for ascending a homologous series of compounds.

(iii) **With methanal**

The general reaction is

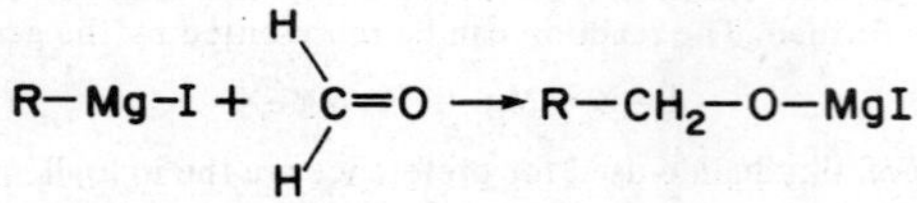

$$R-Mg-I + \underset{H}{\overset{H}{>}}C=O \rightarrow R-CH_2-O-MgI$$

followed by hydrolysis

$$R-CH_2-O-MgI + H_2O \rightarrow \underset{\text{primary alcohol}}{R-CH_2-OH} + Mg(OH)I$$

An example of this reaction is

$$CH_3CH_2-Mg-I + CH_2O = CH_3CH_2CH_2-O-MgI$$
$$\xrightarrow{\text{hydrolysis}} \underset{\text{propanol}}{CH_3CH_2CH_2OH} + Mg(OH)I$$

This is a reaction for synthesising primary alcohols and ascending the homologous series.

(iv) **With other aldehydes**

The general reaction is

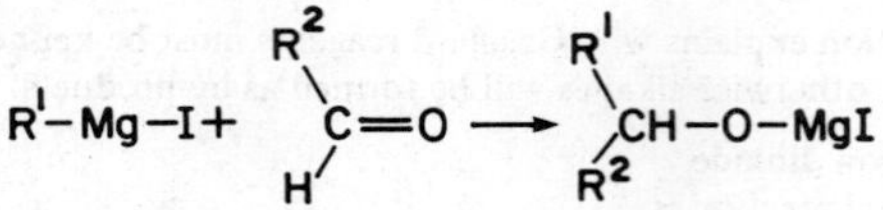

$$R^1-Mg-I + \underset{H}{\overset{R^2}{>}}C=O \rightarrow \underset{R^2}{\overset{R^1}{>}}CH-O-MgI$$

followed by hydrolysis,

$$\underset{R^2}{\overset{R^1}{>}}CH-O-MgI \xrightarrow{\text{hydrolysis}} \underset{R^2}{\overset{R^1}{>}}CH-OH + Mg(OH)I$$

secondary alcohol

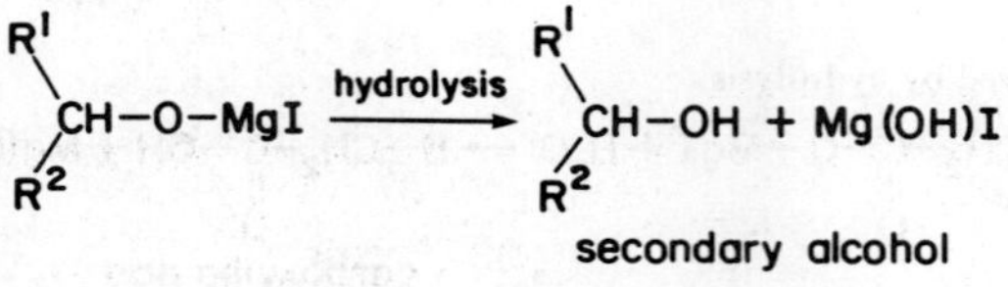

An example of this reaction is

$$CH_3-Mg-I + CH_3-CHO \longrightarrow CH_3-\underset{\underset{H}{|}}{\overset{\overset{CH_3}{|}}{C}}-O-MgI$$

$$CH_3-\underset{\underset{H}{|}}{\overset{\overset{CH_3}{|}}{C}}-OMgI + H_2O \longrightarrow CH_3-\underset{\underset{H}{|}}{\overset{\overset{CH_3}{|}}{C}}-OH + Mg(OH)I$$

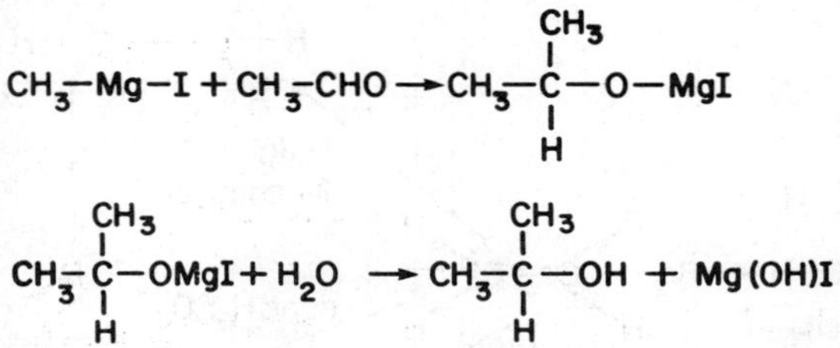

2, methylpropan-2-ol

This is a reaction for synthesising secondary alcohols.

(v) **With ketones**

The general reaction is

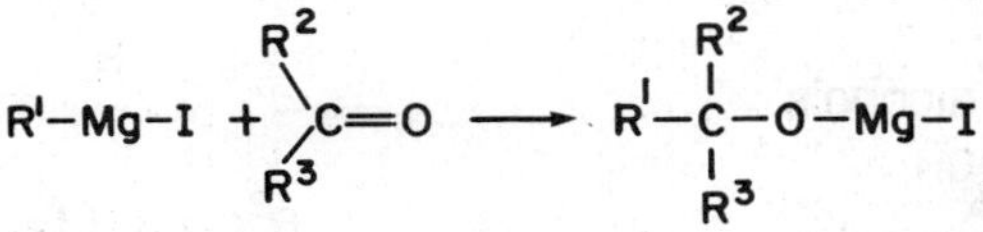

$$R^1-Mg-I + \underset{R^3}{\overset{R^2}{>}}C=O \longrightarrow R^1-\underset{\underset{R^3}{|}}{\overset{\overset{R^2}{|}}{C}}-O-Mg-I$$

followed by hydrolysis

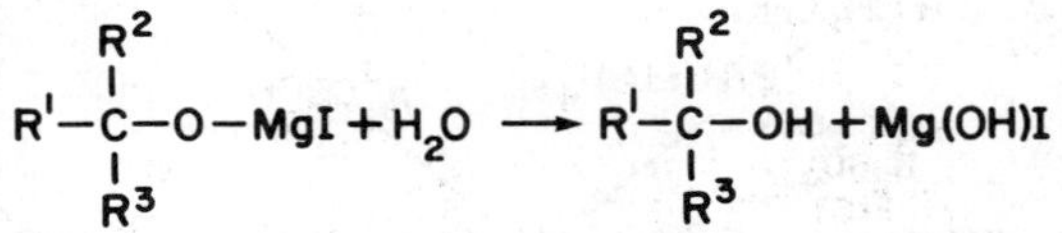

$$R^1-\underset{\underset{R^3}{|}}{\overset{\overset{R^2}{|}}{C}}-O-MgI + H_2O \longrightarrow R^1-\underset{\underset{R^3}{|}}{\overset{\overset{R^2}{|}}{C}}-OH + Mg(OH)I$$

tertiary alcohol

An example of this reaction is

$$CH_3CH_2-Mg-I + \underset{CH_3}{\overset{CH_3}{>}}C=O \longrightarrow CH_3CH_2-\underset{\underset{CH_3}{|}}{\overset{\overset{CH_3}{|}}{C}}-O-MgI$$

$$CH_3CH_2-\underset{\underset{CH_3}{|}}{\overset{\overset{CH_3}{|}}{C}}-O-MgI + H_2O \longrightarrow CH_3CH_2-\underset{\underset{CH_3}{|}}{\overset{\overset{CH_3}{|}}{C}}-OH + Mg(OH)I$$

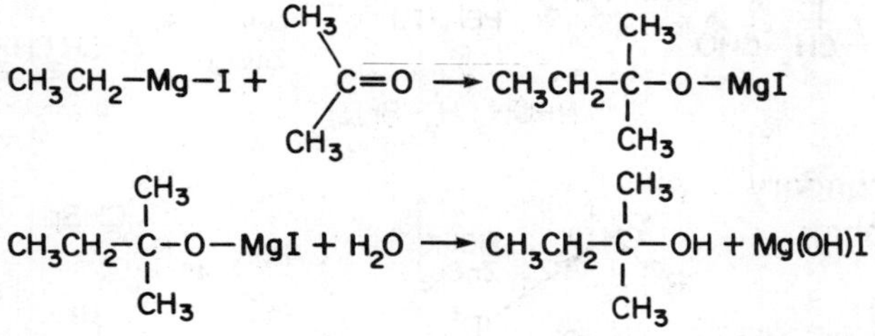

2,methylbutan-2-ol

This reaction is a method of synthesising tertiary alcohols.

7   The variety of reactions and the reactivity of the alkyl halides make them **important as starting materials** and also as **intermediate stages in multistep synthesis** reactions.

8   It is often necessary to devise synthetic pathways from one compound into another. The reactions covered in *Chemistry 2 Checkbook* are necessary for devising such synthetic pathways and these are summarised in *Figs 2 to 5*.

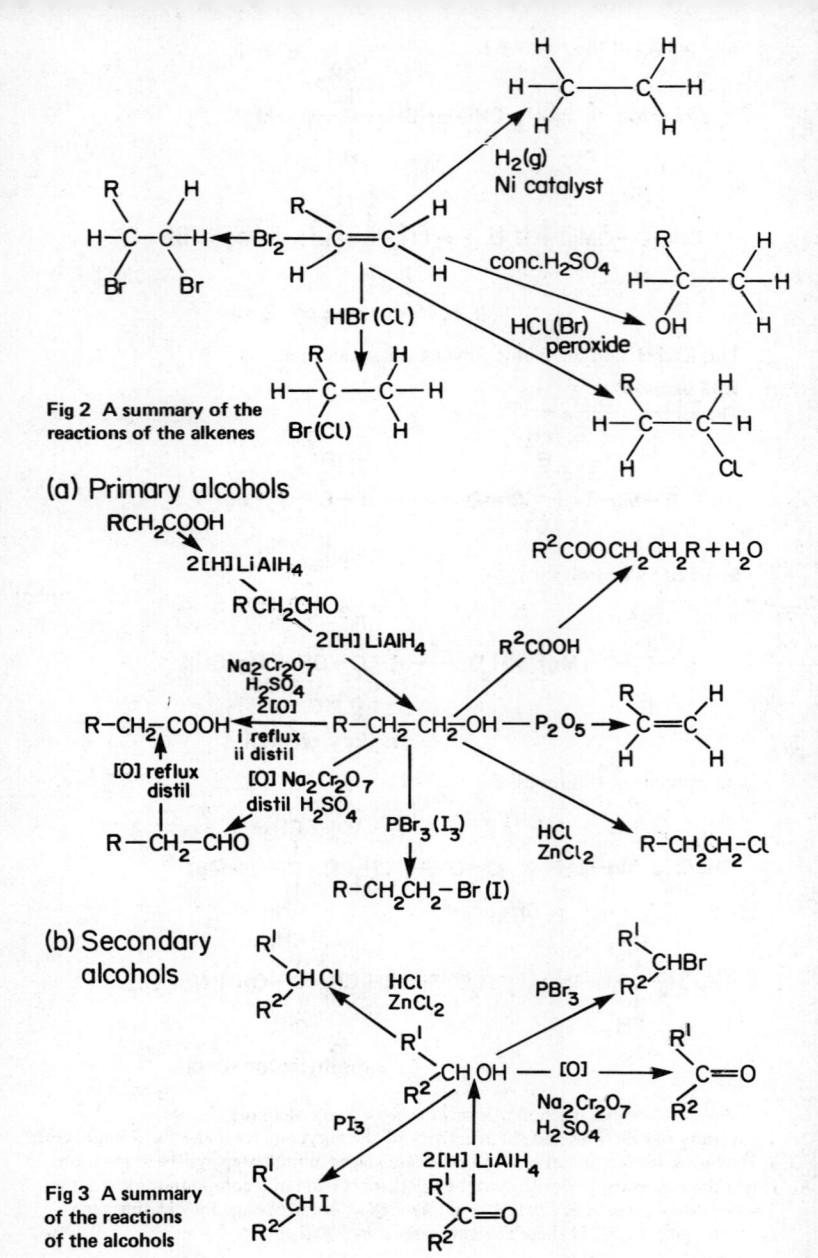

Fig 2 A summary of the reactions of the alkenes

(a) Primary alcohols

Fig 3 A summary of the reactions of the alcohols

(b) Secondary alcohols

$$R\text{ }CO\text{ }Cl$$
↑
$PCl_3/SOCl$

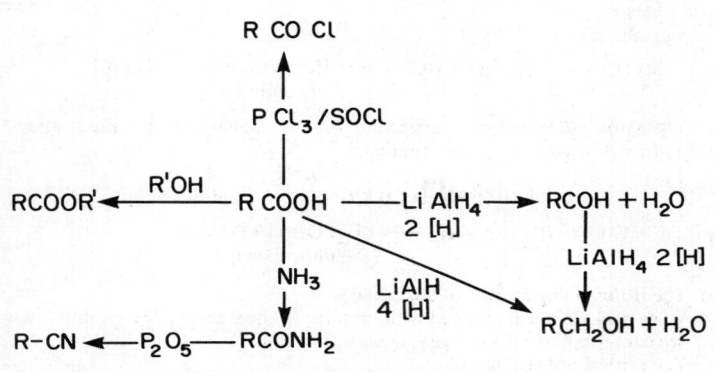

$$RCOOR' \xleftarrow{R'OH} R\text{ }COOH \xrightarrow{LiAlH_4\ 2[H]} RCOH + H_2O$$

$$\downarrow NH_3 \qquad \searrow LiAlH\ 4[H]$$

$$R-CN \xleftarrow{P_2O_5} RCONH_2$$

$$RCOH \xrightarrow{LiAlH_4\ 2[H]} RCH_2OH + H_2O$$

Fig 4 A summary of the reactions of the carboxyllic acids

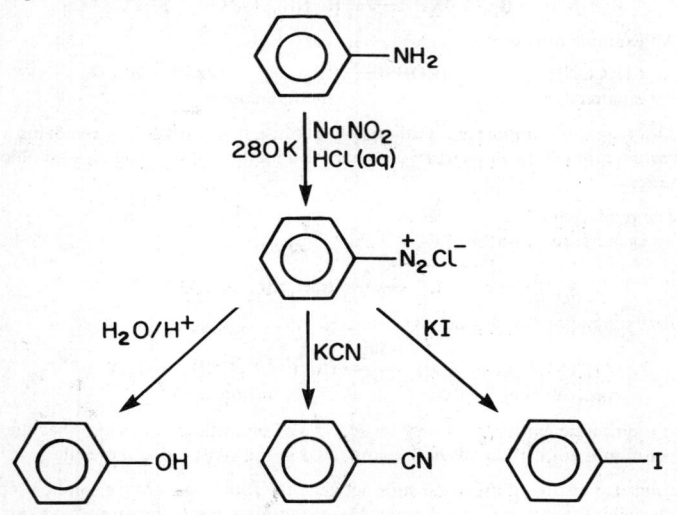

C₆H₅—NH₂

↓ 280 K | NaNO₂ / HCl(aq)

C₆H₅—N₂⁺Cl⁻

↙ H₂O/H⁺   ↓ KCN   ↘ KI

C₆H₅—OH   C₆H₅—CN   C₆H₅—I

Fig 5 Some reactions of primary aryl amines

9 A variety of reactions not previously mentioned but useful in synthetic reactions are

(i) **The hydrolysis of acid nitriles**

The general reaction with acidic solution is

$$R-C\equiv N + H_2O \xrightarrow{H^+} RCONH_2 + H_2O \xrightarrow{H^+} RCOOH + NH_4^+$$

An example of this reaction is the hydrolysis of ethanonitrile with hydrochloric acid. The reaction takes place in two steps, firstly

$$CH_3-CN + H_2O \xrightarrow{HCl} \underset{\text{ethanamide}}{CH_3CONH_2}$$

151

and secondly

$$CH_3CONH_2 + H_2O + HCl \longrightarrow CH_3COOH + H_2O + NH_4Cl$$
$$\text{ethanoic acid}$$

The hydrolysis can also be carried out with an alkaline solution of potassium hydroxide according to the equations

$$CH_3-CN + H_2O \xrightarrow{^-OH} CH_3CONH_2 \quad \text{and secondly}$$
$$CH_3CONH_2 + NaOH \longrightarrow CH_3COONa + NH_3$$
$$\text{sodium ethanoate}$$

(ii) **The Hofman degradation of acid amides**

When acid amides are treated with bromine in aqueous alkaline solution, they are converted into the primary amines.

The general reaction is

$$RCONH_2 + Br_2 + 4KOH \longrightarrow R-NH_2 + 2KBr + K_2CO_3$$

An example of this reaction is

$$CH_3CONH_2 + Br_2 + 4KOH \longrightarrow CH_3-NH_2 + 2KBr + K_2CO_3$$
$$\text{ethanamide} \qquad\qquad\qquad\qquad\qquad \text{methylamine}$$

This reaction is **important synthetically** because it is a method of **removing a carbon atom from a molecule** and hence is a method of **descending a homologous series**.

(iii) **The reduction of acid nitriles**

The general reaction is

$$RCONH_2 + 4H \xrightarrow{LiAlH_4} RCH_2NH_2 + H_2O$$

An example of this reaction is

$$CH_3CH_2CONH_2 + 4H \xrightarrow{LiAlH_4} CH_3CH_2CH_2NH_2 + H_2O$$
$$\text{propanamide} \qquad\qquad\qquad\qquad \text{propylamine}$$

10 When a synthetic pathway is being devised it is of importance to ensure that the correct number of carbon atoms are contained in the synthesised molecule.

11 A knowledge of the interrelationships between the functional groups can be used to determine the identity of unknown organic compounds as shown in *Problems 8 to 10*.

B. WORKED PROBLEMS ON ORGANIC CHEMISTRY

Problem 1 Outline a synthesis for the reaction

$$CH_3CH_2CH_2CH_2-Br \longrightarrow CH_3CH_2CH_2CH_2COOH$$

This reaction involves the introduction of an extra carbon atom into the molecule. This can be achieved by introducing (a) a cyano group or (b) via a Grignard reaction.

(a) Bromobutane reacts with alcoholic potassium cyanide to produce butanonitrile, giving

$$CH_3CH_2CH_2CH_2-Br + KCN \xrightarrow{ethanol} CH_3CH_2CH_2CH_2CN + KBr$$
$$\text{pentanonitrile}$$

Complete hydrolysis of butanonitrile occurs when the compound is refluxed with dilute hydrochloric acid giving

$$CH_3CH_2CH_2CH_2CN + 2H_2O + HCl \xrightarrow{reflux} CH_3CH_2CH_2CH_2COOH + NH_4Cl$$
$$\text{pentanoic acid}$$

This synthesis can be summarised as

$$C_4H_9Br \longrightarrow C_4H_9-CN \longrightarrow C_4H_9CONH_2 \longrightarrow C_4H_9COOH$$

(b) When bromobutane reacts with magnesium turnings in the presence of dry ether and a trace of iodine a Grignard reagent, butyl magnesium bromide, is formed. The equation of the reaction is

$$CH_3CH_2CH_2CH_2Br + Mg \xrightarrow[I_2 \text{ catalyst}]{dry\ ether} CH_3CH_2CH_2CH_2-Mg-Br$$
$$\text{butyl magnesium bromide}$$

The Grignard reagent reacts with carbon dioxide to give an intermediate which on hydrolysis with dilute acid gives pentanoic acid, the reaction being

$$CH_3CH_2CH_2CH_2-Mg-Br + CO_2 \longrightarrow CH_3CH_2CH_2CH_2CO_2-Mg-Br$$
$$\text{intermediate}$$

$$\xrightarrow{dil.\ HCl} CH_3CH_2CH_2CH_2COOH + Mg(OH)Br$$
$$\text{pentanoic acid}$$

The synthesis may be summarised as:

$$C_4H_9-Br \longrightarrow C_4H_9-MgBr \longrightarrow C_4H_9CO_2-MgBr \longrightarrow C_4H_9COOH$$

Problem 2 Outline a synthesis for the reaction

$$CH_3CH_2-CH_2Br \longrightarrow CH_3\underset{Br}{CH}-CH_3$$

The repositioning of a functional group in a carbon chain can be brought about by introducing a double bond into the molecule. Bromopropane can be treated with potassium hydroxide to remove H−Br, giving

$$CH_3-CH_2-CH_2-Br + KOH \longrightarrow CH_3CH_2=CH_2 + H_2O + KBr$$

but a side reaction produces $CH_3CH_2CH_2-OH$.
However propene is a gas which can be collected and treated with hydrogen bromide given by

$$CH_3CH_2=CH_2 + HBr \longrightarrow CH_3\underset{Br}{CH}-CH_3$$

This addition reaction is called a **Markownikov addition**.

The reaction can be summarised as

$$C_3H_7Br \longrightarrow C_3H_6 \longrightarrow CH_3CHBrCH_3$$

Problem 3 Outline a synthesis for the reaction

$$CH_3CH_2CHO \longrightarrow CH_3-\underset{\underset{O}{\|}}{C}-CH_3$$

The repositioning of a functional group is achieved by introducing a carbon to carbon double bond. The aldehyde is converted to a primary alcohol by reduction with lithium aluminium hydride in dry ether given by

$$CH_3CH_2CHO + 2[H] \xrightarrow[\text{dry ether}]{\text{LiAlH}_4} CH_3CH_2CH_2OH$$

Propan-1-ol is then dehydrated to propene by heating it with concentrated sulphuric acid given by

$$CH_3CH_2CH_2OH + H_2SO_4 \xrightarrow{\text{heat}} CH_3-CH=CH_2 + H_2O + H_2SO_4$$

Addition of hydrogen bromide to the propene results in the formation of 2-bromopropane the equation being

$$CH_3-CH=CH_2 + HBr \longrightarrow CH_3-\underset{\underset{Br}{|}}{CH}-CH_3$$

The reaction of 2-bromopropane with potassium hydroxide produces the secondary alcohol propan-2-ol, i.e.

$$CH_3-\underset{\underset{Br}{|}}{CH}-CH_3 + KOH \longrightarrow CH_3-\underset{\underset{OH}{|}}{CH}-CH_3 + KBr$$

Oxidation of the secondary alcohol with sodium dichromate (VI) and sulphuric acid produces the required ketone, propanone, i.e.

$$CH_3-\underset{\underset{OH}{|}}{CH}-CH_3 \xrightarrow[\substack{\text{H}_2\text{SO}_4 \\ \text{distil}}]{\text{Na}_2\text{Cr}_2\text{O}_7} CH_3-\underset{\underset{O}{\|}}{C}-CH_3$$

The synthesis can be summarised as

$$CH_3CH_2CHO \longrightarrow CH_3CH_2CH_2OH \longrightarrow CH_3CH=CH_2 \longrightarrow CH_3-\underset{\underset{Br}{|}}{CH}-CH_3$$
$$\longrightarrow CH_3-\underset{\underset{OH}{|}}{CH}-CH_3 \longrightarrow CH_3-\underset{\underset{O}{\|}}{C}-CH_3$$

Problem 4 Outline a possible synthesis for the reaction

$$CH_3CH_2-OH \longrightarrow CH_3CH_2CH_2-OH$$

This reaction involves the introduction of an additional carbon atom into the carbon chain. This is most easily achieved by introducing a cyano group into the molecule. This cannot be achieved by a direct reaction of ethanol, consequently ethanol is first converted into bromoethane, given by

$$3CH_3CH_2-OH + PBr_3 \longrightarrow 3CH_3CH_2-Br + H_3PO_3$$

Bromoethane reacts with potassium cyanide in alcoholic solution, the equation being

$$CH_3CH_2-Br + KCN \xrightarrow{alcohol} CH_3CH_2CN + KBr$$

Ethanonitrile can be hydrolysed by refluxing with dilute acid, first to the acid amide and finally to the acid. The equation of this reaction is

$$CH_3CH_2-CN + H_2O \xrightarrow{H^+} CH_3CH_2\underset{NH_2}{C}=O + H_2O \xrightarrow{H^+} CH_3CH_2-\underset{OH}{C}=O + NH_3$$

The propanoic acid is reduced with lithium aluminium hydride to propanal and further to propan-1-ol, as shown by

$$CH_3CH_2COOH + 2[H] \xrightarrow{LiAlH_4} \underset{\text{propanal}}{CH_3CH_2CHO} + H_2O \quad \text{and}$$

$$CH_3CH_2CHO + 2[H] \xrightarrow{LiAlH_4} \underset{\text{propan-1-ol}}{CH_3CH_2CH_2OH} + H_2O$$

The reaction can be summarised as

$$C_2H_5OH \longrightarrow C_2H_5-Br \longrightarrow C_2H_5CN \longrightarrow C_2H_5CONH_2 \longrightarrow C_2H_5COOH$$
$$\longrightarrow C_2H_5CHO \longrightarrow C_3H_7OH$$

(*Note: An alternate route via a Grignard reagent can also be used.*)

Problem 5 Outline a synthesis for the reaction

$$CH_3CH_2-OH \longrightarrow CH_3-NH_2$$

This reaction involves the removal of a carbon atom from the carbon chain. The most suitable reaction to bring about this change is to use the Hofmann degradation of amides to amines. The alcohol is converted into the carboxylic acid with sodium dichromate (VI) and sulphuric acid and refluxing, as shown by

$$CH_3CH_2OH + 2[O] \xrightarrow[\substack{H_2SO_4\\ \text{reflux}}]{Na_2Cr_2O_7} CH_3COOH + H_2O$$

The carboxylic acid is converted to the amide by conversion to ammonium ethanoate and heating the salt, i.e.

$$CH_3COOH + NH_3 \longrightarrow CH_3COONH_4 \longrightarrow CH_3CONH_2 + H_2O$$

The amide is then treated with bromine and potassium hydroxide, giving

$$CH_3CONH_2 + Br_2 + 4KOH \longrightarrow CH_3NH_2 + K_2CO_3 + 2KBr$$

This reaction is the synthetically important Hofmann degradation.
The synthesis can be summarised as

$$C_2H_5-OH \longrightarrow CH_3COOH \longrightarrow CH_3CONH_2 \longrightarrow CH_3NH_2$$

Problem 6 Outline a synthesis for the reaction

$$CH_3OH \longrightarrow \underset{CH_3}{CH_3\overset{|}{C}HOH}$$

This reaction involves the introduction of two extra carbon atoms and the change in functional group from a primary alcohol to a secondary alcohol. The shortest synthetic route for such a conversion is via a Grignard reagent. The alcohol must first be converted to a halogeno alkane, preferably the iodoalkane, as shown by

$$3CH_3OH + PI_3 \longrightarrow 3CH_3I + H_3PO_3$$
$$\text{iodomethane}$$

The phosphorous triiodide is formed *in situ* from red phosphorus and iodine. The iodomethane is treated with magnesium turnings in dry ether with a trace of iodine to form methyl magnesium iodide, i.e.

$$CH_3-I + Mg \xrightarrow[I_2 \text{ catalyst}]{\text{dry ether}} CH_3-Mg-I$$

The reaction between this Grignard reagent and ethanal forms an intermediate which on hydrolysis gives the secondary alcohol, shown by

$$CH_3-MgI + CH_3CHO \longrightarrow CH_3-\underset{\underset{CH_3}{|}}{CHO}-Mg-I$$

intermediate

$$\xrightarrow{\text{dil. HCl}} CH_3-\underset{\underset{CH_3}{|}}{CHOH} + Mg(OH)I$$

propan-2-ol

This synthesis can be summarised as

$$CH_3OH \longrightarrow CH_3I \longrightarrow CH_3-MgI \longrightarrow CH_3\underset{\underset{CH_3}{|}}{CHO}-MgI \longrightarrow CH_3\underset{\underset{CH_3}{|}}{CHOH}$$

Problem 7 Outline a synthesis for the reaction

$$\underset{\text{O}}{\underset{\|}{\text{C6H5-C-NH}_2}} \longrightarrow C_6H_5-OH$$

This reaction involves the loss of a carbon atom from the molecule, and this can be achieved by using the Hofmann degradation. The equation for this reaction is

$$C_6H_5-\underset{\underset{O}{\|}}{C}-NH_2 + Br_2 + 4KOH \longrightarrow C_6H_5-NH_2 + 2KBr + K_2CO_3$$

phenylamine

The substitution of the $-NH_2$ group by an $-OH$ group can be brought about via a diazotisation reaction. When phenylamine is treated with a solution of sodium nitrite and hydrochloric acid at a temperature below 293 K, benzene diazonium chloride is formed. The reagent involved in this reaction is nitrous acid which is formed *in situ*, i.e.

$$\underset{}{\bigcirc}-NH_2 + HNO_2 \xrightarrow[292K]{\begin{array}{c}HCl\\NaNO_2\end{array}} \underset{}{\bigcirc}-\overset{+}{N_2}Cl^- + H_2O$$

benzene diazonium chloride

When benzene diazonium chloride is hydrolysed with dilute acid above 293 K, phenol is formed, as shown by

$$\underset{}{\bigcirc}-N_2Cl + H_2O \xrightarrow{H^+} \underset{}{\bigcirc}-OH + N_2 + HCl$$

The synthesis can be summarised as

$$C_6H_5CONH_2 \longrightarrow C_6H_5-NH_2 \longrightarrow C_6H_5-N_2Cl \longrightarrow C_6H_5OH$$

Problem 8 Identify the compounds A, B, C and D from the following data. Two compounds A and B have the molecular formula C_3H_8O, A is oxidised with sodium dichromate and sulphuric acid to a compound C which forms an orange precipitate with 2,4-dinitrophenylhydrazine and shows positive reactions with Fehlings solution and ammoniacal silver nitrate. When B is oxidised in the same way a colourless liquid D is formed which reacts with 2,4-dinitrophenylhydrazine not with Fehlings solution or ammoniacal silver nitrate.

A consideration of the reactions of C and D show that C must be an aldehyde and D a ketone since both functional groups give orange precipitates with 2,4-dinitrophenylhydrazine.

$$\underset{R^2}{\overset{R^1}{\diagdown}}C=O + H_2N-NH-\underset{}{\bigcirc}\underset{NO_2}{\overset{NO_2}{\diagdown}} = \underset{R^2}{\overset{R^1}{\diagdown}}C=N-NH-\underset{}{\bigcirc}\underset{NO_2}{\overset{NO_2}{\diagdown}}+H_2O$$

R^1 and R^2 can be hydrogen or alkyl groups

Considering the number of carbon atoms present the only possible structures for C is

```
      H  H
      |  |
  H — C— C— C=O       propanal
      |  |  |
      H  H  H
```

Similarly for D the only structure is

```
      H     H
      |     |
  H — C— C— C — H     propanone
      |  ‖  |
      H  O  H
```

Since C is produced by the oxidation of A, then A must be a primary alcohol. The only possible primary alcohol with the formula C_3H_8O is

```
      H  H  H
      |  |  |
  H — C— C— C— O— H
      |  |  |
      H  H  H
```

Since D is produced by the oxidation of B, then B must be a secondary alcohol. The only possible secondary alcohol with the formula C_3H_8O is

```
      H  H  H
      |  |  |
   H—C—C—C—H
      |  |  |
      H  O  H
         |
         H
```

Hence it can be deduced that A, B, C and D are propan-1-ol, propan-2-ol, propanal and propanone respectively.

Problem 9 Analysis of an organic liquid showed it to contain 64.86% of carbon, 13.51% of hydrogen and 21.63% of oxygen. Calculate the empirical formula of the liquid.

When the percentages of the elements are given it is convenient to consider 100 g of the compound. This quantity of the compound would contain 64.86 g of C, 13.51 g of H and 21.63 g of O. The calculation of the empirical formula is set out conveniently as shown in the table below.

Element	Weight	Number of moles	Molar ratio		Relative number of atoms
Carbon	64.86	$\frac{64.86}{12} = 5.405$	$\frac{5.405}{1.351}$	=	4
Hydrogen	13.51	$\frac{13.51}{1} = 13.51$	$\frac{13.51}{1.35}$	=	10
Oxygen	21.63	$\frac{21.63}{16} = 1.351$	$\frac{1.351}{1.351}$	=	1

(Number of moles = $\frac{\text{weight of the element}}{\text{atomic weight of the element}}$, the molar ratio is found by dividing each number of moles by the smallest number of moles.)
Hence the empirical formula of the organic liquid is $C_4H_{10}O$.

Problem 10 An organic liquid, X, was found to contain 66.4% carbon, 5.53% hydrogen and 28.07% chlorine, and to have a molecular weight of 126.5. The addition of sodium hydroxide solution to X at room temperature brought about no reaction. Suggest a possible structure(s) for X using this data.

Firstly find the empirical formula by considering 100 g of the compound. The calculation is arranged conveniently as shown in the table below.

Element	Weight of element	Number of moles	Molar ratio	Relative number of atoms
Carbon	66.4	$\frac{66.4}{12} = 5.53$	$\frac{5.53}{0.79}$	7
Hydrogen	5.53	$\frac{5.53}{1} = 5.53$	$\frac{5.53}{0.79}$	7
Chlorine	28.07	$\frac{28.07}{35.5} = 0.79$	$\frac{0.79}{0.79}$	1

The empirical formula is C_7H_7Cl, thus the empirical formula weight is

$(7 \times 12) + (7 \times 1) + 35.5 = 126.5$.

Since the empirical formula weight is the same as the molecular weight the molecular formula must also be C_7H_7Cl.

When compounds have such a similar ratio of C and H the compound can be assumed to be a benzene type molecule. The possible structures are

(a) benzyl chloride (CH₂—Cl on benzene ring)
(b) 2-chlorotoluene (CH₃ and Cl ortho on benzene ring)
(c) 3-chlorotoluene (CH₃ and Cl meta on benzene ring)
(d) 4-chlorotoluene (CH₃ and Cl para on benzene ring)

Since structure (a) would be readily hydrolysed by sodium hydroxide it can be discounted. Structures (b), (c) and (d) are all resistant to hydrolysis. Since no information is given to distinguish between these three, any one could be the structure of X.

C. FURTHER PROBLEMS ON ORGANIC CHEMISTRY

(a) SHORT ANSWER PROBLEMS

Fill in the missing words

1 The sub-division of halogenoalkanes into primary, secondary and tertiary molecules depends on the number of .... atoms on the carbon atom .... to the halogen.

2 The homologous series $C_nH_{2n+1}Cl$ will give rise to .... isomers when n is ....

3 The reaction between halogenoalkanes and alkali metal hydroxides can produce .... or .... depending upon the conditions used.

4 The reaction between iodoethane and magnesium forms .... which is classified as a .... reagent.

5 The displacement of a halogen atom from a halogenoalkane by an —OH group is called .... substitution.

6 The synthesis of an alkene from halogenoalkanes is called an .... reaction.

7 The formation of Grignard reagents must be carried out under .... conditions because .... can be formed as a by-product of the reaction.

8 Tertiary alcohols can be synthesised from Grignard reagents by reaction with ....

9 The synthesis of acid nitriles is a useful method for .... a homologous series.

10 The .... of acid amides can be used to descend a homologous series.

159

(b) MULTI-CHOICE PROBLEMS (answers on page 181)

Select the correct answer from those given
Problems 1 to 14 refer to *Fig 6*

1. The reaction conditions A are
   (a) H$_2$(g) with a nickel catalyst;
   (b) phosphorus tribromide;
   (c) aqueous NaOH;
   (d) lithium aluminium hydride.

2. The reaction product 1 is
   (a) propan-1-ol;
   (b) butan-1-ol;
   (c) propan-2-ol;
   (d) butan-2-ol.

3. The reaction conditions B are
   (a) potassium cyanide;
   (b) lithium aluminium hydride;
   (c) hydrochloric acid;
   (d) aqueous KOH.

4. The reaction product 2 is
   (a) 1,chloropropane;
   (b) ethyl propanoate;
   (c) propyl ethanoate;
   (d) 2,chloropropane.

Fig 6

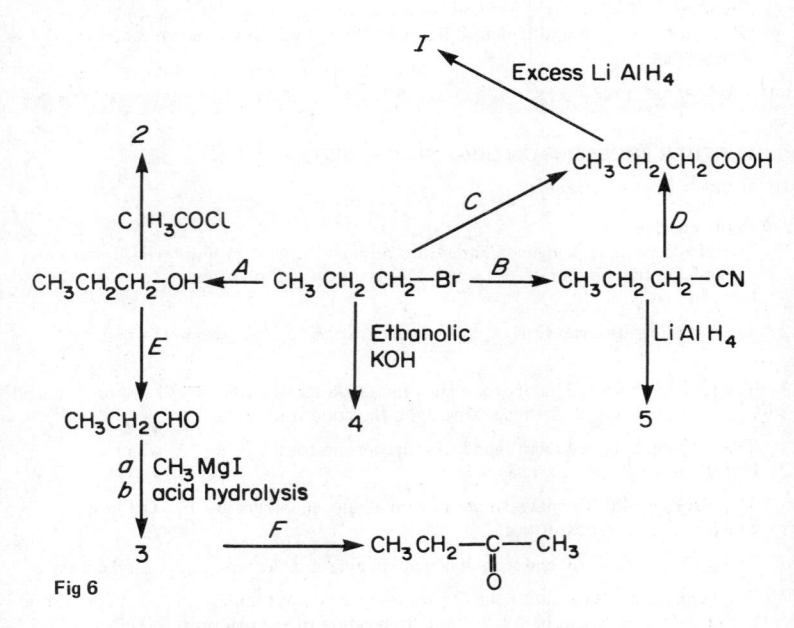

5. The conversion using conditions C can be described as
   (a) an elimination reaction;
   (b) ascending a homologous series;
   (c) a substitution reaction;
   (d) an esterification.

6. The reaction product 3 is
   (a) butan-1-ol;
   (b) propan-1-ol;
   (c) butanal;
   (d) butan-2-ol.

7. The conversion using conditions D can be described as
   (a) ascending a homologous series;
   (b) a hydrolysis reaction;
   (c) a reduction reaction;
   (d) an elimination reaction.

8. The reaction product 4 is
   (a) propene;
   (b) sodium propoxide;
   (c) propan-1-ol;
   (d) propan-2-ol.

9. The reaction conditions E are
   (a) lithium aluminium hydride;
   (b) phosphorus pentoxide;
   (c) acidified sodium dichromate;
   (d) hydrogen and a nickel catalyst.

10. The reaction product 5 is
    (a) propylamine;
    (b) butylamine;
    (c) propanal;
    (d) butanal.

11. The two sets of reaction conditions which are the same are
    (a) A and F;
    (b) C and F;
    (c) D and F;
    (d) E and F.

12. An example of esterification is shown by the formation of reaction product
    (a) 1; (b) 2; (c) 4; (d) 5.

13. An example of an elimination reaction is shown by the formation of reaction product
    (a) 1; (b) 3; (c) 4; (d) 5;

14. The two sets of reaction conditions which can be classified as hydrolysis reactions are
    (a) A and D;
    (b) D and E;
    (c) B and F;
    (d) B and C.

15. When a primary aryl amine is treated with sodium nitrite and sulphuric acid below 293 K, the reaction is called
    (a) an amination reaction;
    (b) a Grignard reaction;
    (c) a diazotisation reaction;
    (d) an oxidation reaction.

16. When an iodoalkane reacts with magnesium in dry ether and a trace of iodine, the reaction is called
    (a) a Grignard reaction;
    (b) a Hofmann degradation reaction;
    (c) a diazotisation reaction;
    (d) a reduction reaction.

17. When an acid amide reacts with bromine and potassium hydroxide solution the reaction is called
    (a) a Grignard reaction;
    (b) a Hofmann degradation reaction;
    (c) a diazotisation reaction;
    (d) an elimination reaction.

18. When a Grignard reagent is added to propanal and the reaction product is hydrolysed, the main product will be
    (a) a primary alcohol;
    (b) a secondary alcohol;
    (c) a tertiary alcohol;
    (d) a carboxylic acid.

19. In a synthetic pathway designed to increase the length of the carbon skeleton of a molecule by one carbon atom, which of the following groups must be introduced?
    (a) a Br group;
    (b) an OH group;
    (c) a CN group;
    (d) an NH_2 group.

20 For the classification of chloroalkanes which of the following should not be included in the same group

(a) $CH_3CH_2CH_2Cl$;

(b) $CH_3CH_2-\underset{\underset{CH_2}{|}}{CH}-CH_3$
       Cl

(c) $CH_3CH_2\underset{\underset{Cl}{|}}{CH}-CH_3$;

(d) $C_6H_5-CH_2-Cl$.

(c) CONVENTIONAL PROBLEMS

1 Draw a radial flow chart to outline the reactions of bromopropane.

2 Draw a radial flow chart to outline the reactions of ethyl magnesium iodide.

3 What is meant by the term *in situ*? Illustrate your answer with suitable examples.

4 Explain what is meant by the terms (a) ascending a homologous series, and (b) descending a homologous series. Give suitable examples to show how (a) and (b) can be carried out.

5 Select examples from the following list of reactions which could be used to convert $R-CH_2-OH$ to $R-CN$.

(i) $R-CH_2OH \xrightarrow[H_2SO_4]{Na_2Cr_2O_7} R-CHO + H_2O$

(ii) $RCONH_2 \xrightarrow{P_2O_5} R-CN + H_2O$

(iii) $3R-CH_2OH + PBr_3 \longrightarrow 3R-CH_2-Br + H_3PO_3$

(iv) $R-CHO \xrightarrow[H_2SO_4]{Na_2Cr_2O_7} RCOOH$

(v) $RCONH_2 + Br_2 + 4KOH \longrightarrow RNH_2 + 2KBr + K_2CO_3$

(vi) $RCOOH + NH_3 \longrightarrow RCOONH_4$

(vii) $R-Br + Mg \longrightarrow R-Mg-Br$

(viii) $R-Mg-Br + CO_2 \xrightarrow{dil.\ HCl} RCOOH$

(ix) $R^1OH + RCOOH \longrightarrow RCOOR$

(x) $RCOOH \xrightarrow{LiAlH_4} RCH_2OH$

6 Using the reactions given in *Problem 5*, how could $R-CN$ be converted into $RCOOR$

7 Using the reactions given in *Problem 5*, how could $R-Br$ be converted into $R-CH_2-Br$?

8 Devise a synthetic route for the conversion of propan-1-ol, $CH_3CH_2CH_2OH$ into propanone $CH_3-\underset{\underset{O}{\|}}{C}-CH_3$

9 Devise a synthetic route for the conversion of ethanoic acid, CH_3COOH into propanoic acid CH_3CH_2COOH.

10 Devise a synthetic route for the conversion of but-1-ene, $CH_3CH_2CH=CH_2$ into 2,methyl propanonitrile $CH_3CH_2\underset{\underset{CN}{|}}{CH}-CH_3$

11 Devise a synthetic route for the conversion of propene, $CH_3CH=CH_2$ into
(a) methyl propanoate, and (b) propyl ethanoate.

12 Devise a synthetic route for the conversion of benzene, ⟨O⟩–H, into 2,phenyl propan-2-ol.

$$CH_3-\underset{\underset{C_6H_5}{|}}{\overset{\overset{OH}{|}}{C}}-CH_3$$

13 Devise a synthetic route for the conversion of butanone $CH_3CH_2-\underset{\underset{O}{\|}}{C}-CH_3$

into butan-1-ol.

14 Devise a synthetic route for the conversion of propanonitrile into propan-1-ol.

15 Devise a synthetic route for the conversion of ethyl ethanoate into ethylamine.

16 Analysis of an organic compound Y gave 76.6% carbon 6.38% hydrogen and 17.02% of oxygen. An aqueous solution of Y showed a *pH* value less than seven, and formed a white precipitate with bromine water.
Calculate the empirical formula of Y and suggest a structure consistent with these reactions.   [C_6H_6O, O –OH]

17 Identify A, B, C and D using the following data.
An organic liquid A, was found to contain 35% carbon, 6.57% hydrogen and 58.43% bromine. When A was treated with ethanolic sodium hydroxide a mixture of hydrocarbons B and C was formed. 10 cm³ of each hydrocarbon required 60 cm³ of oxygen for complete combustion, and 1 mole of B or C each reacted with 1 mole of hydrogen to form the same product D. Write equations for the reactions in order to identify A, B, C and D.
[$CH_3-CHBr-CH_2-CH_3$; $CH_3CH=CHCH_3$; $CH_3CH_2CH=CH_2$; C_4H_{10}]

18 An organic liquid X was oxidised completely with sodium dichromate and sulphuric acid to give a compound Y which on analysis gave 40% carbon, 6.7% hydrogen and 53.3% oxygen. When X and Y are refluxed together with an acid catalyst the resulting solution contains a neutral compound Z which does not react with sodium. Identify X, Y and Z, from this information giving the appropriate equations of reactions.   [C_2H_5OH; CH_3COOH; $CH_3COOC_2H_5$]

19 Identify the compounds H, I and J from the following data, giving equations for the reactions and drawing their structural formulae. A neutral organic liquid H, on analysis gave 76.6% carbon, 6.38% hydrogen and 17.02% oxygen. On hydrolysis with sodium hydroxide H gave a solution which on acidification gave a white precipitate I, and a solution of J. Ether extraction of this solution and evaporation gave pure J which showed a violet colour with neutral iron (*III*) chloride solution.
[$C_6H_5COOC_6H_5$; C_6H_5COOH; C_6H_5OH]

20 A fuming organic liquid L on analysis gave 30.58% carbon, 3.82% hydrogen, 20.38% oxygen and 45.22% chlorine. On reaction with ethanolic ammonia a neutral substance was obtained M which on reduction with lithium aluminium hydride in dry ether gave a solution from which an alkaline gas N was released on

boiling with sodium hydroxide solution. Suggest possible structures for L, M and N and write equations for the reactions which have taken place.

[CH_3COCl; CH_3CONH_2; $CH_3CH_2NH_2$]

21 Assign the structures of the compounds E, F, G and H using the following data. A basic organic liquid E, on analysis gave 77.42% carbon, 7.52% hydrogen and 16.06% nitrogen. When E is treated with sodium nitrate and hydrochloric acid at a temperature below 283 K a substance F is formed in the solution. When the solution of F is reacted with potassium cyanide in the presence of copper (I) cyanide a product G is produced which on reduction with lithium aluminium hydride gives a basic liquid H of molecular weight 107.

[$C_6H_5NH_2$; $C_6H_5N_2Cl$; C_6H_5CN; $C_6H_5CH_2NH_2$]

22 Use the following information to suggest the possible structures of the compounds S, T, U, V and W writing appropriate equations for the reactions used. A compound S on reduction with $LiAlH_4$, gave an organic liquid T which reacted with sodium. Dehydration of T with concentrated sulphuric acid at 440 K gave a gaseous hydrocarbon U. The reaction of U with hydrogen bromide gave a mono-bromo alkane V. Hydrolysis of V with aqueous hydroxide gave an organic liquid which reacted with sodium. Oxidation of V with $Na_2Cr_2O_7$ and H_2SO_4 gave a neutral organic liquid W, which contained 66.67% carbon, 11.11% hydrogen and 22.22% oxygen, and reacted with 2,4-dinitrophenylhydrazine to give an orange precipitate but did not reduce Fehlings solution.

[C_3H_7CHO; $C_2H_5CH=CH_2$; $C_2H_5CHBrCH_3$; $C_2H_5CHOHCH_3$; $C_2H_5COCH_3$]

10 Polymerisation in organic chemistry

A. MAIN POINTS CONCERNING POLYMERISATION IN ORGANIC CHEMISTRY

1 (i) If two molecules of a compound can be combined together by a chemical reaction of the type

$$A + A \longrightarrow A-A$$

the single molecules of A are called **monomers** and the molecules composed of two molecules of A are called **dimers**. Similarly if three molecules of A join together in the form $A-A-A$ the resultant molecule is called a **trimer**. When a large and uncertain number of molecules of A link up into a **giant molecule**, the molecule is called a **polymer** and can be represented by the equation

$$nA \longrightarrow -A-A-A-A-A-A-A- \quad \text{etc.}$$

This joining together of molecules is called **addition polymerisation**.

(ii) If two different compounds can react in a similar way, for example,

$$nA + nB \longrightarrow -A-B-A-B-A-B-A-B- \quad \text{etc.}$$

The polymer formed from **two different monomers** is called a **co-polymer**. This type of polymerisation is found in the **condensation co-polymerisation** of nylons and the **addition co-polymerisation** of certain elastomers.

2 The simplest type of polymerisation takes place between molecules containing a carbon to carbon double bond. For example when ethene $CH_2=CH_2$ is polymerised the reaction can be represented by the equation

$$nCH_2=CH_2 \longrightarrow H-(CH_2-CH_2)_n-H$$
$$\textbf{monomer} \qquad\qquad \textbf{polymer}$$

where n is a large number (up to 10^5) and the polymer is a **long chain hydrocarbon** of the type

$$-CH_2-CH_2-CH_2-CH_2-CH_2-CH_2-CH_2-CH_2- \quad \text{etc.}$$

Other examples of addition polymerisation are shown in *Table 1*.

3 (i) The method of preparation of the addition polymers has a marked effect upon the physical properties of the polymer.

(ii) When ethene is heated at 500 K under a pressure of 2×10^6 kPa in the presence of oxygen as catalyst it gives **low density polyethene** of molecular

TABLE 1 Some thermoplastic polymers

Monomer		Polymer	
Name	Structure	Name	Structure
ethene	H₂C=CH₂	polyethene (polythene)	$-(CH_2-CH_2)_n-$
propene	CH₃(H)C=CH₂	polypropene (polypropylene)	$-(CH(CH_3)-CH_2)_n-$
styrene	C₆H₅(H)C=CH₂	polystyrene	$-(CH(C_6H_5)-CH_2)_n-$
chloroethene	Cl(H)C=CH₂ (G shown in source)	polychloroethene (polyvinyl chloride)	$-(CHCl-CH_2)_n-$
methyl, 2-methyl propenoate	CH₃(H)C=C(H)(COOCH₃)	polymethyl-2, methyl propenoate (perspex)	$-(C(CH_3)(H)-C(H)(COOCH_3))_n-$
tetra fluoro-ethene	F₂C=CF₂	polytetrafluoroethene (P.T.F.E.)	$-(CF_2-CF_2)_n-$

Note. Popular names in brackets

weight up to 300,000. This type of **polyethene** becomes plastic at approximately **393 K**.
(iii) When ethene is bubbled into xylene containing a **Ziegler Natta** type of catalyst (*Problem 3*) the polymer formed has a much higher molecular weight and becomes plastic at approximately **403 K** and is called **high density polyethene**.
(iv) The **length of the polymer chains** is dependent upon not only the method of preparation but also upon the use of **additives** called **inhibitors** which can control the degree of polymerisation.
(v) Addition polymers formed using a free radical initiator produce **atactic** polymers, whereas those formed using Ziegler Natta catalyst produce **isotactic** polymers (*Problem 2*).

4 Addition polymers, which are solid at room temperature, become soft on heating and can be **moulded** into shape using **pressurised dies**. On cooling the polymer once more becomes solid. This process can be repeated provided the polymer is not decomposed. Polymers showing this type of behaviour are called **thermoplastic polymers**.

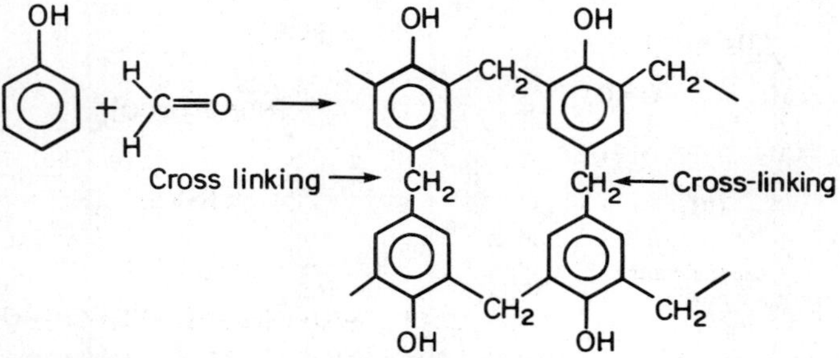

Fig 1 The phenol-methanal thermosetting polymer

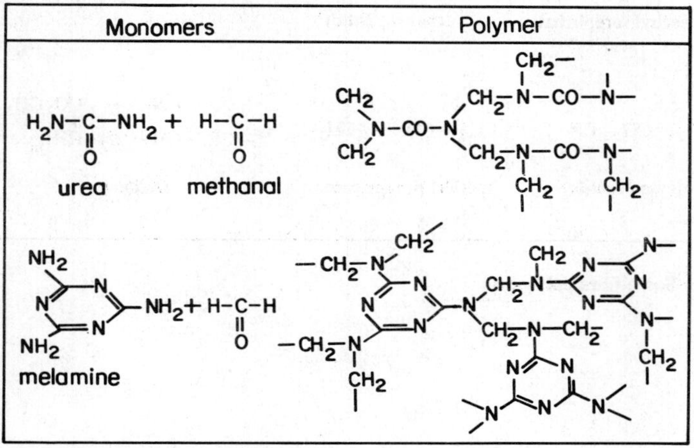

Fig 2 Some thermosetting polymers

Monomers	Polymer
$H_2N-(CH_2)_6NH_2$ + $HO_2C(CH_2)_4COOH$	$H[NH(CH_2)_6NH-CO(CH_2)_4CO_2]_nOH$
1,6-diamino hexane 1,6-hexandioc acid	6,6-Nylon
$H_2N(CH_2)_6NH_2$ + $ClOC(CH_2)_8COCl$	$H[NH(CH_2)_6-NH-CO(CH_2)_8CO]_nOCl$
1,10-decandioyl chloride	6,10-Nylon
caprolactam (cyclic structure: $CH_2-CH_2-CH_2-CH_2-CH_2-C(=O)-NH$ ring)	$[NH(CH_2)_5CO]_n$ 6,Nylon
$CH_3O_2C-C_6H_4-CO_2CH_3$ + $HO(CH_2)_2OH$ dimethyl terephthalic acid ethan-1,2-diol	$CH_3O[CO-C_6H_4-CO-CH_2-CH_2-O]_nH$ Terylene
$CH_2=CH-CN$ $CH_2=CHCO_2CH_3$ propeno-l-nitrile methyl propenoate	$[CH_2-\underset{CN}{CH}-CH_2-\underset{CO_2CH_3}{CH}]_n$ Acrilan

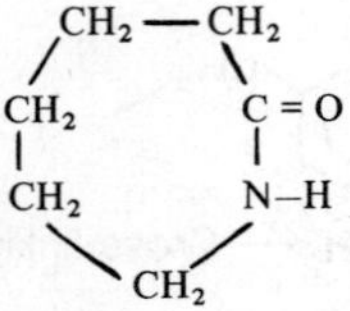

Fig 3 Some fibre polymers

5. When two different monomers react together there are a variety of polymer types possible depending on the nature of the two monomers. These can be classified as (i) **thermosetting** plastics, (ii) **condensation fibre** polymers, and (iii) **elastomers**.

6. When **phenol** and **methanal** react together with an acid catalyst a polymer is formed which is **rigid** and **cannot be softened by heating**. This is due to **extensive cross-linking** taking place between the molecules. The structure of this polymer which is called a **thermosetting** polymer is shown in *Fig 1*. The properties of these polymers are quite different to the thermoplastic polymers (see *Problem 4*). Some examples of thermosetting polymers are shown in *Fig 2*.

7. When a **diamine** and a **di-carboxylic acid** or **di-carboxylic acid chloride** are reacted, a long chain condensation reaction takes place resulting in a **fibrous** polymer. A general reaction can be written as

$$H_2N-R-NH_2 + ClOC-R-COCl \longrightarrow H_2N-R\overline{[NH-CO]}RCOCl + HCl$$
  diamine   di-acid chloride

The dotted line shows the part of the molecule where **condensation** occurs and is a **peptide type linkage**. When large amounts of these molecules are used the equation which represents the reaction is

$$n\ H_2N-R-NH_2 + n HOOC-R-COOH \longrightarrow H\text{-}[NH-R-NH-CO-R-COO]_n\text{-}H + (2n-1)H_2O$$
  diamine   di-acid

Molecules of this type are called **nylons** and examples are shown in *Fig 3* and discussed in *Problem 5*.

8. (i) **Elastomers** can be prepared from the polymerisation of a **diene** or by the co-polymerisation of a diene with a **substituted alkene**. The diene usually used for the formation of **synthetic** elastomers is **buta-1, 3-diene** or a substituted buta-1, 3-diene. For example,

2, methylbuta-1, 3-diene   poly 2,methylbuta-1,3-diene

or

2, chlorobuta-1,3-diene   poly 2, chlorobuta-1,3-diene

169

Both of these polymers retain a **carbon to carbon double bond** which is a necessary component of an **elastomer**.

An example of co-polymerisation is the reaction between buta-1,3-diene and phenylethene (styrene) which can be represented as:

$$4n\,CH_2{=}CH{-}CH{=}CH_2 + n\,CH_2{=}CH{-}C_6H_5 \longrightarrow \{\!\!\{\,CH_2{-}CH{=}CH{-}CH_2\}_4\,CH_2{-}\underset{H}{\overset{C_6H_5}{C}}\,\}_n$$

S.B.R.

This is one of the most widely used synthetic rubbers and has the trivial name of **styrene butadiene rubber** and is abbreviated to **S.B.R.**

(ii) Other forms of rubber which have special properties can also be prepared in a similar way. For example the copolymerisation of buta-1,3-diene and propanonitrile gives **nitrile rubber** which is resistant to chemicals and can be used for any purpose involving chemicals.

$$2n\,CH_2{=}CH{-}CH{=}CH_2 + n\,CH_2{=}CHCN \longrightarrow \{\!\!\{\,CH_2{-}CH{=}CH{-}CH_2\}_2\,CH_2{-}\underset{H}{\overset{CN}{C}}\,\}_n$$

nitrile rubber

(iii) The process of converting these compounds into elastomers is called **vulcanisation** and is brought about by introducing **sulphur** into the polymer. The sulphur **links together** the long chain molecules of polymer introducing a **degree of elasticity**.

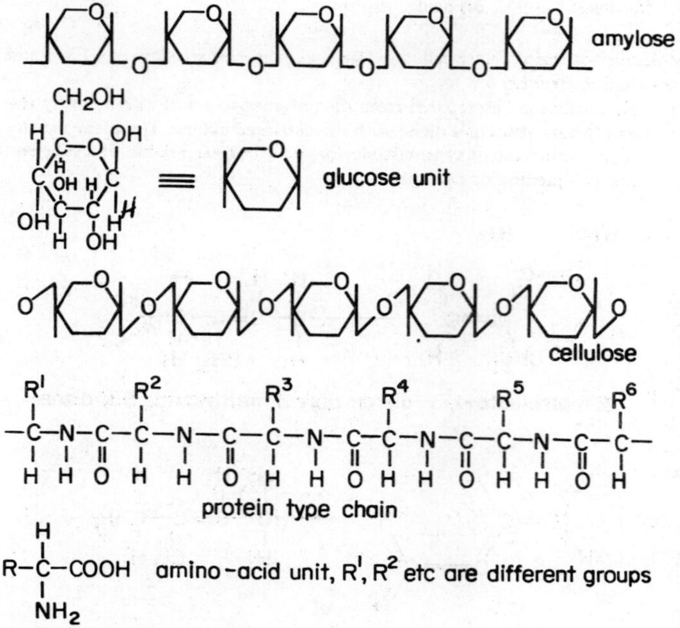

Fig 4 Some natural polymers

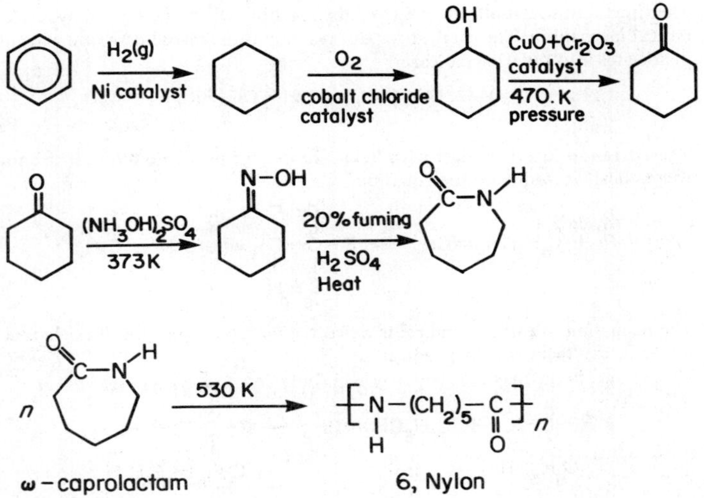

Fig 5 The synthesis of 6, Nylon

9. The properties of polymers can be **modified** by the use of additives. The additives can be classified as (a) **plasticisers**, which make the polymers more **flexible**, (b) **dyes**, which introduce **colour** to the polymers, (c) **fillers**, which can be used to make polymers **more rigid** and (d) **anti-oxidants** which cut down the amount of oxidation in the polymers.

10. In addition to synthetic polymers there are many polymeric molecules found in **nature**. Starch is an example of a **polysaccharide** and is composed of **glucose** units joined together by condensation. The major components are **amylose** and **amylopectin** which are shown in *Fig 4*. **Cellulose** is a further example of a polysaccharide which is also based on glucose. Another source of polymers in nature are the **proteins** which are composed of **amino-acids** joined together. Up to forty amino-acids joined together are classified as **polypeptides**, whereas **over forty** are classified as **proteins**. These polymers are quite different to synthetic polymers in that they contain a greater variety of monomer units. The number of different amino-acids which occur in nature are twenty, and the arrangement of a selection of these can be numerous. An example of a protein type chain is shown in *Fig 5*.

B. WORKED PROBLEMS ON POLYMERISATION IN ORGANIC CHEMISTRY

Problem 1 Explain the terms **initiation, propagation** and **termination** used in describing polymerisation. Use the polymerisation of phenylethene to illustrate your answer.

The three terms relate to the stages of the reaction which takes place by **a free radical** mechanism. The catalyst for this reaction is dibenzoyl peroxide which dissociates into two free radicals

$$C_6H_5-CO-O-O-CO-C_6H_5 \rightarrow 2C_6H_5COO \rightarrow 2C_6H_5\dot{} + 2CO_2$$
Free Radicals

These free radicals then react with the phenylethene molecule to produce another free radical, according to the equation

$$R\cdot + C_6H_5CH=CH_2 \longrightarrow R-\underset{\underset{C_6H_5}{|}}{\overset{\overset{H}{|}}{C}}-\underset{\underset{H}{|}}{\overset{\overset{H}{|}}{C}}\cdot \quad \text{where R· is } C_6H_5\dot{}$$

The formation of this free radical is called the initiation step. Another phenylethene molecule can react with this radical

$$R-\underset{\underset{C_6H_5}{|}}{\overset{\overset{H}{|}}{C}}-\underset{\underset{H}{|}}{\overset{\overset{H}{|}}{C}}\cdot + C_6H_5CH=CH_2 \longrightarrow R-\underset{\underset{C_6H_5}{|}}{\overset{\overset{H}{|}}{C}}-\underset{\underset{H}{|}}{\overset{\overset{H}{|}}{C}}-\underset{\underset{H_6C_5}{|}}{\overset{\overset{H}{|}}{C}}-\underset{\underset{H}{|}}{\overset{\overset{H}{|}}{C}}\cdot$$

This reaction takes place on many occasions, building up the long chain polymer molecule and is called the **propagation** step.

The growth of the molecule can be stopped in a variety of ways. For example, two free radicals could combine:

$$R\{\underset{\underset{C_6H_5}{|}}{\overset{\overset{H}{|}}{C}}-\underset{\underset{H}{|}}{\overset{\overset{H}{|}}{C}}\}_n\cdot + \cdot\{\underset{\underset{C_6H_5}{|}}{\overset{\overset{H}{|}}{C}}-\underset{\underset{H}{|}}{\overset{\overset{H}{|}}{C}}\}_m R \rightarrow R\{\underset{\underset{C_6H_5}{|}}{\overset{\overset{H}{|}}{C}}-\underset{\underset{H}{|}}{\overset{\overset{H}{|}}{C}}\}_n\{\underset{\underset{H}{|}}{\overset{\overset{H}{|}}{C}}-\underset{\underset{C_6H_5}{|}}{\overset{\overset{H}{|}}{C}}\}_m R$$

(*n* and *m* can be quite different or similar)

This is called a **termination** reaction. This final stage of the reaction is dependent upon the concentration of the free radicals in the reaction, which is **small** during the propagating stage but **increases** as the **phenylethene is used up**. The reaction can be stopped by the addition of a reagent called an **inhibitor** which will react with the free radicals present.

A polymerisation of this type is called a chain reaction.

Problem 2 What is the difference between an atactic polymer, an isotactic polymer, and a syndiotactic polymer.

When substituted alkenes are polymerised a mixture of products can be obtained. If propene is considered as an example, one structure is

Where the dotted lines represent the direction into the page and the full lines the direction out of the page. This **random orientation** of methyl groups is called an **atactic** structure.

Another possible structure is

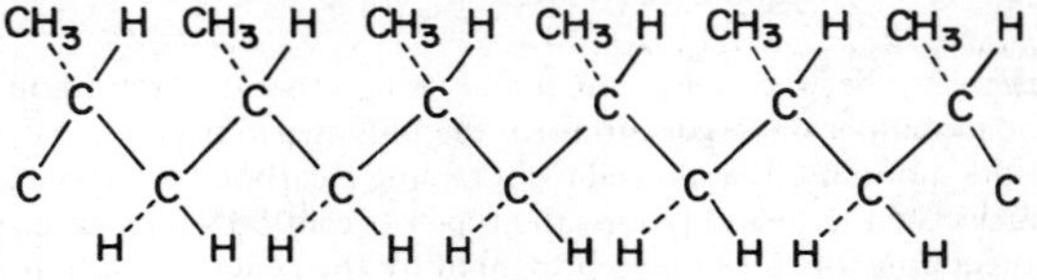

In this structure **all of the methyl groups have the same orientation** and this is called an **isotactic** structure.

A third possibility is

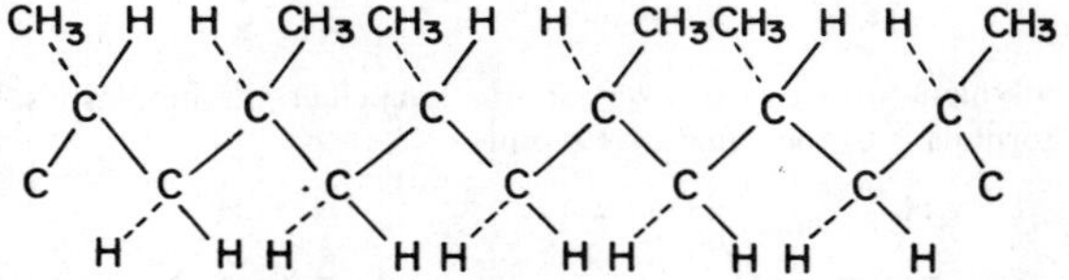

In this structure the **orientation** of the methyl groups are **alternately behind and in front** of the page and this regularity is called a **syndiotactic** structure.

Problem 3 Explain how propene is polymerised using a Ziegler Natta catalyst.

The Ziegler Natta catalysts contain two main components, aluminium triethyl and a titanium chloride or alkoxide. The catalysts are thought to react together to form a titanium complex.

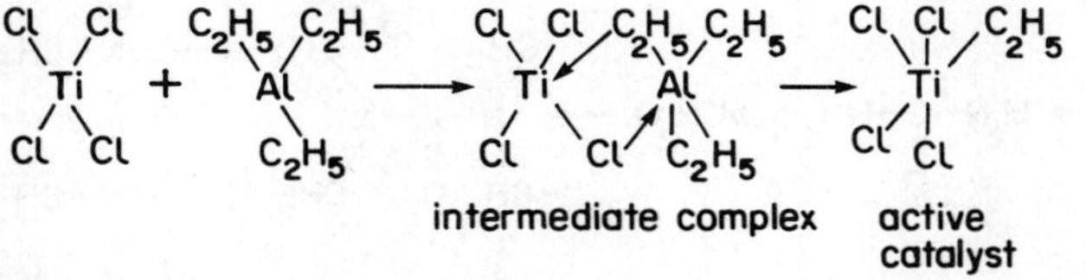

intermediate complex   active catalyst

This catalyst is thought to react with propene in the following way

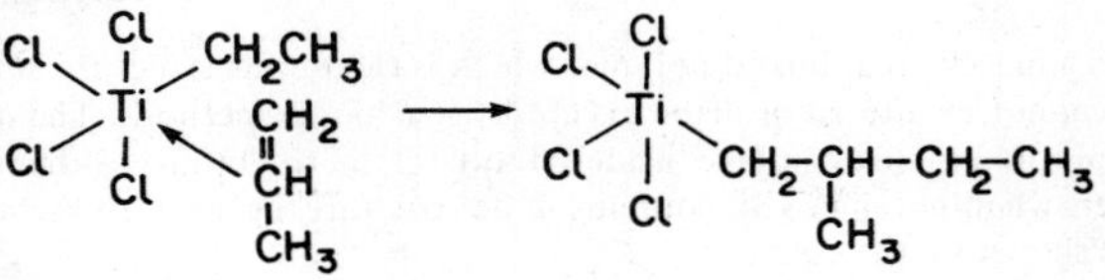

The next step is

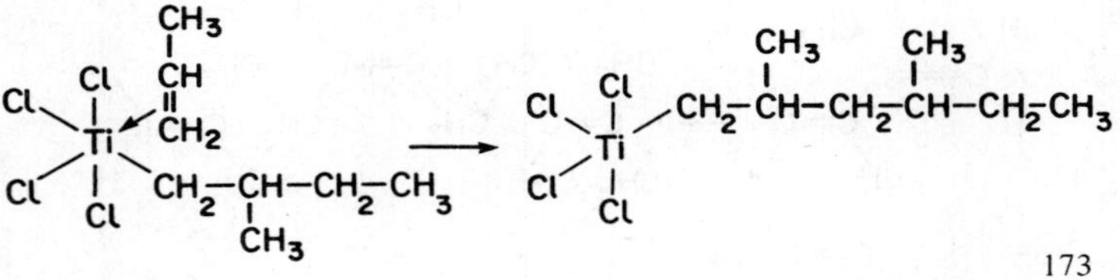

These are the propagating steps and the regularity of the addition of propene gives the isotactic form of the polypropene polymer.

Problem 4 Discuss how monomers and polymers are related in thermoplastics, thermosetting polymers and elastomers.

The relationship between a monomer and its polymer depends upon the reaction which the monomer undergoes to form the polymer molecules.

When the monomer is a molecule containing a carbon to carbon double bond (sometimes called the **vinyl group**) the type of reaction which takes place is an addition reaction which can be represented by the general equation

$$n \: \overset{H}{\underset{H}{C}} = \overset{H}{\underset{X}{C}} \longrightarrow \left(\overset{H}{\underset{H}{C}} - \overset{H}{\underset{X}{C}} \right)_n$$

The polymers formed in this way are the long chain thermoplastics. If X in the general formula is Cl the equation becomes

$$n \: \overset{H}{\underset{H}{C}} = \overset{H}{\underset{Cl}{C}} \longrightarrow \left(\overset{H}{\underset{H}{C}} - \overset{H}{\underset{Cl}{C}} \right)_n$$

vinyl chloride   P.V.C.

The resulting polymers are long chain molecules of high molecular weight. Thermosetting plastics are not composed of a single monomer, but are formed when two different monomers react together. A typical example is the polymer formed when urea and methanal react together.

urea–methanal polymer

This is a highly cross-linked polymer which is rigid in its structure, and once formed cannot be altered in shape except by machining methods. The monomer of natural rubber latex can be considered to be 2, methylbuta-1, 3-diene. This monomer, when polymerised, contains in its structure a carbon to carbon double bond, as shown by the equation

Synthetic rubbers or elastomers are formed between buta-1, 3-diene and another monomer by the process of co-polymerisation. For example, when buta-1, 3-diene and styrene polymerise together a polymer known as SBR is formed, the abbreviation standing for styrene-butadiene-rubber.

$$4n\ CH_2=CH-CH=CH_2 + n\ CHC_6H_5 \rightarrow \{CH_2-CH=CH-CH_2\}_4 CH_2-\underset{C_6H_5}{\overset{H}{C}}\}_n$$

These polymers all have carbon to carbon double bonds which allows a certain degree of cross-linking and flexibility. The synthetic polymers which are formed from a single monomer are usually derivatives of buta-1, 3-diene, for example, poly-2-chlorobuta-1, 3-diene (neoprene).

Problem 5 What type of polymers have been synthesised for use in the production of man-made fibres.

The copolymerisation of diamines and diacids takes place to give a polymeric material which can be extruded and spun into fibres. The class of polymers formed in this way are the nylons, the name being derived from New York, and London where the polymers were discovered. The reaction which takes place is a condensation reaction, resulting in the formation of a peptide type linkage, for example

$$H_2N-R'-NH_2 + HO_2C-R^2-CO_2H \rightarrow H_2N-R'\underset{H}{\overset{}{-}}N-\underset{O}{\overset{\|}{C}}+R^2-CO_2H$$

peptide type linkage

This reaction takes place many thousands of times to produce long chain molecules, which when intertwined display remarkable strength. The composition of R^1 and R^2 is designated in the type of nylon formed. The most common are 6,6,Nylon made from 1,6-diaminohexane and 1,6-hexandioc acid, and 6,10 Nylon in which the diamine is the same but the diacid is 1,10 decandioc acid. A more ready reaction takes place using diacid chlorides than the diacids themselves.

An alternative nylon called 6,Nylon can be prepared from a single monomer as shown in *Fig 5*. This is a particularly popular type of material due to the ready availability of the starting material.

Another type of polymer used extensively in clothing materials are the polyesters, for example

$$2n \underset{H}{\overset{H}{C}}=CH-CN + 2n \underset{H}{\overset{H}{C}}=\underset{CO_2CH_3}{\overset{H}{C}} \longrightarrow \left(\underset{H\ H\ H}{\overset{H\ CN\ H}{C-C-C}}-\underset{CO_2CH_3}{\overset{H}{C}}-\underset{H\ H\ H}{\overset{H\ CN\ H\ H}{C-C-C-C}}-\underset{CO_2CH_3}{\overset{H}{C}} \right)_n$$

propeno-1-nitrile **methyl propenoate** **Acrilan**

Problem 6 Explain what is meant by the term 'free radical'. How are these species able to initiate addition polymerisation reaction.

When a covalent bond in a molecule is broken such that one of the two electrons is retained by each of the separated groups, the process is called homolytic fission and results in the formation of free radicals. This reaction can be represented by the equation

$$X-Y \longrightarrow X\cdot + Y\cdot$$

Where the · represents the electrons from the broken covalent bond.

The reagents used to form free radicals for polymerisation reactions can be organic peroxides, for example, benzoyl peroxide. The photochemical decomposition of benzoyl peroxide can be represented by the equation

$$Ph-\underset{O}{\overset{\|}{C}}-O-O-\underset{O}{\overset{\|}{C}}-Ph \xrightarrow{U.V.\ light} 2\ Ph-\underset{O}{\overset{\|}{C}}-O\cdot$$

This free radical undergoes further decomposition according to the equation

$$Ph-\underset{O}{\overset{\|}{C}}-O\cdot \longrightarrow Ph\cdot + CO_2$$

phenyl free radical

When this phenyl free radical comes into contact with an alkene $RCH=CH_2$, the double bond reacts with the free radical in the following way,

$$Ph\cdot + \underset{R}{\overset{R}{C}}=\underset{R}{\overset{R}{C}} \longrightarrow Ph-\underset{H\ H}{\overset{R\ H}{C-C}}\cdot \quad (1)$$

This free radical will react with another alkene molecule to form

$$Ph-\underset{H\ H}{\overset{R\ H}{C-C}}\cdot + \underset{H}{\overset{R}{C}}=\underset{H}{\overset{H}{C}} \longrightarrow Ph-\underset{H\ H\ H\ H}{\overset{R\ H\ R\ H}{C-C-C-C}}\cdot \quad (2)$$

This process of beginning the chain reaction is called initiation, i.e. reaction (1), the continuation of the reaction being the propagation of the reaction, i.e. reaction (2).

Problem 7 Explain the difference between an addition polymer and a condensation polymer.

Addition polymerisation takes place either between identical alkene molecules to form thermoplastics

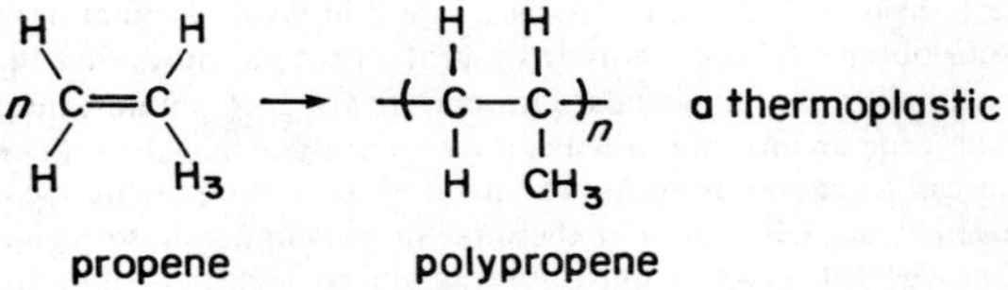

$$n \begin{array}{c} H \\ | \\ C=C \\ | \quad | \\ H \quad H_3 \end{array} \longrightarrow \left(\begin{array}{cc} H & H \\ | & | \\ C - C \\ | & | \\ H & CH_3 \end{array} \right)_n \quad \text{a thermoplastic}$$

propene → polypropene

a thermoplastic

A condensation polymerisation takes place between two different molecules resulting in the formation of a small molecule like water or hydrogen chloride in addition to the polymer. A typical reaction is that between 1,6-diaminohexane and hexanedioyl chloride to form 6,6-nylon and hydrogen chloride

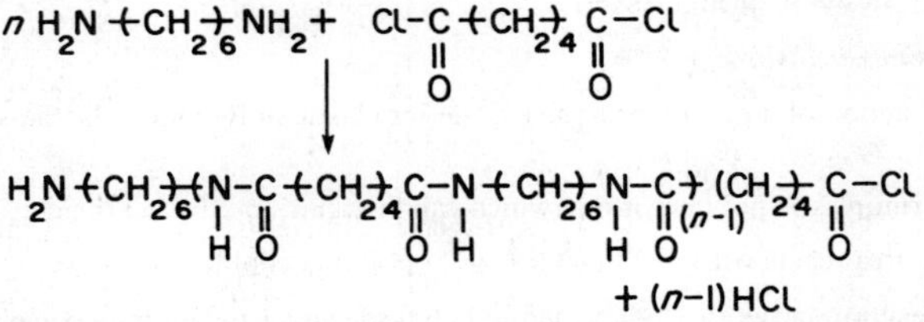

$$n\; H_2N(CH_2)_6NH_2 + Cl-C(CH_2)_4C-Cl$$
$$\quad\quad\quad\quad\quad\quad\quad\quad\quad \| \quad\quad\quad \|$$
$$\quad\quad\quad\quad\quad\quad\quad\quad\quad O \quad\quad\quad O$$

↓

$$H_2N(CH_2)_6\{N-C(CH_2)_4C-N(CH_2)_6N-C\}(CH_2)_4C-Cl$$
$$\quad\quad\quad\quad\; | \;\; \|\quad\quad\quad \|\;\; |\quad\quad\quad\quad | \;\; \|_{(n-1)}\quad \|$$
$$\quad\quad\quad\quad H \; O\quad\quad\;\; O\; H\quad\quad\quad\;\; H\; O\quad\quad\quad O$$

$$+ (n-1)HCl$$

or possibly a phenol and methanal, to form a thermosetting plastic. The reaction is shown below,

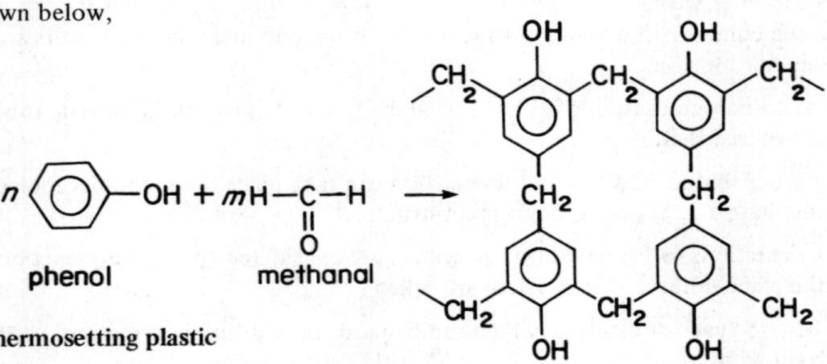

$$n \;\text{phenol}-OH + m\;H-C-H \longrightarrow$$
$$\quad\quad\quad\quad\quad\quad\quad \|$$
$$\quad\quad\quad\quad\quad\quad\quad O$$

phenol   methanal

a thermosetting plastic

Problem 8 Why are proteins and carbohydrates classified as polymers? What simple experiments can be used to give evidence of such classification?

Proteins and carbohydrates are compounds of high molecular weight. Most organic chemicals have molecular weights of less than 500, and any which have larger values than these are suspected of being polymeric.

Starch, which is a major part of many foodstuffs, is a carbohydrate. If a solution of starch is refluxed with a solution of hydrochloric acid, after extracting the organic material the only compound which can be identified by thin layer chromatography is glucose $C_6H_{12}O_6$. Thus it can be concluded that the carbohydrate, starch, is composed of the monomer glucose. The chemical terms given to these compounds are polysaccharide and monosaccharide respectively.

Protein sources are more difficult to work with because they are much more complex. However, it is relatively simple to break a protein source down into its constituents, again using acid hydrolysis. The thin layer chromatographic analysis of a mixture obtained from the hydrolysis of a protein shows that they are composed of a number of amino-acids. The amounts of each amino-acid present can be investigated using an enzyme called carboxypeptidase, and the sequence in which they occur can be found using fluorodinitrobenzene for a technique called N-terminal analysis. Discussion of these techniques in detail is outside the scope of this text, however it serves to illustrate that amino-acids are copolymerised to form proteins.

C. FURTHER PROBLEMS ON POLYMERISATION

(a) SHORT ANSWER PROBLEMS

Fill in the missing words

1   The reaction of a monomer to give a thermoplastic polymer can be classified as an ....

2   A thermoplastic polymer is one which can be .... by heating.

3   When urea reacts with methanal a ...... polymer is obtained.

4   The reaction between 1,6-hexanedioyl chloride and 1,6-diaminohexane produces a polymer called ....

5   In the condensation reaction to form fibre type polymers the monomers are held together by ....

6   The co-polymerisation of .... and .... gives the synthetic rubber known as S.B.R.

7   In order that an addition polymerisation can take place the monomer molecule must have a .... bond in its structure.

8   The reactions to form addition polymers are considered to be chain reactions which take place in three stages. These are called ...., ..., ...

9   The two types of catalysts which can be used for addition polymerisation are classified as .... and .... catalysts.

10 An example of a natural polymer is amylose from starch. The monomer of this polymer is ....

11 When amino-acids are joined together in natural polymers, the polymers are called .... or .... depending on the number of amino-acid molecules present in the molecule.

12 The polymerisation of propene with a peroxide gives a polymer whose structure is said to be ...., whereas a Ziegler catalyst gives a polymer with an .... structure.

13 In co-polymerisation reactions the three types of polymers which are formed are ...., ... and ....

14 The numbers 6 and 10 in the name 6,10 Nylon refer to the number of .... in the .... and the ....

15 The polymerisation of $F_2C=CF_2$ gives .... , a stable polymer used as a heat-resistant covering for cooking utensils.

(b) MULTI-CHOICE PROBLEMS (answers on page 181)

Select the correct answer from those given
Problems 1 to 7 refer to Fig 6

1 The reaction which produces a thermoplastic polymer is
 (a) A; (b) B; (c) C; (d) D.

2 The reaction which produces an elastomer is
 (a) A; (b) B; (c) C; (d) D.

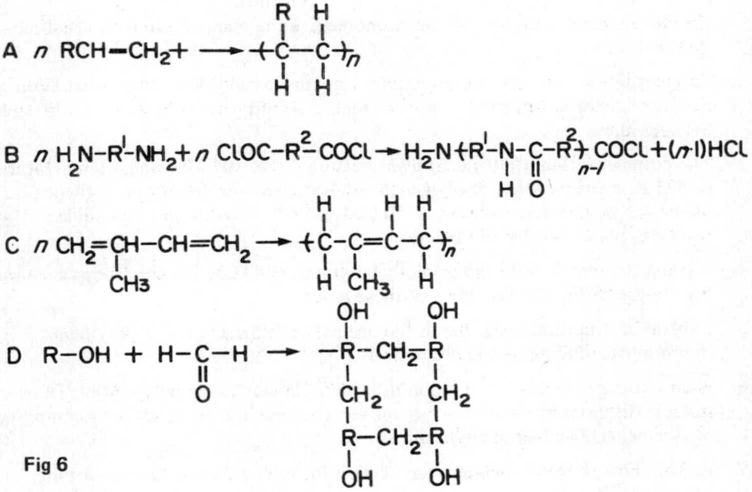

A n RCH=CH$_2$ + ⟶ $+\!\!\left(\!\!\begin{array}{c}R\ H\\|\ \ |\\C-C\\|\ \ |\\H\ H\end{array}\!\!\right)_{\!\!n}$

B n H$_2$N–R^1–NH$_2$ + n ClOC–R^2–COCl ⟶ H$_2$N$\{$R^1–N–C–R$^2\}_{n-1}$COCl + $(n\text{-}1)$HCl
  with N–H and C=O on the middle group

C n CH$_2$=CH–CH=CH$_2$ ⟶ $+\!\!\left(\!\!\begin{array}{c}H\ \ \ H\ H\\|\ \ \ \ |\ \ |\\C-C=C-C\\|\ \ \ \ |\ \ |\\H\ CH_3\ H\end{array}\!\!\right)_{\!\!n}$
 with CH$_3$ branch

D R–OH + H–C–H ⟶ structure with OH, CH$_2$, R groups in network
     ‖
     O

Fig 6

3 The reaction which produces a fibre type polymer is
 (a) A; (b) B; (c) C; (d) D.

4 The reaction which produces a thermosetting polymer is
 (a) A; (b) B; (c) C; (d) D.

5 The reaction which can be classified as a condensation polymerisation is
 (a) A; (b) B; (c) C; (d) D.

6 The most likely reaction to produce polystyrene would be a reaction of the type
 (a) A; (b) B; (c) C; (d) D.

7 The most likely reaction to produce 6,10 Nylon would be a reaction of the type
 (a) A; (b) B; (c) C; (d) D.

8. The monomer units of a polypeptide are
   (a) aldehydes;
   (b) amino-acids;
   (c) dienes;
   (d) diamines.

9. The compound required for the formation of an elastomer with buta-1,3-diene is
   (a) 1,6-diamino hexane;
   (b) hexandioyl choride;
   (c) propanonitrile;
   (d) urea.

10. The compound required for the formation of a thermosetting polymer with methanal is
    (a) benzene;
    (b) phenylamine;
    (c) benzaldehyde;
    (d) phenol.

(c) CONVENTIONAL PROBLEMS

1. What type of polymerisation reactions do the following monomers take part in
   (a) but-1-ene;
   (b) hexandioc acid;
   (c) butadiene;
   (d) chloroethene;
   (e) decandioyl chloride;
   (f) urea.
   Give an example using each of the monomers in the manner you have classified them.

2. Polymerisation reactions are sometimes classified as addition and condensation reactions. Select a suitable example of each type of reaction to show the difference between them.

3. The polymerisation of ethene at high pressure (20×10^4 kPa) and a temperature of 473 K in the presence of oxygen as catalyst gives low density polyethene of a molecular weight ranging between 50,000 and 300,000. Suggest a possible reaction mechanism for this reaction.

4. Explain the terms atatic and isotactic polymers, and state the conditions necessary for the preparation of polymers of these types.

5. Explain in structural terms the difference between thermoplastic polymers, thermosetting polymers and elastomers.

6. What structural feature is common to both 6,6,Nylon and a polypeptide. Draw suitable diagrams to illustrate your answer. (Assume the polypeptide is composed of glycine, alanine and phenylalanine).

7. Explain how polychloroethene can be used for such different uses as clothing and water pipes.

8. Make an investigation of a consumable item (e.g. a motorcycle, or a vacuum cleaner) to establish the types of polymers used in its construction. Classify each component polymer type and suggest a naturally occurring material that could be used in its place.

9. Why are quite different machining techniques necessary for manufacturing items from thermoplastics and thermosetting polymers.

10. Polymers which are classified as rubbers do not show elastomeric properties until they have been vulcanised. What is meant by this term? Draw suitable diagrams to show the effect it has on the polymer.

Answers to problems

Chapter 1 (page 13)
1 (d); 2 (c); 3 (b); 4 (b); 5 (a); 6 (c); 7 (d); 8 (c); 9 (d); 10 (d).

Chapter 2 (page 27)
1 (a); 2 (d); 3 (b); 4 (a); 5 (c); 6 (d); 7 (a); 8 (d); 9 (a); 10 (a).

Chapter 3 (page 43)
1 (c); 2 (b); 3 (c); 4 (a); 5 (d); 6 (b); 7 (a); 8 (d); 9 (a); 10 (c).

Chapter 4 (page 54)
1 (b); 2 (d); 3 (b); 4 (d); 5 (b).

Chapter 5 (page 66)
1 (c); 2 (c); 3 (d); 4 (a); 5 (b); 6 (a); 7 (c); 8 (a); 9 (b); 10 (b).

Chapter 6 (page 90)
1 (b); 2 (d); 3 (c); 4 (a); 5 (d); 6 (c); 7 (b); 8 (a); 9 (d); 10 (b).

Chapter 7 (page 115)
1 (a); 2 (c); 3 (d); 4 (a); 5 (c); 6 (c); 7 (b); 8 (b); 9 (d); 10 (a);
11 (a); 12 (d); 13 (c); 14 (b); 15 (d).

Chapter 8 (page 137)
1 (a); 2 (b); 3 (a); 4 (b); 5 (b); 6 (a); 7 (d); 8 (b); 9 (c); 10 (d);
11 (b); 12 (b); 13 (c); 14 (a); 15 (d); 16 (b); 17 (c); 18 (d);
19 (c); 20 (a).

Chapter 9 (page 160)
1 (c); 2 (b); 3 (a); 4 (b); 5 (b); 6 (d); 7 (b); 8 (a); 9 (c); 10 (b);
11 (d); 12 (b); 13 (c); 14 (a); 15 (c); 16 (a); 17 (b); 18 (c);
19 (c); 20 (c).

Chapter 10 (page 179)
1 (d); 2 (c); 3 (b); 4 (d); 5 (b); 6 (a); 7 (b); 8 (b); 9 (c); 10 (d).

Index

Acids, 30
Acid amide, 123
Acid chloride, 123
Acid dissociation constant K_a, 31–41
Acid nitrate, 123
Acidic oxides, 75, 76, 87
Acrilan, 168
Activation energy, 93, 94, 100
Active mass, 96
Acylium ion, 131, 135
Addition polymer, 177
Addition polymersation, 165, 167
Addition reactions, 122–124, 133
Additives to polymers, 167. 171
Aldehydes, 123
  mechanism of reactions, 129
Aldehyde ammonia, 123
Alkane, 123
Alkenes, 123
  reaction flow chart, 150
Alkyl halides, 143
  reactions with
    alcoholic ammonia, 146
    aqueous alkine, 145
    ethanolic alkaline, 145
    ethanolic potassium cyanide, 146
    magnesium, 147
Aluminium chloride as a Lewis acid, 135
Aluminium oxide, 78
Aluminium triethyl, 173
Amide ion as a base, 32
Amines,
  preparation from alkyl halides, 146
Amino-acid, 170
Ammonia,
  as an acid, 33
  as a base, 32, 33
  formation, 9
  in buffers, 41
  in reaction mechanisms, 134
  with alkyl halides, 146
  with iodomethane, 146
Ammonium chloride in buffers, 41
Ammonium ethanoate, 155
Ammonium ion as an acid, 32
Amphoteric oxides, 73, 75, 76, 87
Amylose, 170

Anions, 4
Antimony, 76, 88
Arrhenius, 93, 100, 101
Arrow notation, 124, 127, 128
Arsenic, 76, 88
Atatic polymers, 167, 172

Base dissociation constant K_b, 31–33, 41
Bases, 30
Basic oxides, 75, 76
Benzamide, 156
Benzene electrophilic substitution, 125, 130, 134, 138
Benzene diazonium chloride, 151, 157
  hydrolysis of, 151
  with potassium cyanide, 151
  with potassium iodide, 151
Benzoic acid dissociation, 39
Benzyl chloride, 159
Bi-molecular collisions, 93, 99
Bismuth, 76, 88
Body centred cubic, 72
Boltzmann, 93, 99, 100
Bond dissociation energies, 2
  of chlorine, 12
  of hydrogen, 7, 9, 10, 11
  of nitrogen, 9
Born Haber cycle, 3
  of caesium iodide, 13
  of calcium sulphide, 6
  of calcium oxide, 4, 5
  of sodium chloride, 5
Bragg, 57, 59
  equation, 60, 61, 64
Bromine, bond energy, 2
Bromoalkanes, 123, 144
  preparation from,
    hydrogen bromide, 144
    phosphorus tribromide, 144
1, Bromobutane, 152
  with sodium hydroxide, 146
2, Bromobutane, reaction mechanism, 132
Bromoethane, 155
  with sodium hydroxide, 145
1, Bromopropane, 144, 153

2, Bromopropane, 144, 153
Bronsted-Lowry, 30
Buffer solutions, 32, 39, 40, 41
Butane,
  combustion, 10
  formation, 10
Buta-1, 3-diene, 169, 170
Butan-2-ol reaction mechanism, 132
But-1-ene reaction mechanism, 132
But-2-ene reaction mechanism, 132
Butyl magnesium bromide, 153
  preparation of pentanoic acid, 153

Cadmium iodide structure, 56
Calcium sulphide,
  formation, 6
  lattice energy, 6
Caesium,
  atomisation, 13
  ionisation, 13
Caesium chloride structure, 56–58, 61, 63, 64
Caesium iodide,
  formation, 13
  lattice energy, 13
Calcium,
  atomisation, 6
  ionisation, 6
Calcium fluoride, 58
  crystal structure, 61
Calcium oxide, 4
Canonical structures, 127
ω-caprolactam, 168, 171
Carbocation, 131
  acylium, 135
  methyl, 135
Carbohydrate, 177
Carbon, 69
  atomisation, 7, 10
  combustion, 10
  properties, 75, 87
Carboxylic acid from Grignard reagents, 147
  reaction flow chart, 151
Cations, 4
Cellulose, 170
Chain reaction, 131, 172
Chemical energetics, 1
Chloride ion as a base, 32
Chlorides, 69
  of group IV, 75, 87
  of group V, 76, 89
Chlorine, bond energy, 2, 4, 11
  electron affinity, 4
  radicals, 131
  with a Lewis acid, 135

Chloroalkanes, 143
  preparation using hydrogen chloride, 143
  using thionyl chloride, 143
2, Chlorobuta-1, 3-diene, 169
Chloroethane, 144
  formation, 8, 9
  preparation, 143
Chloroethanoic acid dissociation, 37
Chloroethene, 166
Chloromethane,
  reaction mechanism, 131
  with a Lewis acid, 135
Chloromethylbenzenes, 159
Chloronium ion, 134
2-Chloropropane preparation of, 143
  reaction with sodium hydroxide, 146
Cobalt chloride catalyst, 171
Collision theory, 93, 100
Condensation fibre polymers, 169
Condensation reaction, 134
Conjugate acids, 32
Conjugate acid base pairs, 30, 33
Conjugate bases, 32
Co-polymers, 156, 169
4:2 co-ordination, 56, 58, 63
4:4 co-ordination, 56, 58, 63
6:3 co-ordination, 56, 53
6:6 co-ordination, 56, 57, 61
8:4 co-ordination, 56, 61
8:8 co-ordination, 56, 61
Covalent bonding, 2
Covalent crystal structures, 57, 58, 59
β-cristobalite structure, 56, 58, 59
Cyanohydrin, 123
Cydohexane, 171
Cyclohexanol, 171
Cydohexanone, 171

d-block, 69, 70, 69
  atomic radii, 74
  colour, 74
  complex ions, 80
  oxidation states, 74
  paramagnetism, 74
  properties, 74
1, 10-decanedioc acid, 168, 175
Degree of dissociation, 25, 31, 34, 35, 36, 38, 39
Deliquescence, 48
Diamine, 169
1, 6, diaminohexane, 168, 175
Dibenzoyl peroxide, 172, 176
Di-carboxylic acid, 169
Di-carboxylic acid chloride, 169

Diene, 169
Diffraction, 59
Dimers, 165
Dimethylterephthalic acid, 168
Dinitrogen pentoxide, 81, 83
Dinitrogen oxide, 81, 82
Dinitrogen tetroxide, 81, 83
Dinitrogen trioxide, 81, 82
2, 4-dinitrophenylhydrazine, 157
Disodium oxide, 78
Disulphur dichloride bonding, 86
Distribution coefficient, 47
Distribution of energies of gas molecules, 101
Distribution of velocities of gas molecules, 94

Efflorescence, 48
Elastomers, 169, 170, 174, 175
Electron deficient, 124, 130
Electronegativity, 122, 124, 126, 127
Electronic configuration of the elements, 71
Electrophiles, 124, 125, 130, 131
Electrophilic addition, 124, 133
   to alkene, 130
   to carbonyl compounds, 129
Electrophilic centre, 124
Electrophilic substitution, 125, 133, 138
Elimination reactions, 122, 123, 126, 133
   alkyl halides, 132, 145
   carbonyl compounds, 129, 134
Endothermic enthalpy, 4
Endothermic reaction, 18
   reaction profile, 95, 101
   with a catalyst, 97
Enthalpy, 1
Enthalpy of formation, 2
   of ammonia, 9
   of butane, 10
   of chloroethane, 8, 9
   of ethane, 14
   of ethanol, 8, 9
   of hydrogen chloride, 8, 9
   of hydrogen peroxide, 14
   of hydrogen sulphide, 11
   of phosphorus oxychloride, 8, 9
   of phosphorus pentachloride, 8, 9
   of phosphorus trichloride, 12
   of sodium chloride, 3, 5
Enthalpy of reaction, 8, 14, 26
Equilibria,
   gaseous, 17,
   heterogeneous, 46
   ionic, 30

Equilibrium constant K_c, 47, 50
Equilibrium constant K_p, 17, 48, 49
   units, 19
Esterification mechanism, 136
Ethanamide hydrolysis, 151
   Hofmann degradation, 152
   reduction, 152
Ethanal with a Grignard reagent, 156
Ethan-1, 2-diol, 168
Ethanoate ion as a base, 32
Ethanoic acid, 33, 136, 155
   dissociation, 38
   from hydrolysis, 152
   in buffers, 40
Ethanol, 155
   esterification mechanism, 136
   formation, 8, 9
   with thiony chloride, 143
Ethanoyl chloride with a Lewis acid, 135
Ethene, 166
   hydrogenation, 11
   mechanism, 129
   polymerisation, 165
Ethylmagnesium iodide with water, 147
   with methanal, 148
   with propanone, 149
Exothermic enthalpy, 4
Exothermic reaction, 18
   reaction profile, 95, 101
   with a catalyst, 97

Fibre polymers, 168
First order reactions half life, 98, 105, 106, 108
   graphs, 103, 105, 106
   integrated rate equation, 98, 107, 108
Free radical, 125, 131, 140, 176
   in polymerisation,
Fluorine,
   bond energy, 2
   electron affinity, 4
Fluorite structure, 56, 57, 58
Fluoro alkanes, 145
Fluoromethane, 144

Gaseous equilibria, 17
Germanium, 69
   properties, 75, 87
Glucose, 170, 178
Group IV, 69
   properties, 75, 87
Grignard reagent, 153, 156

Grignard reagents, 147
reactions with, water 147
 with aldehydes, 148
 with carbon dioxide, 147
 with ketones, 149
 with methanal, 148

Halogen carrier, 135
Halogeno alkanes, 143
Hess's Law, 3, 6, 7, 8, 10, 11, 12
Heterogeneous equilibria, 46
Heterogeneous reaction, 46
Hexagonal close packed, 72
1, 6, hexanedioc acid, 168, 175
Hofmann degradation, 155, 156
 of acid amides, 152
Homogeneous reactions kinetic theory, 93
Homolytic fission, 126, 131
Hydrazine, 134, 139
Hydrides, 69
 of group IV, 75, 87
 of group V, 76, 88
Hybridised orbitals, 84, 86
Hydrochloric acid, 33
Hyrogenation of ethene, 11
Hydrogen bond energy, 2, 7, 9, 10, 11
 combustion, 10
Hydrogen bromide bond energy, 2
Hydrogen chloride bond energy, 2
 formation, 8, 9
Hydrogen fluoride bond energy, 2
Hydrogen iodide bond energy, 2
Hydrogen ions, 30, 31, 34
Hydrogen sulphide formation, 11
Hydrolysis of acid nitriles, 151
 ethanonitrile, 151
Hydrolysis of chlorides, 77
Hydrolysis of esters, 136
 of propanonitrile, 137
Hydrolysis of Grignard reagents, 147, 148
Hydroxide ions, 31
Hydroxylamine, 129

Ideal gas law, 17
Immiscible solvents, 47
Inductive effects, 126, 127
Inhibitor, 167
Initial rate of reaction, 98, 112, 113
Initiation, 171
Inorganic chemistry, 69
Integrated rate equations, 98
Iodine bond energy, 2, 13
 electron affinity, 13

Iodoalkanes, 145
 preparation from,
  hydrogen iodide, 145
  phosphorus triodide, 145
1, iodobutane, 144
2, iodobutane, 144
2, iodo, 2, methylpropane, 144
Iodomethane, 156
Iodomethane with ammonia, 147
Ionic compounds, 1
Ionic crystal structures, 57, 59
Ionic equilibria, 30
Iron (III) bromide, 135
Iron (III) chloride Lewis acid, 135
Isomers, 143, 144
Isotatic polymers, 167, 172
Isotopic labelling, 136

Ketones mechanism of reaction, 129
Kinetic theory of matter, 93, 99, 100

Lattice crystal structures, 56
Layer structures, 56, 58
Lead, 69
 properties, 75, 87
Lewis acid, 131, 135
Lithium aluminium hydride, 150, 151, 154, 155

Markownikov addition, 153
Maxwell, 93, 99, 100
Mean bond energy, 2
 of C–C, 7, 10, 11
 of C=C, 9
 of C–H, 10, 11
 of N–H, 11
 of P–Cl, 11
 of S–H, 12
Mesomeric effects, 126, 127
Metallic character, 69
Metallic physical properties, 77
Methanal, 169, 174, 177
Methane, 7
 formation, 7
Methane radical reaction, 131
Methanoic acid, 32
 dissociation, 36
Methylamine, 155
Methylamine degradation product, 152
2, methylbuta-1, 3-diene, 169, 174
2, methylbutan-2-ol from Grignard reaction, 149

185

Methyl magnesium iodide, 156
2, methylpropanoic acid from Grignard reagent, 148
2, methylpropan-2-ol from Grignard reaction, 149
Methyl, 2, methylpropenoate, 166
Methylpropenoate, 168, 176
Mole fraction, 17–24, 48, 49
Molecular rearrangement reaction kinetics, 114
Monomers, 165

Neoprene, 175
Nickel, 171
   as a catalyst, 150
Nitric acid, 32
Nitrile rubber, 170
Nitrobenzene, 123
Nitrogen bond energy, 2, 9
Nitrogen dioxide, 81, 82
Nitrogen oxide, 81, 82
Nitrogen oxides, 76, 81, 88
Nitrogen trichloride, 83, 84
   bonding, 84
Nitronium ion, 125, 130
Nitrous acid, 156
Nitrous acid dissociation, 34
Non-metallic character, 69
Normal distribution, 94, 100, 101
Nucleophilic centre, 124
Nucleophiles, 124, 125, 129, 131, 132
Nucleophilic addition, 133, 124
   to alkene, 130, 138
   to carbonyl compounds, 129
Nucleophilic substitution, 125, 133
   to alkyl halides, 132, 134
Nucleophilic substitution bromoethane, 145
   iodopropane, 146
Nucleophilic substitution reaction kinetics, 114
Nylon, 169
6, nylon, 168, 171, 175
6, 6 nylon, 168, 177
6, 10 nylon, 168, 175

Octahedral site, 62
Order of reaction, 96, 98
Organic chemistry, 143
Ostwald's dilution law, 31, 36, 37
Oxidation states, 69
   of d-block, 74
   of group IV, 75
   of group V, 76

Oxides, 69
   of group IV, 75, 87
   of group V, 76, 88
Oxyacids, 73
Oxygen, bond energy, 2

p-Block, 69, 70, 79
   covalent radii, 73
   ionic radii, 73
   melting point, 73
   oxidation state, 73
   properties, 73
pK_a, 32, 33, 34, 41
pK_b, 31, 33, 42
Partial pressure, 17–24, 48, 49
Partition coefficient, 47, 51, 52
Pentanonitrile, 153
Pentanoic acid, 153
Periodic table, 69, 70
Perspex, 166
pH, 31, 33, 34, 37, 39, 40, 41
Phenol, 157, 169, 177
Phenylamine, 151, 156
Phenylamine as a base, 32
Phenylethene, 170, 171, 172
Phosphides, 85
Phosphorus,
   atomisation, 12
   bond energy, 2
Phosphorus, 76
   structure of allotropes, 88
Phosphorus oxychloride formation, 8, 9
Phosphorus pentachloride bonding, 84
Phosphorus pentachloride formation, 8, 9
Phosphorus pentachloride, 83
   structure, 84
Phosphorus tribromide, 154
Phosphorus trichloride bonding, 84
Phosphorus trichloride formation, 12
Phosphorus trichloride, 83
   structure, 84
Phosphorus trichloride, 156
pOH, 32, 33, 42
Polarisation, 122, 124, 126, 127, 131, 136
Polychloroethene, 166
Poly, 2, chlorobuta-1, 3-diene, 169, 175
Polyethene, 166
Polyethene,
   high density, 167
   low density, 165
Polymerisation, 165

Poly, 2, methylbuta-1, 3-diene, 169
Polymethyl, 2, methylpropenoate, 166
Polypeptides, 170
Polypropene, 166, 177
Polysaccharide, 171
Polystyrene, 166
Polytetrafluoroethane, 166
Potassium cyanide, 155
Potassium cyanide with alkylhalides, 146
Potassium cyanide substitution, 153
Potassium ethanoate in buffers, 40
Primary alcohols from Grignard reagents, 148
Primary alcohols reaction flow chart, 150
Propagation, 171
Propanal, 154, 155, 157
Propan-1-ol, 154, 155, 157
Propan-2-ol, 156, 158
Propan-2-ol with hydrogen chloride, 143
Propanoic acid, 155
Propanoic acid,
  dissociation, 36
  in buffers, 41
Propanonitrile, 155, 170
Propanol from Grignard reaction, 148
Propanone, 157
  reaction mechanism, 134
  with hydrazine, 139
Propene, 154, 166, 177
Propene polymerisation, 172, 173
Propeno-1-nitrile, 168, 176
Propylamine, 152
Propylmagnesium iodide with carbon dioxide,
Protein, 170, 177
Proton acceptor, 30
Proton donor, 30

Radius ratio, 57, 59, 61, 62, 64
Rate constant, 94
Rate of reaction, 93, 94, 101
Reaction kinetics, 93
Reaction profiles, 91, 102
  catalysed reactions, 97
  multi-step reaction, 96, 103
Reaction mechanism, 93, 96, 113, 122
Rearrangement reactions, 122, 123, 126
Reduction of propanamide, 152
Rock-salt structure, 56, 58
Root mean square velocity, 100
Rutile structure, 56, 57, 58

s-block, 69, 70, 78
  covalent radii, 72
  ionic radii, 72
  ionisation energies, 72
  properties, 72
SBR rubber, 170, 175
Second order reaction,
  graphs, 103
  integrated rate equation, 98, 109, 110
Secondary alcohol from Grignard reaction, 148
Secondary alcohols reaction flow chart, 150
Silane formation, 14
Silicon, 69
  atomisation, 14
  properties, 75, 87
Sodium, 4
  atomisation, 4
  ionisation, 4
Sodium chloride structure, 56, 57, 58, 61, 64
  formation, 5
  lattice energy, 4
Sodium ethanoate in buffers, 40
Sodium propanoate in buffers, 41
Standard enthalpy, 1
  of atomisation, 4
  of carbon, 7, 10
  of sulphur, 11
  of phosphorus, 12
  of silicon, 14
Standard enthalpy of atomisation table, 15
Standard enthalpy of combustion of carbon, 10
  of butane, 10
  of hydrogen, 10
Standard enthalpy of dilution, 1
Standard enthalpy of electron affinity, 1, 2
  of sulphur, 6
Standard enthalpy of electron affinity table, 15
Standard enthalpy of formation table, 16
Standard enthalpy of ionisation, 1, 2
  of caesium, 13
Standard enthalpy of ionisation energies, table, 15
Standard enthalpy of lattice energy, 1
  of caesium iodide, 13
Standard enthalpy of neutralisation, 1
Standard enthalpy of solution, 1
Starch, 171, 177

Strong acids, 31
Strong base, 31
Styrene, 166, 170
Substitution reaction, 122, 123, 125, 133
Sulphur dichloride, 87
Sulphur dichloride bonding, 86
Sulphur, electron affinity, 4
   atomisation, 6, 11
Sulphur hexafluoride, 87
   bonding, 86
Sulphur oxidation states, 86
Sulphur tetrafluoride, 87
   bonding, 86
Sulphur trioxide, 78
   polarisation, 130
Sulphuric acid, 32
Supersaturated, 47
Sydiotactic polymer, 172

Tertiary alcohols from Grignard reactions, 149
Terylene, 168
Tetrafluoroethene, 166
Thermoplastic, 174, 177
Thermoplastic polymers, 167
Thermosetting polymers, 169, 173
Thionyl chloride with carboxylic acids, 151

Tin, 69
   properties, 75, 87
Titanium chloride, 173
Titanium dioxide, 59
Triangular site, 62
Trimer, 165

Ultraviolet light, 125, 131
Unit cell, 63, 66, 68
Urea, 174

Vacant d-orbitals, 83
Vinyl chloride, 174
Vulcanisation, 170

Water,
   as an acid, 32, 33
   as a base, 32, 33
Water of crystalisation, 47
Weak acids, 31
Weak base, 31
Wurtzite structure, 56, 58

X-ray crystallography, 57, 59, 64

Zero order reaction, 103
Ziegler Nalta catalyst, 167, 173
Zinc blende structure, 56, 57, 58, 63

Butterworths Technician Series

Mathematics

Mathematics for Technicians 1
F Tabberer

1978 192 pages 246 × 189 mm
0 408 00326 X Limp Illustrated

Mathematics for Technicians 2
F Tabberer

1978 156 pages 246 × 189 mm
0 408 00371 5 Limp Illustrated

Science

Physical Science for Technicians 1
R McMullan

1978 96 pages 246 × 189 mm
0 408 00332 4 Limp Illustrated

Building Construction, Civil Engineering, Surveying and Architecture

Building Technology 1
J T Bowyer

1978 96 pages 246 × 189 mm
0 408 00298 0 Limp Illustrated

Building Technology 2
J T Bowyer

1978 96 pages 246 × 189 mm
0 408 00299 9 Limp Illustrated

Building Technology 3
J T Bowyer

1980 104 pages 246 × 189 mm
0 408 00411 8 Limp Illustrated

Civil Engineering Technology 3
B J Fletcher and S A Lavan

1980 96 pages 246 × 189 mm
0 408 00426 6 Limp Illustrated

•Construction Science and Materials 2
D Watkins and J Fincham

1981 192 pages approx 246 × 189 mm
0 408 00488 6 Limp Illustrated

•Site Surveying and Levelling 2
W S Whyte and R E Paul

1981 160 pages approx 246 × 189 mm
0 408 00532 7 Limp Illustrated

Heating and Hot Water Services for Technicians
K Moss

1978 168 pages 246 × 189 mm
0 408 00300 6 Limp Illustrated

Electrical, Electronic and Telecommunications Engineering

Electrical Drawing for Technicians 1
F Linsley

1979 96 pages 246 × 189 mm
0 408 00417 7 Limp Illustrated

Telecommunications Systems for Technicians 1
G L Danielson and R S Walker

1979 112 pages 246 × 189 mm
0 408 00352 9 Limp Illustrated

•Transmission Systems for Technicians 2
G L Danielson and R S Walker

1981 72 pages approx 246 × 189 mm
0 408 00562 9 Limp Illustrated

•Radio Systems for Technicians 2
G L Danielson and R S Walker

1981 96 pages approx 246 × 189 mm
0 408 00561 0 Limp Illustrated

•Radio Systems for Technicians 3
G L Danielson and R S Walker

1982 112 pages approx 246 × 189 mm
0 408 00588 2 Limp Illustrated

Electrical and Electronic Principles 2
I R Sinclair

1979 96 pages 246 × 189 mm
0 408 00433 9 Limp Illustrated

Electrical and Electronic Applications 2
D W Tyler

1980 204 pages 246 × 189 mm
0 408 00412 6 Limp Illustrated

Electronics for Technicians 2
S A Knight

1978 112 pages   246 × 189 mm
0 408 00324 3   Limp   Illustrated

Electronics for Technicians 3
S A Knight

1980 160 pages   246 × 189 mm
0 408 00458 4   Limp   Illustrated

Electrical Principles for Technicians 2
S A Knight

1978 144 pages   246 × 189 mm
0 408 00325 1   Limp   Illustrated

Electrical and Electronic Principles 3
S A Knight

1980 160 pages   246 × 189 mm
0 408 00456 8   Limp   Illustrated

•Electrical and Electronic Principles 4/5
S A Knight

1982 176 pages approx   246 × 189 mm
0 408 01109 2   Limp   Illustrated

Mechanical, Production, Marine and Motor Vehicle Engineering

Vehicle Technology 1
M J Nunney

1980 112 pages   246 × 189 mm
0 408 00461 4   Limp   Illustrated

•Vehicle Technology 2
M J Nunney

1981 96 pages approx   246 × 189 mm
0 408 00594 7   Limp   Illustrated

•Engine Technology 1
M J Nunney

1981 120 pages approx   246 × 189 mm
0 408 00511 4   Limp   Illustrated

Manufacturing Technology 2
P J Harris

1979 96 pages   246 × 189 mm
0 408 00410 X   Limp   Illustrated

•Manufacturing Technology 3
P J Harris

1981 104 pages approx   246 × 189 mm
0 408 00493 2   Limp   Illustrated

•Fabrication, Welding and Metal Joining Processes — A textbook for Technicians and Craftsmen
C Flood

1981 160 pages approx   246 × 189 mm
0 408 00448 7   Limp   Illustrated

•Materials Technology for Technicians 2
W Bolton

1981 128 pages approx   246 × 189 mm
0 408 01117 3   Limp   Illustrated

•Materials Technology for Technicians 3
W Bolton

1982 128 pages approx   246 × 189 mm
0 408 01116 5   Limp   Illustrated

•Materials Technology 4
W Bolton

1981 128 pages approx   246 × 189 mm
0 408 00584 X   Limp   Illustrated

Mechanical Science for Technicians 3
W Bolton

1980 128 pages   246 × 189 mm
0 408 00486 X   Limp   Illustrated

•Mechanical Science for Higher Technicians 4/5
D H Bacon and R C Stephens

1981 256 pages approx   234 × 156 mm
0 408 00570 X   Limp   Illustrated

•Thermodynamics for Technicians 3/4
D H Bacon and R C Stephens

1982 96 pages approx   234 × 156 mm
0 408 01114 9   Limp   Illustrated

Engineering Instrumentation and Control
W Bolton

1980 144 pages   246 × 189 mm
0 408 00462 2   Limp   Illustrated